S0-AJJ-669

Wed Exam

FUNDAMENTALS OF COLLEGE

ALGEBRA

AND ELEMENTARY FUNCTIONS

CUMMINGS PUBLISHING COMPANY MENLO PARK, CALIFORNIA

RICHARD E. JOHNSON   The University of New Hampshire

LONA LEE LENDSEY   Oak Park and River Forest High School

WILLIAM E. SLESNICK   Dartmouth College

GRACE E. BATES   Mount Holyoke College

Copyright © 1974 by Cummings Publishing Company, Inc.
Philippines Copyright 1974

All rights reserved. No part of this publication may be reproduced,
stored in a retrieval system, or transmitted, in any form or by any
means, electronic, mechanical, photocopying, recording, or
otherwise, without the prior written permission of the publisher.
Printed in the United States of America.
Published simultaneously in Canada.
Library of Congress Catalog Card Number 73-90822

ISBN: 0-846-53398-7

ABCDEFGHIJKL-MA-7987654

Cummings Publishing Company, Inc.
2727 Sand Hill Road
Menlo Park, California 94025

Preface

The first three chapters of this text cover the basic topics in algebra that every student of mathematics should know. They include the symbolism of algebra, the manipulation of algebraic expressions, and the solution of first-degree equations and inequalities.

Functions are introduced in Chapter 4, followed by a study of polynomial, exponential, and logarithmic functions in succeeding chapters. Chapters 7 and 8 contain the standard topics in trigonometry essential for students of the physical sciences and of more advanced mathematics courses.

A feature of this edition is Chapter 10 on matrices and determinants. The echelon method used on the augmented matrix of a system of linear equations gives a simple, straightforward way of solving the system. Also it shows how to solve a system of linear equations using determinants.

Complex numbers are introduced in Chapter 9. Then in Chapter 11 the analytic geometry of circles, ellipses, hyperbolas, and parabolas is briefly studied.

There are extensive lists of exercises at the end of each section. These are graded into three levels of difficulty. Enrichment material is presented through many exercises in the third level of difficulty. Each chapter has a set of review exercises at the end. Appendix A–Axioms of Algebra, Appendix B–Tables, and answers to odd-numbered exercises appear in the back of the book.

R.E.J.
L.L.L.
W.E.S.
G.E.B.

Contents

1 · Numbers and Operations

1–1 REAL NUMBERS

The number system used in elementary mathematics is the so-called *real number system*. We can get some idea of the nature of this system by looking at the decimal representation of numbers. Thus, $\frac{3}{2}$ has decimal representation

$$\frac{3}{2} = 1.5,$$

$\frac{7}{3}$ has decimal representation

$$\frac{7}{3} = 2.333\ldots, \qquad \text{(infinitely many 3's)}$$

$\sqrt{2}$ has decimal representation

$$\sqrt{2} = 1.4142\ldots, \qquad \text{(infinitely many digits)}$$

π has decimal representation

$$\pi = 3.1415\ldots, \qquad \text{(infinitely many digits)}$$

and so on. Roughly speaking, the real number system consists of all numbers represented by decimals, finite or infinite. Special kinds of real numbers are discussed below.

The ordinary operations of addition and multiplication can be performed with real numbers. These operations have familiar properties.

$$x + y = y + x \qquad \text{(commutative axiom of addition)}$$
$$x(y + z) = xy + xz \qquad \text{(distributive axiom)}$$

and many more. If you wish to review the axioms, you will find them listed in the appendix.

1-2 INTEGERS AND RATIONAL NUMBERS

The system of integers consists of positive integers, negative integers, and zero. If we imagine the integers arranged in a line as indicated below, they will extend endlessly in both directions.

$$\ldots, -10^9, \ldots, -4, -3, -2, -1, 0, 1, 2, 3, 4, \ldots, 10^9, \ldots$$

In this line, the positive integers are to the right of 0, and the negative integers are to the left of 0.

Since the sum of two integers and the product of two integers are again integers, we say the system of integers is *closed* with respect to addition and multiplication. The identity elements of the real number system, 0 and 1, are also integers. Remember,

$$x + 0 = x \qquad \text{(0 is the identity element of addition)};$$
$$x \cdot 1 = x \qquad \text{(1 is the identity element of multiplication)}.$$

Each integer has an additive inverse which is an integer. Thus, -8 is the additive inverse of 8, meaning

$$8 + (-8) = 0.$$

113 is the additive inverse of -113, meaning

$$(-113) + 113 = 0.$$

Not every nonzero integer has a multiplicative inverse which is an integer. For example, 8 has multiplicative inverse $\frac{1}{8}$, meaning

$$8 \cdot \tfrac{1}{8} = 1,$$

and $\frac{1}{8}$ is not an integer.

Another important subsystem of the real number system is the rational number system. We recall that a number is called *rational* if it can be expressed as a quotient of two integers. For example, each of the numbers

$$\frac{1}{5}, \quad \frac{-6}{8}, \quad \frac{4}{3}, \quad \frac{-100}{-101}, \quad 3.14159$$

is rational. Each integer n is also a rational number since $n = n/1$. Consequently, the rational number system contains the system of integers.

Each rational number can be expressed in many different ways as a quotient of two integers. For example, 2/4, 3/6, 1/2, and 13/26 are different numerals for the same rational number one-half, and 6/14, $-15/-35$, 3/7, 21/49, and $-3/-7$ are different ways of representing the same rational number three-sevenths. If we are given two quotients of integers, we can tell whether they represent the same rational number by the following rule. If a, b, c, and d are integers with $b \neq 0$ and $d \neq 0$, then

$$\frac{a}{b} = \frac{c}{d} \quad \textit{if, and only if,} \quad a \cdot d = b \cdot c.$$

For example,

$$\frac{3}{7} = \frac{6}{14} \quad \text{since} \quad 3 \cdot 14 = 7 \cdot 6, \quad \text{or } 42.$$

A nonzero rational number a/b is said to be expressed in *simplest form* if $b > 0$ and the integers a and b are relatively prime, that is, if the greatest common divisor (g.c.d.) of a and b is 1. For example, the rational number 3/7 is expressed in simplest form, since $7 > 0$ and the g.c.d. of 3 and 7 is 1. We shall not prove it here, but the simplest form of a rational number is *unique*. If a/b is the simplest form of a rational number, then any other representation has the form na/nb for some nonzero integer n.

The rational number system is *closed* with respect to the operations of addition, multiplication, subtraction, and division (except by zero). In other words, if a and b are rational numbers, then so are $a + b$, $a \cdot b$, $a - b$, and $a \div b$, with the exception that $a \div b$ is undefined if $b = 0$.

Exercises

Write each of the following rational numbers as a quotient of integers and express each answer in simplest form.

1. (a) $\frac{24}{64}$ (b) $\frac{98}{1008}$ 2. (a) 3.14   (b) 1.414

Find the decimal representation for each of the following rational numbers.

3. (a) $\frac{3}{8}$ (b) $\frac{5}{6}$ 4. (a) $\frac{9}{40}$ (b) $\frac{2}{7}$

Perform the indicated operations, and express each answer in simplest form.

5. (a) $\frac{3}{4} - \frac{2}{3}$ (b) $\frac{4}{15} - \frac{7}{20}$

6. (a) $\frac{3}{4} \cdot (-\frac{2}{3})$ (b) $\frac{66}{65} \times \frac{13}{44}$

7. (a) $\frac{3}{4} \div (-\frac{2}{3})$ (b) $-\frac{38}{45} \div \frac{57}{70}$

8. (a) $\frac{4}{39} - \frac{5}{52} + \frac{6}{65}$ (b) $\frac{12}{75} - \frac{7}{60} - \frac{11}{30}$

9. (a) $(\frac{4}{5} + \frac{3}{15}) \div (-\frac{5}{9})$ (b) $(2\frac{1}{8} - 1\frac{5}{16}) \div 3$

10. (a) $(\frac{5}{2} - \frac{5}{3}) \times \frac{36}{15}$ (b) $(\frac{4}{17} \times \frac{85}{64}) + (\frac{111}{52} \times \frac{39}{74})$

11. (a) $\frac{7}{8}(\frac{19}{57} - \frac{1}{3})$ (b) $(\frac{17}{68} - \frac{1}{4}) \div (-\frac{13}{17})$

Which, if any, of the following systems are closed?

12. The set of positive integers with respect to subtraction

13. The set of integers with respect to subtraction

14. The set of negative integers with respect to addition

15. The set of negative integers with respect to multiplication

16. The set of integers with respect to division

17. The set of positive rational numbers with respect to division

18. The set of even integers with respect to addition

19. The set of odd integers with respect to multiplication

20. The set of positive rational numbers with respect to subtraction

21. The set of rational numbers with respect to subtraction

22. The set of negative rational numbers with respect to addition

23. The set of negative rational numbers with respect to multiplication

24. The set of rational numbers with respect to division

25. The set of nonzero rational numbers with respect to division

26. (a) Name six rational numbers between 0 and 1, between 0 and $\frac{1}{2}$, between 0 and $\frac{1}{4}$, between 0 and $\frac{1}{10}$, and between 0 and a when $a > 0$.
(b) How many rational numbers are there between any two rational numbers?

27. (a) What is the largest integer that is less than $\frac{137}{56}$?
(b) What is the smallest integer that is greater than $\frac{137}{56}$?
(c) What integer is nearest to $\frac{137}{56}$?

---

28. (a) Can you find a largest rational number which is less than $\frac{137}{56}$? Explain your answer.
(b) Can you find a smallest rational number which is greater than $\frac{137}{56}$? Explain your answer.

29. Is the set $\{-1, 0, 1\}$ closed with respect to any of the operations of arithmetic? If so, name them.

30. For which operations of arithmetic is the set of multiples of 3 closed?

31. If $S = \{x \mid x = 3^n, n$ a positive integer$\}$, is S closed with respect to any arithmetic operations? If so, name them.

32. Describe a subset of the rational numbers which is closed
(a) under $+$, $-$, and $\times$, but not $\div$.
(b) under $\times$, but not $+$.
(c) under $+$ and $-$, but not $\times$.

33. Suppose p/q represents a nonzero rational number expressed in simplest form. Describe the set of values for q so that p/q has a finite decimal representation.

1–3   IRRATIONAL NUMBERS

There are many real numbers which cannot be expressed as a quotient of two integers. Such real numbers are called *irrational numbers*. For example, it may be shown that $\sqrt{2}$, π, $\sqrt[3]{7} - 3$, and $\sqrt{29}/4$ are irrational numbers.

We may obtain many irrational numbers by taking square roots, cube roots, and so on, of positive rational numbers. The real number y is called a *square root* of x if $y^2 = x$; a *cube root* of x if $y^3 = x$; and so on. Thus, since $4^2 = 16$, 4 is a square root of 16; and since $4^3 = 64$, 4 is a cube root of 64. One of the properties of the real number system is that every positive real number has a positive square root, cube root, and so on.

There is an interesting question about rational numbers: what positive rational numbers have *rational* square roots? In other words, under what conditions is a given rational number the square of another rational number? To answer this question, let a/b be a positive rational number expressed in simplest form. If there exists another positive rational number x/y, also in simplest form, such that

$$\left(\frac{x}{y}\right)^2 = \frac{a}{b},$$

then we must have

$$\frac{x^2}{y^2} = \frac{a}{b}.$$

Now, if the integers x and y are relatively prime, then so are the integers x^2 and y^2. Hence, the rational number x^2/y^2 is expressed in simplest form. Since x^2/y^2 and a/b are simplest forms for the same rational number, and the simplest form of a rational number is unique, we must have

$$x^2 = a \quad \text{and} \quad y^2 = b.$$

Therefore, we can make the following statement.

The positive rational number a/b, expressed in simplest form, is the square of another rational number if, and only if, the integers a and b are squares of integers.

The squares of the positive integers, in order, are

1,　4,　9,　16,　25,　36,　49,　64,　81,　100,　121,　144, ...

These numbers are called *perfect squares.* Hence, only rational numbers such as

$$\frac{4}{9}, \frac{36}{81}, \frac{121}{144}$$

have rational square roots.

Knowing which rational numbers have rational square roots, we can easily give examples of irrational numbers. All we need do is select a rational number in simplest form, such as $\frac{7}{3}$ or $\frac{5}{1}$, for which the two integers involved are not both perfect squares. Then the positive square root of the number must be irrational. For example,

$$\sqrt{\tfrac{7}{3}} \quad \text{and} \quad \sqrt{5}$$

are irrational numbers. We recall that for a positive number x, the symbol $\sqrt{x}$ designates the *positive square* root of x, and the symbol $-\sqrt{x}$ denotes the negative square root of x. *Negative numbers do not have real square roots.*

If x is a rational number and y is an irrational number, then $x + y$ must be irrational. To see that this is so, let $z = x + y$. Then $y = z - x$, and y is rational if both z and x are rational, because the set of rational numbers is closed under subtraction. Since we assumed that y was irrational, z must be irrational. Similarly, if x is a nonzero rational number and y is irrational, then xy is irrational. Neither the sum nor the product of two irrational numbers need be irrational. For example, $3 - \sqrt{2}$ and $3 + \sqrt{2}$ are two irrational numbers whose sum and product are both rational:

$$(3 - \sqrt{2}) + (3 + \sqrt{2}) = 6,$$
$$(3 - \sqrt{2}) \times (3 + \sqrt{2}) = 3^2 - (\sqrt{2})^2, \text{ or } 7.$$

Hence, the set of irrational numbers is *not closed* under either addition or multiplication.

Exercises

1. Select from the following those numbers which have rational square roots:

$$\tfrac{4}{7}, \tfrac{3}{64}, \tfrac{25}{16}, \tfrac{5}{45}, \pi^2, (\tfrac{2}{3})^2, -144, .0121, \sqrt{16}, \sqrt{25}$$

2. (a) List five irrational numbers between 2 and 3.
   (b) List five irrational numbers between -3 and -3.5.

3. (a) Show that $\sqrt{18}$ is between 4.2 and 4.3.
   (b) Show that $-\sqrt{26}$ is between -5 and -5.1.

4. (a) Show that $\sqrt{32}$ is between 5.6 and 5.7.
   (b) Show that $\sqrt{32}$ is between 5.65 and 5.66.

5. (a) Compute $(3.5)^2$ to see whether $\sqrt{13}$ is closer to 3 or to 4.
   (b) Find the integer closest to $\sqrt{42}$.

6. (a) What is the largest integer that is less than $\sqrt{7}$?
   (b) What is the smallest integer that is greater than $\sqrt{7}$?
   (c) What integer is nearest to $\sqrt{7}$?
   (d) Can you find a largest rational number which is less than $\sqrt{7}$?
   (e) Can you find a smallest rational number which is greater than $\sqrt{7}$?

7. Find approximations to $\sqrt{3}$ by determining
   (a) the consecutive integers between which $\sqrt{3}$ lies.
   (b) the consecutive integers between which $10\sqrt{3}$ lies (the largest integer which has a square less than 300 and the smallest integer which has a square greater than 300).
   (c) the consecutive integers between which $100\sqrt{3}$ lies.

8. (a) Compute $(2.5)^3$ to see whether $\sqrt[3]{15}$ is closer to 2 or to 3.
   (b) Find the integer closest to $\sqrt[3]{95}$.

9. (a) Between which two consecutive integers does $-\sqrt[3]{100}$ lie?
   (b) What is the largest integer that is less than $-\sqrt[3]{100}$?
   (c) Is there a largest rational number which is less than $-\sqrt[3]{100}$?

Find the sum of each of the following pairs of irrational numbers.

10. (a) $4 + \sqrt{3}, 4 - \sqrt{3}$ (b) $\sqrt{2} + 8, \sqrt{2} - 8$

11. (a) $\sqrt{6} + \sqrt{7}, \sqrt{6} - \sqrt{7}$ (b) $3\sqrt{2} - \sqrt{5}, \sqrt{5} - 3\sqrt{2}$

Find the product of each of the following pairs of irrational numbers.

12. (a) $5 + \sqrt{3}, 5 - \sqrt{3}$ (b) $\sqrt{2} - \sqrt{5}, \sqrt{2} + \sqrt{5}$

13. (a) $5 + \sqrt{3}, 5 - \sqrt{3}$ (b) $3\sqrt{2} + \sqrt{7}, 3\sqrt{2} - \sqrt{7}$

14. What restrictions on a, b, c and d will guarantee that
(a) $(a + b\sqrt{7}) + (c + d\sqrt{7})$ be rational?
(b) $(a + b\sqrt{7}) \times (c + d\sqrt{7})$ be rational?

15. Is the set

$$\{a + b\sqrt{7} \,|\, a \text{ and } b \text{ rational}\}$$

closed under any of the operations of arithmetic? Explain your answer.

16. (a) If we define the *greatest integer* in any real number r to be that integer n for which $n \leq r < n + 1$, what is the *greatest integer* n in each of the following real numbers: 3.01, 3.99, $\sqrt{2}$, $5 + \sqrt{2}$, -2.1, -2.5?
(b) Describe those numbers for which the *greatest* integer is also the *nearest* integer. Illustrate.

1-4   ALGEBRAIC EXPRESSIONS

In the formula

$$A = lw$$

for the area A of a rectangle having length l and width w, the symbols A, l, w are called variables. A *variable* is a symbol (usually a letter of the alphabet) which can be assigned values from some set. The variables A, l, and w above can be assigned values from the set of positive numbers.

An expression involving numbers, variables, and operations is called an *algebraic expression*. Such an expression becomes a number when values are assigned to the variables. For example,

$$3x - 2y + 7$$

is an algebraic expression involving the variables x and y. If we let $x = 2$ and $y = 5$, then $3x - 2y + 7$ becomes

$$3 \cdot 2 - 2 \cdot 5 + 7,$$

or

$$6 - 10 + 7, \quad \text{or } 3.$$

Similar algebraic expressions can be combined by addition or subtraction, as illustrated below.

Problem 1.   Find $(7x + 3y - 4) + (2x - 5y + 3)$.

Solution. We combine like terms.

$$(7x + 3y - 4) + (2x - 5y + 3)$$
$$= (7x + 2x) + (3y - 5y) + (-4 + 3)$$
$$= (7 + 2)x + (3 - 5)y - 1$$
$$= 9x - 2y - 1$$

Problem 2. Find $(x^2 - 3xy + 2y^2) + (4x^2 + 3xy + 7y^2)$.

Solution. We combine terms containing like variables.

$$(x^2 - 3xy + 2y^2) + (4x^2 + 3xy + 7y^2)$$
$$= (x^2 + 4x^2) + (-3xy + 3xy) + (2y^2 + 7y^2)$$
$$= (1 + 4)x^2 + (-3 + 3)xy + (2 + 7)y^2$$
$$= 5x^2 + 0xy + 9y^2$$
$$= 5x^2 + 9y^2$$

We used the facts above that $x^2 = 1 \cdot x^2$ and that $0xy = 0$.

The negative of a sum of numbers is the sum of the negatives.

$$-(x + y) = (-x) + (-y)$$

Therefore, to subtract a sum of numbers we add their negatives.

$$z - (x + y) = z + (-x) + (-y)$$

This fact is used in the following problem.

Problem 3. Find $(9a - 4b + 3c) - (8a + 5c - 2d)$.

Solution. First,

$$(9a - 4b + 3c) - (8a + 5c - 2d)$$
$$= 9a - 4b + 3c + (-8a) + (-5c) + 2d$$

Then we collect like terms.

$$= (9a - 8a) - 4b + (3c - 5c) + 2d$$
$$= (9 - 8)a - 4b + (3 - 5)c + 2d$$
$$= a - 4b - 2c + 2d$$

Problem 4. Find $(7x + 11y - 4) - (14x - 3y + 7)$.

Solution. We proceed as above.

$$(7x + 11y - 4) - (14x - 3y + 7)$$
$$= 7x + 11y - 4 - 14x + 3y - 7$$
$$= (7x - 14x) + (11y + 3y) + (-4 - 7)$$
$$= -7x + 14y - 11$$

Exercises

Find the value of each of the given algebraic expressions when $x = 3$ and $y = 2$.

1. (a) $4x + 5y - 6$ (b) $2x + 3y + 1$
    (c) $6x + 8y - 5$ (d) $2x + 2y - 7$

2. (a) $9x^2 - 2xy + y^2$ (b) $x^2 - 10xy + 25y^2$
    (c) $10x^2 - 12xy + 26y^2$ (d) $8x^2 + 8xy - 24y^2$

3. (a) $x^2 - 4xy + 4y^2$ (b) $9x^2 + 6xy + y^2$
    (c) $(x - 2y)^2$ (d) $(3x + y)^2$

Find the required sum or difference. Evaluate the given expression when $a = 2$ and $b = -3$. Evaluate your simplified answer when $a = 2$ and $b = -3$. Do the two values agree?

4. $(6a - 5b + 8) + (2a + 3b - 5)$

5. $(9 - b - 7a) + (6 + 7b - 2a)$

6. $(a^2 - 6ab + 9b^2) + (a^2 + 6ab + 9b^2)$

7. $(2a^2 - ab - b^2) - (3a^2 - 4ab - 3b^2)$

Find the required sum or difference.

8. $(8x + 4y - 5) + (3x - 4y + 4)$

9. $(2x - 5y + 3) + (9x + 8y - 4)$

10. $(7x + 3y - 4) + (x - y + 4)$

11. $(8x + 5y - 2) - (6x - 3y - 8)$

12. $(14x - 3y + 7) - (7x + 11y - 4)$

13. $(5x - y - 6) - (-5x + y + 6)$

14. Add:
$$6x^2 - 7xy + y^2$$
$$3x^2 + \ xy - y^2$$

15. Subtract:
$$6x^2 - 7xy + y^2$$
$$3x^2 + \ xy - y^2$$

1-5   MULTIPLICATION OF ALGEBRAIC EXPRESSIONS

We recall the exponential notation that allows us to write x^2 in place of $x \cdot x$; y^6 in place of $y \cdot y \cdot y \cdot y \cdot y \cdot y$; 2^5 in place of $2 \cdot 2 \cdot 2 \cdot 2 \cdot 2$. By definition,

$$x^n = \overbrace{x \cdot x \cdot \ldots \cdot x}^{n \text{ factors}}, \quad n \text{ any positive integer.}$$

Thus, we can write 10^9 in place of one billion; and 2^{10} in place of 1024. We call x^n *the nth power of x.* Of course, the special cases of x^2 and x^3 are called the *square* and *cube* of x, respectively.

Two powers of x can be multiplied to give another power of x. For example,

$$x^2 \cdot x^4 = \overbrace{(x \cdot x) \cdot (x \cdot x \cdot x \cdot x)}^{6 \text{ x's}}$$
$$= x^6.$$

Thus,

$$x^2 \cdot x^4 = x^{2+4}.$$

Always,

$$x^m \cdot x^n = \overbrace{\underbrace{(x \cdot x \cdot \ldots \cdot x)}_{m \text{ x's}} \cdot \underbrace{(x \cdot x \cdot \ldots \cdot x)}_{n \text{ x's}}}^{(m+n) \text{ x's}}$$
$$= x^{m+n}.$$

This result is important enough to be given a name:

THE FIRST LAW OF EXPONENTS

$$x^m \cdot x^n = x^{m+n} \quad \text{*for all positive integers m and n.*}$$

We use this law in multiplying algebraic expressions, as shown below.

Problem 1.   Find $(3x^3y) \cdot (4x^5y^7)$.

Solution.   We first realign the factors with like ones next to each other.

$$(3x^3y) \cdot (4x^5y^7) = (3 \cdot 4) \cdot (x^3x^5) \cdot (y \cdot y^7)$$

By definition, $y = y^1$. Hence, by the first law of exponents,

$$(3x^3y)(4x^5y^7) = 12x^{3+5}y^{1+7}$$
$$= 12x^8y^8.$$

Problem 2.　Find $(7a^2b^3c^5) \cdot (8a^3b^3c^4)$.

Solution.　Proceeding as above,

$$(7a^2b^3c^5) \cdot (8a^3b^3c^4) = (7 \cdot 8) \cdot (a^2a^3) \cdot (b^3 \cdot b^3) \cdot (c^5 \cdot c^4)$$
$$= 56a^{2+3}b^{3+3}c^{5+4}$$
$$= 56a^5b^6c^9.$$

A power of a product can be expressed as a product of powers. For example,

$$(xy)^3 = (xy) \cdot (xy) \cdot (xy)$$
$$= (x \cdot x \cdot x) \cdot (y \cdot y \cdot y)$$
$$= x^3y^3.$$

By the same argument, we obtain the following.

THE SECOND LAW OF EXPONENTS

$$(xy)^n = x^ny^n \qquad \textit{for every positive integer } n.$$

Problem 3.　Find $(3xy)^4$.

Solution.　By the second law of exponents, extended to three factors,

$$(3xy)^4 = 3^4x^4y^4$$
$$= 81x^4y^4.$$

How do we find a power of a power? For example, what is $(x^2)^3$? By definition,

$$(x^2)^3 = \overbrace{x^2 \cdot x^2 \cdot x^2}^{3\ x^2\text{'s}}.$$

Thus,

$$(x^2)^3 = x^{2 \cdot 3}$$
$$= x^6.$$

This illustrates the following law.

THE THIRD LAW OF EXPONENTS

$$(x^m)^n = x^{mn} \quad \textit{for all positive integers m and n.}$$

Problem 4. Find $(-2a^4b)^3$.

Solution.

$$
\begin{aligned}
(-2a^4b)^3 &= (-2)^3(a^4)^3b^3 && \text{(second law of exponents)} \\
&= -8a^{4\cdot3}b^3 && \text{(third law of exponents)} \\
&= -8a^{12}b^3
\end{aligned}
$$

An algebraic expression such as $3x^2y$ or $8a^3bc^2$ is called a *monomial* (one term); such as $x + 3y$ or $ab - 4a$ is called a *binomial* (two terms); such as $3x^2 - 4x + 1$ or $a^2x + by + 4cz^2$ is called a *trinomial* (three terms); and so on. Products involving monomials, binomials, and so on, can be found as illustrated below.

Problem 5. Find $3x \cdot (4x + 2y)$.

Solution. $3x \cdot (4x + 2y) = 3x \cdot 4x + 3x \cdot 2y$ (distributive axiom)

$$= 12x^2 + 6xy$$

Problem 6. Find $(5x - 2y) \cdot (3x + 7y)$.

Solution.   Think of this product as $a \cdot (b + c)$, where $a = (5x - 2y)$, $b = 3x$, $c = 7y$. By the distributive axiom,

$$a \cdot (b + c) = a \cdot b + a \cdot c.$$

Thus,

$$(5x - 2y) \cdot (3x + 7y) = (5x - 2y) \cdot 3x + (5x - 2y) \cdot 7y.$$

Now use the distributive axiom with each term on the right side.

$$
\begin{aligned}
(5x - 2y) \cdot (3x + 7y) &= 5x \cdot 3x + (-2y) \cdot 3x + 5x \cdot 7y + (-2y) \cdot 7y \\
&= 15x^2 - 6xy + 35xy - 14y^2
\end{aligned}
$$

Adding the like terms $-6xy + 35xy = (-6 + 35)xy$, we get

$$(5x - 2y) \cdot (3x + 7y) = 15x^2 + 29xy - 14y^2.$$

Exercises

Correct each of the following false statements:

1. $x \cdot x^8 = x^8$ **2.** $3^2 \cdot 3^4 = 9^6$

3. $(x^5)^2 = x^{25}$ **4.** $(2x^5)^2 = 2x^{10}$

5. $(3x^4)^2 = 6x^8$ **6.** $-(-5x^3)^2 = 25x^6$

7. $-2x(7x - 3y) = -14x^2 - 6xy$ **8.** $(5x - 2y)^2 = 25x^2 + 4y^2$

9. $(3x - 5y)(2x + 7y) = 6x^2 - 11xy - 35y^2$

10. $(6x + y)(6x - y) = 36x^2 - 12xy + y^2$

Use the first law of exponents to find

11. $(5x^3y^2) \cdot (2xy^4)$ **12.** $(-7x^2y^5z^4) \cdot (9x^3y^4z)$

Use the second law of exponents to find

13. $(-3xy)^2$ **14.** $(-\frac{2}{3}xyz)^5$

Use the third law of exponents to find

15. $(x^9)^2$ **16.** $(2^6)^3$

Perform the indicated operations, and express each answer in simplest form. State the laws used.

17. $7^2 \cdot 7^6 \cdot 7$ **18.** $5 \cdot 5^2 \cdot 5^3$

19. $x^2 \cdot x \cdot x^4$ **20.** $(-6x^3y)(-2x^3y^2)$

21. $(-2xy)^5$ **22.** $(4x^3y)^2$

23. $-(-5xy^4)^3$ **24.** $(-3a^2b^3)^4 \cdot (-\frac{1}{3}ab^5)^4$

25. $(-1.5a^4b)^7(\frac{2}{3}ab^2)^7$ **26.** $5x(3x + 7y)$

27. $3xy(2x - 7y)$ **28.** $-2x^2(6x - 5y)$

29. $2x(3x + y) + y(3x + y)$ **30.** $3x(5x - 2y) - 4y(5x - 2y)$

31. $(2x + y)(3x + y)$ **32.** $(3x - 4y)(5x - 2y)$

33. $(2x - 5y)(7x + 3y)$ **34.** $(5x - 2y)(3x + 4y)$

35. $(4x + 9y)(4x - 9y)$ **36.** $(4x + 9y)(4x + 9y)$

37. $(4x - 9y)^2$ **38.** $(4x + 9y)^3$

1-6   DIVISION OF ALGEBRAIC EXPRESSIONS

If we divide two powers of a variable x, one of three situations might arise. These three cases are illustrated below.

$$x^4 \div x^4 = \frac{x^4}{x^4} = 1$$

$$x^6 \div x^4 = \frac{x \cdot x \cdot x \cdot x \cdot x \cdot x}{x \cdot x \cdot x \cdot x} = x^{6-4} = x^2$$

$$x^4 \div x^6 = \frac{x \cdot x \cdot x \cdot x}{x \cdot x \cdot x \cdot x \cdot x \cdot x} = \frac{1}{x^{6-4}} = \frac{1}{x^2}$$

Of course, we never allow x to equal 0 because division by 0 is undefined.

The three cases described above can be condensed into the following statement.

THE FOURTH LAW OF EXPONENTS

$$\frac{x^m}{x^n} = \begin{cases} 1 & \text{if } m = n \\ x^{m-n} & \text{if } m > n \\ \dfrac{1}{x^{n-m}} & \text{if } n > m \end{cases} \qquad \text{for all positive integers } m \text{ and } n.$$

We use this result in the following problems.

Problem 1.   Find $(3a^3b^2) \div (2ab^5)$.

Solution. $\dfrac{3a^3b^2}{2ab^5} = \dfrac{3}{2} \cdot \dfrac{a^3}{a^1} \cdot \dfrac{b^2}{b^5}$

$$= \frac{3}{2} \cdot a^{3-1} \frac{1}{b^{5-2}}$$

$$= \frac{3}{2} \cdot a^2 \cdot \frac{1}{b^3}, \quad \text{or} \quad \frac{3a^2}{2b^3}.$$

Problem 2.   Find $(-12x^5y^4) \div (4x^2y^4)$.

Solution. $\dfrac{-12x^5y^4}{4x^2y^4} = \dfrac{-12}{4} \cdot \dfrac{x^5}{x^2} \cdot \dfrac{y^4}{y^4}$

$$= -3 \cdot x^{5-2} \cdot 1$$

$$= -3x^3$$

Problem 3.   Find $(4a^3x^3 - 5a^4x) \div (2a^2x^3)$.

Solution.   A sum of terms is divided by a monomial by dividing each term by the monomial.

$$\frac{4a^3x^3 - 5a^4x}{2a^2x^3} = \frac{4a^3x^3}{2a^2x^3} - \frac{5a^4x}{2a^2x^3}$$

$$= \frac{4}{2} \cdot a^{3-2} \cdot 1 - \frac{5}{2} \cdot a^{4-2} \cdot \frac{1}{x^{3-1}}$$

$$= 2a - \frac{5a^2}{2x^2}$$

Exercises

Perform the indicated operations and express each answer in simplest form.

1. $x^5 \div x^5$ **2.** $x^{12} \div x^{10}$

3. $x^{10} \div x^{12}$ **4.** $x^8 \div x^4$

5. $x^4 \div x^8$ **6.** $5^{20} \div 5^4$

7. $24x^2y^3 \div (6x^5y^2)$ **8.** $(36xy^4) \div (18xy^2)$

9. $(12x^2y) \div (36x^5y)$ **10.** $(-7x^2y^3) \div (14x^5y^2)$

11. $\dfrac{5^6 \cdot 2^4}{5^4 \cdot 2^3}$ **12.** $\dfrac{7^6 \cdot 3^3}{7^8 \cdot 3^2}$

13. $(8x^3y^3 - 6x^4y) \div (2x^2y)$ **14.** $(8x^3y^3 - 6x^4y) \div (10x^3y^4)$

15. $(8x^3y^3 - 6x^4y) \div (-8x^3y^3)$ **16.** $(30x^4y^3 + 6x^5y^2) \div (-30x^4y^2)$

1-7 ADDITION OF FRACTIONS

We recall how to add two rational numbers.

$$\frac{2}{9} + \frac{4}{5} = \frac{2 \cdot 5}{9 \cdot 5} + \frac{4 \cdot 9}{5 \cdot 9}$$

$$= \frac{10}{45} + \frac{36}{45}$$

$$= \frac{46}{45}$$

For all fractions a/b and c/d,

$$\frac{a}{b} + \frac{c}{d} = \frac{ad + bc}{bd}.$$

Sometimes we can find a common denominator for two rational numbers which is less than their product. For example,

$$\frac{5}{6} + \frac{2}{27} = \frac{5 \cdot 9}{6 \cdot 9} + \frac{2 \cdot 2}{27 \cdot 2}$$

$$= \frac{45}{54} + \frac{4}{54}$$

$$= \frac{49}{54}$$

Actually, 54 is the least common denominator (l.c.d.) of these two fractions; and it is less than their product $6 \cdot 27 = 162$.

The method described above can be used in adding fractions involving algebraic expressions. Some examples are given below.

Problem 1. Find $\dfrac{3x}{2y^2} + \dfrac{4y}{6x}$.

Solution. The l.c.d. is evidently $6xy^2$. That is, this is the common denominator having the least coefficient (6) and the least powers of x and y.

$$\frac{3x}{2y^2} + \frac{4y}{6x} = \frac{3x \cdot 3x}{2y^2 \cdot 3x} + \frac{4y \cdot y^2}{6x \cdot y^2}$$

$$= \frac{9x^2}{6xy^2} + \frac{4y^3}{6xy^2}$$

$$= \frac{9x^2 + 4y^3}{6xy^2}.$$

Problem 2. Find $\dfrac{2a^2}{3bc^2} - \dfrac{4b}{9a^2c^3}$.

Solution. The l.c.d. evidently is $9a^2bc^3$.

$$\frac{2a^2}{3bc^2} - \frac{4b}{9a^2c^3} = \frac{2a^2 \cdot 3a^2c}{3bc^2 \cdot 3a^2c} - \frac{4b \cdot b}{9a^2c^3 \cdot b}$$

$$= \frac{6a^4c}{9a^2bc^3} - \frac{4b^2}{9a^2bc^3}$$

$$= \frac{6a^4c - 4b^2}{9a^2bc^3}$$

Problem 3. Find $\dfrac{7}{x^2} - \dfrac{4}{x} + 5$.

Solution. The term 5 is considered to be the fraction $\frac{5}{1}$.

$$\frac{7}{x^2} - \frac{4}{x} + 5 = \frac{7}{x^2} - \frac{4 \cdot x}{x \cdot x} + \frac{5 \cdot x^2}{1 \cdot x^2}$$

$$= \frac{7}{x^2} - \frac{4x}{x^2} + \frac{5x^2}{x^2}$$

$$= \frac{7 - 4x + 5x^2}{x^2}$$

Exercises

Find the following sums (that is, write each sum as a single fraction).

1. $\frac{2}{7} + \frac{3}{7}$ **2.** $\frac{2}{7} + \frac{3}{5}$

3. $\frac{5x^2}{6} + \frac{x}{6}$ **4.** $\frac{5x^2}{2} + \frac{x}{3}$

5. $\frac{6}{x} + \frac{7}{x^2}$ **6.** $\frac{9}{x^2} - \frac{5}{x} + 8$

7. $\frac{2x}{3y^2} + \frac{5y}{12x}$ **8.** $\frac{3c^2}{5ab^2} - \frac{4b^2}{15a^2c^2}$

9. $\frac{2}{x^2} + \frac{3}{x} + \frac{4}{xy}$ **10.** $\frac{x}{y} + \frac{y}{x} + \frac{1}{3}$

11. $\frac{x}{2y} + 3 + \frac{y}{2x}$ **12.** $\frac{2x}{y} - 1 + \frac{y}{8x}$

Examine each statement and tell for what values of x, if any, the statement is true.

13. $\frac{x-1}{x^2-x} = \frac{1}{x}$ **14.** $\frac{1}{x-1} - \frac{1}{(x-1)^2} = \frac{x-2}{(x-1)^2}$

15. $\frac{5-x}{5+x} = -1$ **16.** $\frac{8+x^3}{8-x^3} = 1$

1-8   INTEGRAL EXPONENTS

Exponential notation was introduced into mathematics in the seventeenth century by the Frenchman René Descartes. With this notation, the astronomer can very simply express the approximate distance from the earth to the farthest visible star as 6×10^{19} miles, instead of 60,000,000,000,000,000,000 miles.

We saw previously that

$$\overbrace{x^n = x \cdot x \cdot \ldots \cdot x}^{n\ x\text{'s}}, \quad n \text{ any positive integer.}$$

The number n in x^n is called the exponent of x^n, and x^n is called the nth *power* of x.

By the fourth law of exponents

$$\frac{x^m}{x^n} = x^{m-n} \quad \text{if } m > n.$$

What happens if we insist that the above equation be true even if $m < n$? This will mean, for example, that

$$\frac{x^3}{x^7} = x^{3-7} = x^{-4},$$

and

$$\frac{x^5}{x^5} = x^{5-5} = x^0.$$

Therefore, it will mean that

$$x^{-4} = \frac{1}{x^4}$$

and

$$x^0 = 1.$$

We have some reason, consequently, for *defining*

$$x^0 = 1 \quad \text{for every nonzero number } x, \text{ and}$$

$$x^{-n} = \frac{1}{x^n} \quad \text{for every positive integer } n \text{ and every nonzero number } x.$$

In this way, the nth power of every nonzero number is defined for every integer n, whether n is positive, negative, or zero.

For example,

$$2^{-4} = \frac{1}{2^4} = \frac{1}{16}$$

$$3^0 = 1$$

$$\left(\frac{1}{5}\right)^{-2} = 5^2 = 25 \qquad \left(\text{because } \frac{1}{1/5} = 5\right)$$

Having defined zero and negative exponents, it can be shown that the following laws of *exponents* are true for all integral exponents.

$$x^m \cdot x^n = x^{m+n} \qquad \text{(first law)}$$

$$\frac{x^m}{x^n} = x^{m-n} \qquad \text{(fourth law)}$$

$$(x^m)^n = x^{mn} \qquad \text{(third law)}$$
$$(xy)^n = x^n y^n \qquad \text{(second law)}$$
$$\left(\frac{x}{y}\right)^n = \frac{x^n}{y^n} \qquad \text{(fifth law)}$$

Only the last one has not already been discussed.

Problem 1. Express $\dfrac{a^7 b^3}{a^2 b^5}$ as a product of powers of a and b.

Solution. We have

$$\frac{a^7 b^3}{a^2 b^5} = \frac{a^7}{a^2} \cdot \frac{b^3}{b^5}$$
$$= a^{7-2} \cdot b^{3-5} = a^5 b^{-2}. \qquad \text{(fourth law)}$$

Problem 2. Express $\dfrac{3x^{-4}y^2 z}{2x^2 y^{-3} z^4}$ in terms of positive powers of the variables.

Solution. We have

$$\frac{3x^{-4}y^2 z}{2x^2 y^{-3} z^4} = \frac{3}{2} \cdot \frac{x^{-4}}{x^2} \cdot \frac{y^2}{y^{-3}} \cdot \frac{z^1}{z^4}$$

$$= \frac{3}{2} \, x^{-4-2} y^{2-(-3)} z^{1-4} \qquad \text{(fourth law)}$$

$$= \frac{3}{2} \, x^{-6} y^5 z^{-3}$$

$$= \frac{3}{2} \cdot \frac{1}{x^6} \cdot y^5 \cdot \frac{1}{z^3}$$

$$= \frac{3}{2} \frac{y^5}{x^6 z^3} \quad \text{or} \quad \frac{3y^5}{2x^6 z^3}$$

Problem 3. Find $(a^{-3}b^2)^{-2}$.

Solution. We proceed as follows.

$$(a^{-3}b^2)^{-2} = (a^{-3})^{-2}(b^2)^{-2} \qquad \text{(second law)}$$
$$= a^6 b^{-4} \qquad \text{(third law)}$$
$$= \frac{a^6}{b^4}$$

Problem 4. Find $\left(\dfrac{5xy^3}{2x^5 y^2}\right)^3$.

Solution.   We have

$$\left(\frac{5xy^3}{2x^5y^2}\right)^3 = \frac{(5xy^3)^3}{(2x^5y^2)^3} \qquad \text{(fifth law)}$$

$$= \frac{5^3x^3(y^3)^3}{2^3(x^5)^3(y^2)^3} \qquad \text{(second law)}$$

$$= \frac{5^3x^3y^9}{2^3x^{15}y^6} \qquad \text{(third law)}$$

$$= \frac{125}{8}\frac{y^{9-6}}{x^{15-3}} \qquad \text{(fourth law)}$$

$$= \frac{125}{8}\frac{y^3}{x^{12}}.$$

Exercises

Perform each of the following multiplications.

1. (a) $3^7 \cdot 3^0$ (b) $(-2)^3(-2)^0$

2. (a) $y^8 \cdot y^0$ (b) $x^0 \cdot x^5$

Perform each of the following divisions, giving each answer in two different forms.

3. (a) $\dfrac{3^2}{3^2}$ (b) $\dfrac{2^4}{2^4}$

4. (a) $\dfrac{y^n}{y^n}$, $y \neq 0$ (b) $x^n \div x^n$, $x \neq 0$

Perform the indicated operations, and express each answer in simplest form. State the laws or definitions used.

5. (a) $1^0 + 2^0 + 3^0$ (b) $5^0 + 6^0 + 7^0$

6. (a) $\dfrac{5^6 \cdot 2^4}{5^1 \cdot 2^3}$ (b) $\dfrac{7^6 \cdot 3^3}{7^8 \cdot 3^2}$

7. (a) $\left(\dfrac{3x^2}{2y^3}\right)^4$ (b) $\left(-\dfrac{2a^2}{3b^4}\right)^2$

8. (a) $\left(\dfrac{2x^4 \cdot x^7}{10y^3 \cdot y}\right)^3$ (b) $-\left(\dfrac{2x}{y^2}\right)^5$

Express as a power of x, or a multiple of a power of x.

9. (a) $\dfrac{5x^{-8}}{15x^{-16}}$ (b) $\dfrac{21x^2}{3x^5}$

10. (a) $\dfrac{x^{-2}}{x^{-5}}$ (b) $\dfrac{2x^6}{6x^{12}}$

11. (a) $(-3x^4)^{-2}$ (b) $(\tfrac{1}{2}x^{-3})^{-4}$

Assume that the value of any variable that appears in a denominator is a nonzero number, and simplify each of the following algebraic expressions. Give answers without negative exponents.

12. (a) $\dfrac{2x^{-3}}{3y^{-2}}$ (b) $\dfrac{(x^{-3})^2 x^5}{x^{-1}}$

13. (a) $\dfrac{x^0}{y^3}$ (b) $0^1 \cdot 1^0$

14. (a) $\left(\dfrac{3xy^2}{5x^3y}\right)\left(\dfrac{10x^4}{21y^5}\right)$ (b) $\left(\dfrac{28a^4b}{7ab^4}\right)^2\left(\dfrac{27ab^5}{54a^5b}\right)^3$

15. (a) $\dfrac{3^6}{2^3 + 2^0}$ (b) $\dfrac{49^3 \cdot 13 \cdot 49^{-3}}{5^2 + 5^0}$

16. (a) $\dfrac{(2 \cdot 10^2)^3 (4 \cdot 10^{-2})^2}{(2 \cdot 10^3)^{-1}}$ (b) $\dfrac{(3 \cdot 10^{-3})(4 \cdot 10^5)}{2 \cdot 10^4}$

Use the third law of exponents to complete each statement.

17. (a) $4^8 = 2^?$ (b) $9^6 = 3^?$

18. (a) $27^6 = 3^?$ (b) $8^5 = 2^?$

19. (a) $2^7 \cdot 4^3 = 2^?$ (b) $3^6 \cdot 81^2 = 3^?$

Express each number as a power of 2 and simplify.

20. (a) $[(\tfrac{1}{4})^6 \cdot 64]^{-3}(32)^{-2}$ (b) $\dfrac{16^3 - 32^4}{4^6 + 8^5}$

Express each number as a power of 3 and simplify.

21. (a) $243^6 \cdot 27^8 \div 81^2$ (b) $\dfrac{\frac{1}{27} + \frac{1}{81}}{\frac{1}{3} - \frac{1}{9}}$

Write the expressions with positive exponents only, and simplify.

22. (a) $3 + 3^{-1}$ (b) $x + x^{-1}$

23. (a) $x^{-2} + y^{-2}$ (b) $z^{-3} - y^{-1}$

24. (a) $(-5xy)^{-3}$ (b) $(-3x^{-4})^2$

25. (a) $(a^{-2}b)^4$ (b) $(x^5x^{-5})^5$

1-9 RADICALS

Knowing that the area of a square is A square inches, we can find the length L, in inches, of a side of the square by the formula

$$L = \sqrt{A}.$$

Similarly, if the volume of a cube is V cubic inches, then the length E, in inches, of an edge of the cube is given by the formula

$$E = \sqrt[3]{V}.$$

We call L the positive square root of A, and E the positive cube root of V. Roots of real numbers are defined in the following way.

Definition of the *n*th root of a number

For every integer n > 1 and all real numbers x and y, the number y is called an nth root of x if, and only if,

$$y^n = x.$$

For a positive number x, we write

$$\sqrt[n]{x}$$

to indicate the *positive* nth *root* of x. In the *radical sign* $\sqrt[n]{x}$, the positive integer n is called the *index*; and x is called the *radicand* in $\sqrt[n]{x}$.

If n is an odd positive integer (such as 3 or 5) and x is a negative number, then

$$\sqrt[n]{x}$$

denotes the negative nth root of x.

One of the unusual, but quite useful, properties of the real number system is that every positive real number x has a unique positive real nth root $\sqrt[n]{x}$. If n is an odd positive integer, every negative real number x has a unique negative real nth root $\sqrt[n]{x}$.

For example,

$$\sqrt{49} = 7, \quad \sqrt[3]{27} = 3, \quad \sqrt[4]{625} = 5, \quad \sqrt[5]{-32} = -2,$$

according to the definition of nth roots. Since an even power of a nonzero number is always positive, in the real number system negative numbers do not have square roots, fourth roots, or, in general, nth roots if n is even.

The following two laws are useful in working with algebraic expressions involving radicals.

LAWS OF RADICALS

$$\sqrt[n]{x \cdot y} = \sqrt[n]{x} \cdot \sqrt[n]{y} \qquad \text{(first law)}$$

$$\sqrt[n]{\frac{x}{y}} = \frac{\sqrt[n]{x}}{\sqrt[n]{y}} \qquad \text{(second law)}$$

These laws are valid for all integers $n > 1$ and all positive real numbers x and y. If n is odd, then they are true for all nonzero real numbers x and y. These laws follow directly from the laws of exponents.

If c/d is a rational number expressed in simplest form, then $\sqrt{c/d}$ is also a rational number if, and only if, the integers c and d are perfect squares, that is, $\sqrt{c}$ and $\sqrt{d}$ are integers. It can be shown in the same way that $\sqrt[n]{c/d}$ is a rational number if, and only if, $\sqrt[n]{c}$ and $\sqrt[n]{d}$ are integers. In this case,

$$\sqrt[n]{\frac{c}{d}} = \frac{\sqrt[n]{c}}{\sqrt[n]{d}}$$

by the second law of radicals. For example,

$$\sqrt[3]{\frac{125}{27}} = \frac{\sqrt[3]{125}}{\sqrt[3]{27}}, \quad \text{or} \quad \frac{5}{3}.$$

An integer is called *square-free* if no factor of it other than 1 is a perfect square. Thus, 14 and 33 are square-free, whereas 44 is not (4 is a perfect-square factor of 44). Every positive integer can be expressed as a product of a perfect-square integer and a square-free integer. For example,

$$45 = 9 \cdot 5, \qquad \text{(9 perfect-square, 5 square-free)}$$
$$150 = 25 \cdot 6. \qquad \text{(25 perfect-square, 6 square-free)}$$

In the same way, every positive integer can be expressed as a product of a perfect-cube integer and a cube-free integer, and so on.

Our remarks above allow us to express the square root of a positive integer in *simplest form* as the product of an integer and the square root of a square-free integer, and similarly for cube roots, and so on. For example,

$$\sqrt{45} = \sqrt{9} \cdot \sqrt{5} = 3\sqrt{5},$$
$$\sqrt{150} = \sqrt{25} \cdot \sqrt{6} = 5\sqrt{6},$$

$$\sqrt[3]{384} = \sqrt[3]{64 \cdot 6} \qquad\qquad \text{(64 perfect-cube, 6 cube-free)}$$
$$= \sqrt[3]{64} \cdot \sqrt[3]{6} = 4\sqrt[3]{6}.$$

Problem 1. Simplify $\sqrt{12a^3}$.

Solution. We have

$$12a^3 = 4a^2 \cdot 3a. \qquad \text{(}4a^2 \text{ a perfect-square, } 3a \text{ square-free)}$$

Hence,

$$\sqrt{12a^3} = \sqrt{4a^2} \cdot \sqrt{3a}$$
$$= 2a\sqrt{3a}.$$

Problem 2. Simplify $\sqrt{\dfrac{54x^5}{5y}}$.

Solution. We have

$$\sqrt{\frac{54x^5}{5y}} = \frac{\sqrt{54x^5}}{\sqrt{5y}}$$
$$= \frac{\sqrt{9x^4 \cdot 6x}}{\sqrt{5y}}$$
$$= \frac{\sqrt{9x^4} \cdot \sqrt{6x}}{\sqrt{5y}}$$
$$= \frac{3x^2 \sqrt{6x}}{\sqrt{5y}}$$

We can eliminate the radical in the denominator by multiplying numerator and denominator by $\sqrt{5y}$.

$$\sqrt{\frac{54x^5}{5y}} = \frac{3x^2\sqrt{6x} \cdot \sqrt{5y}}{\sqrt{5y} \cdot \sqrt{5y}}$$
$$= \frac{3x^2\sqrt{30xy}}{5y}$$

Problem 3. Simplify $\sqrt[3]{81x^5y^{10}}$.

Solution. We have

$$81x^5y^{10} = 27x^3y^9 \cdot 3x^2y. \quad \text{(}27x^3y^9 \text{ perfect-cube, } 3x^2y \text{ cube-free)}$$

Hence, $$\sqrt[3]{81x^5y^{10}} = \sqrt[3]{27x^3y^9} \cdot \sqrt[3]{3x^2y}$$
$$= 3xy^3\sqrt[3]{3x^2y}.$$

Exercises

Complete each of the following simplifications.

1. (a) $\sqrt{20x^5} = \sqrt{4x^4 \cdot ?} = \sqrt{4x^4} \cdot \sqrt{?} = 2x^2 \cdot ?$
   (b) $\sqrt{75x^7} = \sqrt{? \cdot 3x} = \sqrt{?} \cdot \sqrt{3x} = ? \cdot \sqrt{3x}$

2. (a) $\sqrt[3]{24x^7} = \sqrt[3]{8x^6 \cdot ?} = \sqrt[3]{8x^6} \cdot \sqrt[3]{?} = 2x^2 \cdot ?$
   (b) $\sqrt[3]{-54x^{16}} = \sqrt[3]{? \cdot 2x} = \sqrt[3]{?} \cdot \sqrt[3]{2x} = ? \cdot \sqrt[3]{2x}$

Use the fact that $\sqrt{xy} = \sqrt{x} \cdot \sqrt{y}$ to factor each square root and simplify.

3. (a) $\sqrt{45}$ (b) $\sqrt{20}$ **7.** (a) $\sqrt{98}$ (b) $\sqrt{847}$
4. (a) $\sqrt{80}$ (b) $\sqrt{125}$ **8.** (a) $\sqrt{180}$ (b) $\sqrt{210}$
5. (a) $\sqrt{12}$ (b) $\sqrt{27}$ **9.** (a) $\sqrt{2475}$ (b) $\sqrt{3872}$
6. (a) $\sqrt{48}$ (b) $\sqrt{75}$

Simplify each of the following expressions.

10. (a) $\sqrt{175}$ (b) $\sqrt{108}$ **14.** (a) $\sqrt[3]{-250x^6y^8}$ (b) $\sqrt[3]{16xy}$
11. (a) $\sqrt[3]{343}$ (b) $\sqrt[3]{-27}$ **15.** (a) $\sqrt[4]{48x^8y^{10}}$ (b) $\sqrt[4]{162x^6y^{12}}$
12. (a) $\sqrt{27x^4y^3}$ (b) $\sqrt[3]{27x^4y^3}$
13. (a) $\sqrt[5]{-96x^7y^5}$ (b) $\sqrt[5]{-243}$

Complete each of the following simplifications.

16. (a) $\sqrt{\dfrac{12a^3}{5b^3}} = \sqrt{\dfrac{12a^3}{5b^3} \times \dfrac{5b}{5b}} = \sqrt{\dfrac{4a^2}{25b^4} \times ?} = ?\sqrt{?}$

   (b) $\sqrt{\dfrac{18a}{7b}} = \sqrt{\dfrac{18a}{7b} \times \dfrac{7b}{7b}} = \sqrt{\dfrac{9}{49b^2} \times ?} = ?\sqrt{?}$

Write each of the following square roots of rational numbers as a rational number times the square root of a square-free integer.

17. (a) $\sqrt{\frac{1}{5}}$ (b) $\sqrt{\frac{1}{6}}$ **20.** (a) $\sqrt{1\frac{3}{5}}$ (b) $\sqrt{\frac{148}{3}}$
18. (a) $\sqrt{\frac{2}{11}}$ (b) $\sqrt{\frac{4}{7}}$ **21.** (a) $\sqrt{\frac{7}{20}}$ (b) $\sqrt{\frac{35}{6}}$
19. (a) $\sqrt{\frac{3}{8}}$ (b) $\sqrt{\frac{2}{27}}$ **22.** (a) $\sqrt{\frac{49}{24}}$ (b) $\sqrt{\frac{169}{180}}$

Simplify each of the following radicals.

23. (a) $\sqrt{\dfrac{2x^3}{5}}$ (b) $\sqrt[3]{\dfrac{2}{9x}}$ **24.** (a) $\sqrt[3]{\dfrac{8x^4y}{z^5}}$ (b) $\sqrt[5]{\dfrac{2a^6}{3b^7}}$

1–10   ADDITION AND SUBTRACTION OF RADICALS

In adding or subtracting radical expressions, we combine like radicals.

Problem 1.   Find $(\sqrt{24} - 2\sqrt{5}) + (3\sqrt{20} + 5\sqrt{6})$.

Solution.   In simplest form,

$$\sqrt{24} = \sqrt{4 \cdot 6} = 2\sqrt{6}, \qquad \sqrt{20} = \sqrt{4 \cdot 5} = 2\sqrt{5}.$$

Hence,

$$(\sqrt{24} - 2\sqrt{5}) + (3\sqrt{20} + 5\sqrt{6})$$
$$= (2\sqrt{6} - 2\sqrt{5}) + (6\sqrt{5} + 5\sqrt{6})$$
$$= (2\sqrt{6} + 5\sqrt{6}) + (-2\sqrt{5} + 6\sqrt{5})$$
$$= 7\sqrt{6} + 4\sqrt{5}.$$

Problem 2.   Find $(\sqrt{8a^3} + 6\sqrt{10b}) - (\sqrt{90b^3} + \sqrt{18a})$.

Solution.   In simplest form,

$$\sqrt{8a^3} = \sqrt{4a^2 \cdot 2a} = 2a\sqrt{2a},$$
$$\sqrt{90b^3} = \sqrt{9b^2 \cdot 10b} = 3b\sqrt{10b},$$
$$\sqrt{18a} = \sqrt{9 \cdot 2a} = 3\sqrt{2a}$$

Hence,

$$(\sqrt{8a^3} + 6\sqrt{10b}) - (\sqrt{90b^3} + \sqrt{18a})$$
$$= (2a\sqrt{2a} + 6\sqrt{10b}) - (3b\sqrt{10b} + 3\sqrt{2a})$$
$$= 2a\sqrt{2a} + 6\sqrt{10b} - 3b\sqrt{10b} - 3\sqrt{2a}$$
$$= (2a\sqrt{2a} - 3\sqrt{2a}) + (6\sqrt{10b} - 3b\sqrt{10b})$$
$$= (2a - 3)\sqrt{2a} + (6 - 3b)\sqrt{10b}.$$

Exercises

Simplify each radical that is not in simplest form, and find the sum or difference.

1. (a) $\sqrt{50} + 3\sqrt{2}$ (b) $\sqrt{80} + 7\sqrt{5}$
2. (a) $3\sqrt{8} - 5\sqrt{98}$ (b) $7\sqrt{54} - 3\sqrt{24}$
3. (a) $(4\sqrt{12} + 5\sqrt{32}) + (7\sqrt{2} - 2\sqrt{27})$
    (b) $(\sqrt{28} + 3\sqrt{75}) - (\sqrt{63} + 5\sqrt{108})$

4. (a) $6\sqrt{12x} - 5\sqrt{27x^3}$ (b) $\sqrt[3]{24x^2} - 5\sqrt[3]{-81x^5}$

5. (a) $\sqrt{\frac{4}{15}} + 3\sqrt{15}$ (b) $\sqrt{\frac{1}{2}} - \sqrt[3]{\frac{2}{9}}$

6. (a) $(\sqrt{27x^3} + 2\sqrt{72y^5}) - (\sqrt{243x^3} - 3\sqrt{200y^5})$

    (b) $(5\sqrt{72a} + \sqrt{288a}) - (2\sqrt{50a} + \sqrt{242a})$

7. (a) $\sqrt{8x} + \sqrt{2x^3}$ (b) $\sqrt{20x^5} - \sqrt{125x^5}$

8. (a) $\sqrt[3]{\frac{1}{3}} - \sqrt{3}$ (b) $\sqrt{5} - \sqrt[5]{\frac{1}{5}}$

9. Give a pair of values for x and y which makes the following statement false.

$$\sqrt{x - y} = \sqrt{x} - \sqrt{y} \text{ for every positive value of } x \text{ and } y.$$

10. Is the statement $\sqrt{x^2 + y^2} = x + y$ true when $x = 3$, $y = 4$? $x = y = 1$? $x = y = 0$?

1–11   MULTIPLICATION AND DIVISION OF RADICALS

We multiply and divide radicals by using the laws of radicals together with the axioms of algebra.

Problem 1. Simplify $\sqrt{2x^3y} \cdot \sqrt{18xy^4}$.

Solution. Using the first law of radicals,

$$\sqrt{2x^3y} \cdot \sqrt{18xy^4} = \sqrt{2x^3y \cdot 18xy^4}$$
$$= \sqrt{36x^4y^5}$$
$$= \sqrt{36x^4y^4 \cdot y}$$
$$= 6x^2y^2\sqrt{y}.$$

Problem 2. Simplify $\dfrac{\sqrt{18a^3b^5}}{\sqrt{12ab^6}}$.

Solution. Using the second law of radicals,

$$\frac{\sqrt{18a^3b^5}}{\sqrt{12ab^6}} = \sqrt{\frac{18a^3b^5}{12ab^6}}$$

$$= \sqrt{\frac{3a^{3-1}}{2b^{6-5}}} = \sqrt{\frac{3a^2}{2b}}$$

$$= \sqrt{a^2 \cdot \frac{3}{2b}} = a\sqrt{\frac{3}{2b}}.$$

We could change the form of this expression by rationalizing the denominator:

$$a\sqrt{\frac{3}{2b}} = a\sqrt{\frac{3\cdot 2b}{2b\cdot 2b}} = a\sqrt{\frac{6b}{(2b)^2}} = \frac{a}{2b}\sqrt{6b}.$$

Problem 3. Simplify $(2\sqrt{5} + 3\sqrt{2})(\sqrt{5} - 5\sqrt{2})$.

Solution. Multiplying each term of the first binomial by each term of the second, we get:

$$(2\sqrt{5} + 3\sqrt{2})(\sqrt{5} - 5\sqrt{2})$$
$$= 2\sqrt{5}\cdot\sqrt{5} + 2\sqrt{5}\cdot(-5\sqrt{2}) + 3\sqrt{2}\cdot\sqrt{5} + 3\sqrt{2}\cdot(-5\sqrt{2})$$
$$= 2\cdot 5 - 10\sqrt{10} + 3\sqrt{10} - 15\cdot 2$$
$$= -7\sqrt{10} - 20.$$

Problem 4. Simplify $\dfrac{4\sqrt{3} - \sqrt{7}}{\sqrt{7} + \sqrt{3}}$.

Solution. We use the fact that $(\sqrt{7} + \sqrt{3})(\sqrt{7} - \sqrt{3})$ is an integer.

$$(\sqrt{7} + \sqrt{3})(\sqrt{7} - \sqrt{3})$$
$$= \sqrt{7}\cdot\sqrt{7} + \sqrt{7}\cdot(-\sqrt{3}) + \sqrt{3}\cdot\sqrt{7} + \sqrt{3}\cdot(-\sqrt{3})$$
$$= 7 - \sqrt{21} + \sqrt{21} - 3$$
$$= 4$$

Thus,

$$\frac{4\sqrt{3} - \sqrt{7}}{\sqrt{7} + \sqrt{3}}$$
$$= \frac{(4\sqrt{3} - \sqrt{7})(\sqrt{7} - \sqrt{3})}{(\sqrt{7} + \sqrt{3})(\sqrt{7} - \sqrt{3})}$$
$$= \frac{4\sqrt{3}\cdot\sqrt{7} + 4\sqrt{3}\cdot(-\sqrt{3}) - \sqrt{7}\cdot\sqrt{7} - \sqrt{7}\cdot(-\sqrt{3})}{4}$$
$$= \frac{4\sqrt{21} - 12 - 7 + \sqrt{21}}{4}$$
$$= \tfrac{1}{4}(5\sqrt{21} - 19).$$

The method used above to eliminate the radicals in the denominator is called *rationalizing the denominator.*

Exercises

Use the fact that $\sqrt{x} \cdot \sqrt{y} = \sqrt{xy}$ to find the following products.

1. (a) $\sqrt{3} \cdot \sqrt{5}$ (b) $\sqrt{2} \cdot \sqrt{3}$

2. (a) $\sqrt{14} \cdot \sqrt{5}$ (b) $\sqrt{7} \cdot \sqrt{6}$

Use the fact that $\sqrt{x} \div \sqrt{y} = \sqrt{x \div y}$ to find the following quotients.

3. (a) $\sqrt{18} \div \sqrt{3}$ (b) $\sqrt{10} \div \sqrt{5}$

4. (a) $\sqrt{\frac{10}{3}} \div \sqrt{\frac{5}{3}}$ (b) $\sqrt{2\frac{4}{5}} \div \sqrt{\frac{7}{10}}$

Perform the indicated operations and give each answer in simplest form.

5. (a) $\sqrt{3} \cdot \sqrt{6}$ (b) $\sqrt{7} \cdot \sqrt{35}$

6. (a) $\sqrt[3]{4} \cdot \sqrt[3]{10}$ (b) $\sqrt[4]{40} \cdot \sqrt[4]{14}$

7. (a) $3\sqrt{2} \cdot 5\sqrt{2}$ (b) $(4\sqrt{3})^2$

8. (a) $(3\sqrt{2})^3$ (b) $(2\sqrt{3})^3$

9. (a) $\sqrt{20x^3} \cdot \sqrt{30x^7}$ (b) $\sqrt[3]{-10x^7} \cdot \sqrt[3]{-4x^7}$

10. (a) $\sqrt{6} \div \sqrt{12}$ (b) $\sqrt{7xy} \div \sqrt{14x^2y^2}$

11. (a) $\dfrac{\sqrt[3]{16}}{\sqrt[3]{2}}$ (b) $\dfrac{\sqrt[5]{64}}{\sqrt[5]{2}}$

12. (a) $\sqrt{\frac{3}{5}} \div \sqrt{\frac{5}{6}}$ (b) $\sqrt[3]{-5x^2y} \div \sqrt[3]{10xy^5}$

13. (a) $(5 + \sqrt{3})(5 - \sqrt{3})$ (b) $(2\sqrt{3} + 3\sqrt{2})^2$

14. (a) $(3 - \sqrt{5})^2 + \sqrt{180}$ (b) $(\sqrt{6x} - \sqrt{3x^3})^2$

Complete each of the following simplifications.

15. (a) $\dfrac{5 + \sqrt{3}}{5 - \sqrt{3}} = \dfrac{5 + \sqrt{3}}{5 - \sqrt{3}} \cdot \dfrac{5 + \sqrt{3}}{5 + \sqrt{3}} = \dfrac{?}{?}$

(b) $\dfrac{2\sqrt{3} - \sqrt{5}}{2\sqrt{3} + \sqrt{5}} = \dfrac{2\sqrt{3} - \sqrt{5}}{2\sqrt{3} + \sqrt{5}} \cdot \dfrac{2\sqrt{3} - \sqrt{5}}{2\sqrt{3} - \sqrt{5}} = \dfrac{?}{?}$

Rationalize the denominator of each fraction, and simplify.

16. (a) $\dfrac{4}{\sqrt{3} - 1}$ (b) $\dfrac{\sqrt{2} + 3}{\sqrt{2} - 5}$

17. (a) $\dfrac{16}{\sqrt{7} - \sqrt{3}}$ (b) $\dfrac{\sqrt{7} - \sqrt{2}}{\sqrt{7} + \sqrt{2}}$

18. (a) $\dfrac{\sqrt{x} + 3\sqrt{y}}{\sqrt{x} - 3\sqrt{y}}$ (b) $\dfrac{\sqrt{x} - 2\sqrt{y}}{\sqrt{x} + 2\sqrt{y}}$

1–12   RATIONAL EXPONENTS

We have defined the exponential notation x^n for every integer n. It is natural to ask whether x^r can be defined for every rational number r. Of course, we would like to define x^r so that the laws of exponents continue to be valid for rational exponents.

For example, what is a reasonable definition of $x^{1/3}$? If the third law of exponents is to be valid for rational exponents, then we must have

$$(x^{1/3})^3 = x^{1/3 \cdot 3}, \quad \text{or } x.$$

Since $(\sqrt[3]{x})^3 = x$ for every real number x, a natural definition of $x^{1/3}$ is the cube root of x:

$$x^{1/3} = \sqrt[3]{x}.$$

With this example in mind, we define

$$x^{1/n} = \sqrt[n]{x}$$

for every positive integer n and for every real number x for which $\sqrt[n]{x}$ is real. Thus, for example,

$$4^{1/2} = \sqrt{4}, \quad \text{or } 2,$$
$$81^{1/4} = \sqrt[4]{81}, \quad \text{or } 3,$$
$$(-32)^{1/5} = \sqrt[5]{-32}, \quad \text{or } -2.$$

Now that we have defined the $(1/n)th$-power of a real number, let us consider how we might define the $(m/n)th$-power of a number. We first look at a special example, say $8^{2/3}$. If the third law of exponents is to be valid, then we must have

$$8^{2/3} = (8^{1/3})^2$$
$$= (\sqrt[3]{8})^2$$
$$- 2^2, \quad \text{or } 4.$$

With this example in mind, we give the following definition.

Definition of rational exponents

For every pair of integers m and n, with $n > 1$, and for every real number x for which $(\sqrt[n]{x})^m$ is real, we define

$$x^{m/n} = (\sqrt[n]{x})^m.$$

Returning to the example above, we might have computed $8^{2/3}$ as follows.

$$8^{2/3} = (8^2)^{1/3}$$
$$= \sqrt[3]{8^2}$$
$$= \sqrt[3]{64}, \quad \text{or } 4.$$

The fact that the answer is the same as before suggests that the following equation is true for all integers m and n, with $n > 0$, and all nonzero numbers x having a real number nth root.

$$(x^{1/n})^m = (x^m)^{1/n}$$

The truth of the above equation allows us to find $x^{m/n}$ in either one of two ways:

$$x^{m/n} = (x^{1/n})^m$$

or

$$x^{m/n} = (x^m)^{1/n}.$$

For example,

$$4^{3/2} = (\sqrt{4})^3 = 2^3, \quad \text{or } 8,$$
$$4^{3/2} = (4^3)^{1/2} = \sqrt{64}, \quad \text{or } 8.$$

It can be proved that the five laws of exponents are valid for rational exponents as well as for integral exponents. From now on, we shall assume that these laws are true for rational exponents, and we shall use them whenever necessary.

Problem 1. Simplify $3^{2/3} \cdot 9^{1/6}$.

Solution.
$$3^{2/3} \cdot 9^{1/6} = 3^{2/3} \cdot (3^2)^{1/6}$$
$$= 3^{2/3} \cdot 3^{2/6}$$
$$= 3^{2/3+2/6} = 3^1, \quad \text{or } 3.$$

Problem 2. Simplify $(x^{-5/2} \cdot y^{7/3})^6$.

Solution.
$$(x^{-5/2} \cdot y^{7/3})^6 = (x^{-5/2})^6 \cdot (y^{7/3})^6$$
$$= x^{-15} \cdot y^{14}$$
$$= \frac{y^{14}}{x^{15}}$$

Problem 3. Simplify $\sqrt{xy^3} \cdot \sqrt[3]{x^2y}$.

Solution.

$$\sqrt{xy^3} \cdot \sqrt[3]{x^2y} = (xy^3)^{1/2} \cdot (x^2y)^{1/3}$$
$$= x^{1/2} \cdot (y^3)^{1/2} \cdot (x^2)^{1/3} \cdot y^{1/3}$$
$$= x^{1/2} \cdot y^{3/2} \cdot x^{2/3} \cdot y^{1/3}$$
$$= x^{1/2+2/3} \cdot y^{3/2+1/3}$$
$$= x^{7/6} \cdot y^{11/6} \qquad (\text{or } x \cdot x^{1/6} \cdot y \cdot y^{5/6})$$
$$= (x^7 \cdot y^{11})^{1/6} \qquad (\text{or } xy(x^{1/6}y^{5/6})$$
$$= \sqrt[6]{x^7y^{11}} \qquad (\text{or } xy\sqrt[6]{xy^5})$$
$$= \sqrt[6]{(x^6y^6) \cdot (xy^5)}$$
$$= xy\sqrt[6]{xy^5}$$

Exercises

Simplify each of the following expressions.

1. (a) $9^{1/2}$ (b) $27^{2/3}$

2. (a) $9^{-1/2}$ (b) $27^{-2/3}$

3. (a) $64^{5/6}$ (b) $32^{-2/5}$

4. (a) $16^{3/2}$ (b) $8^{-2/3}$

5. (a) $3^{1/2} \cdot 3^{3/2}$ (b) $\dfrac{27^{2/3} - 27^{-2/3}}{9}$

Rewrite each expression, using fractional exponents instead of radicals.

6. (a) $-2\sqrt{y}$ (b) $-x\sqrt{x}$

7. (a) $3\sqrt[4]{4x^3y}$ (b) $2\sqrt[3]{2x^2y}$

8. (a) $\sqrt[3]{(x-y)^2}$ (b) $\sqrt[4]{(x-2y)^5}$

Rewrite each expression, using radicals instead of fractional exponents. Simplify when possible.

9. (a) $(2x)^{4/5}$ (b) $y^{2/3}$

10. (a) $-3x^{1/5}$ (b) $(-3x)^{4/5}$

11. (a) $x^{1/3} - y^{1/3}$ (b) $(x+y)^{1/3}$

Simplify each of the following expressions.

12. $(10^{1/3} \cdot 10^{-1/6})^6$ **13.** $(10^{1/3})^6 + (10^{-1/3})^6$

14. $9^{2/3} \cdot 27^{2/9}$ **15.** $8^{3/2} \cdot 4^{1/4}$

16. $(64x^9)^{2/3}$ **17.** $(36x^2)^{-3/2}$

18. $(x^{1/2} + y^{1/2})(x^{1/2} - y^{1/2})$ **19.** $(e^x - e^{-x})^2$

20. $\left(\dfrac{-x^{1/2}y^{2/3}}{x^{3/4}y^{1/6}} \right)^{12}$ **21.** $(x^{1/2} + y^{1/2})^2$

In Exercises 22 through 25, simplify the expression, following the method of Problem 3, Section 12.

22. $(\sqrt{x^3 y^2})(\sqrt[3]{xy})$

23. $\dfrac{\sqrt[3]{a^2 b}}{\sqrt{ab^3}}$

24. (a) $\sqrt{2}\sqrt[3]{3}$

(b) $\sqrt[4]{2}\sqrt{2}$

25. (a) $\sqrt[3]{\sqrt{2\sqrt{2}}}$

(b) $\sqrt[3]{\sqrt{\sqrt{x}}}$

26. Use fractional exponents to show that $\sqrt[4]{9} = \sqrt{3}$.

27. Show that $\sqrt[6]{x^3} = \sqrt[4]{x^2}$, x nonnegative. Find another way to express this number.

The *index* of the radical $\sqrt[n]{a}$ is the integer n. Use fractional exponents to express each of the following as a single radical with the smallest possible index.

28. (a) $\sqrt[4]{49}$

(b) $\sqrt[8]{25}$

29. (a) $\sqrt[6]{125}$

(b) $\sqrt[6]{4}$

Simplify.

30. $\sqrt[3]{16} \cdot \sqrt[6]{4}$

31. $\sqrt[6]{8} \div \sqrt[4]{25}$

32. $\sqrt[3]{\sqrt{8}}$

33. $\sqrt[3]{\sqrt[5]{64}}$

34. $\sqrt[4]{a^2 b^4} - b\sqrt{a}$

35. $\sqrt[6]{27x^3} - \sqrt{3x}$

1-13 / NUMBER LINES

An interesting feature of the real number system is that it may be used as a scale on a line. Thus, if we choose a unit of length, such as an inch or a centimeter, we may represent the integers as equispaced points (the chosen unit apart) on a line. (See Fig. 1-1.) By bisecting, trisecting, and so on, each unit segment, the rational numbers may also be assigned to points on the line. For example, $\frac{1}{2}$ is assigned to the point halfway between 0 and 1; $-\frac{5}{3}$ is assigned to the point two-thirds of the way from -1 to -2; $\frac{12}{5}$ is assigned to the point two-fifths of the way from 2 to 3; and so on. The point O, which has zero assigned to it, is called the *origin*.

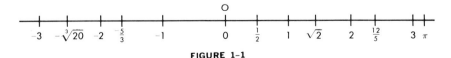

FIGURE 1-1

Each irrational number can also be assigned to a point on the line. For example, we may find the point having $\sqrt{2}$ assigned to it in the way indicated in Fig. 1–2. In this figure, the partially drawn circle has its center at the origin and a radius of $\sqrt{2}$. Hence, it will intersect the given line at the point having $\sqrt{2}$ assigned to it.

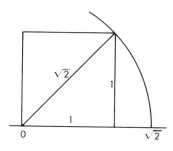

FIGURE 1–2

It is not possible to construct the point assigned to every real number by the method used for $\sqrt{2}$. For example, it is impossible (by means of straightedge and compass alone) to construct the point assigned to the irrational number π. However, we can imagine that there is a point representing π.

Each real number is assigned to a unique point on the line, and each point on the line has a unique real number assigned to it. A line having a real-number scale on it is called a *number line*. The number assigned to a point on the number line is called the *coordinate* of the point.

A number line may be assigned a *direction*. We shall always take the direction as that from the origin, O, toward the point with coordinate 1. Thus, if we imagine ourselves walking from left to right along the number line in Fig. 1–3, we are walking in the direction of the line, called the *positive direction*. We would be walking counter to the direction of the line, or in the *negative direction*, if we walked from right to left. The direction of a number line is indicated by an arrowhead as shown in Fig. 1–3. If point A on the line has coordinate a, then A is to the *right* of the origin O if, and only if, $a > 0$. Similarly, point B with coordinate b is to the *left* of O if, and only if, $b < 0$.

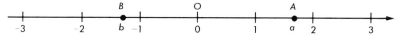

FIGURE 1–3

The distance between two points on a yardstick may be found by subtracting the coordinates of the two points. For example, the distance between points A and B on the yardstick of Fig. 1–4 is $29 - 21$, or 8 inches. It is possible to find the distance between any two points on a number line in the same way if the two points are on the same side of the origin. This situation is similar to our yardstick in Fig. 1–4.

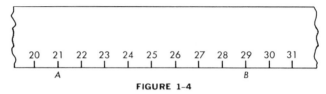

FIGURE 1–4

If two points are on opposite sides of the origin, as are C and D in Fig. 1–5, then how do we find the distance between them? By counting

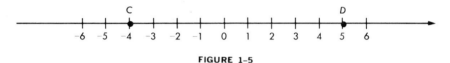

FIGURE 1–5

unit intervals we see that the distance between C and D is 9. If we subtract the coordinate of C from that of D, we get

$$5 - (-4) = 5 + 4, \quad \text{or } 9.$$

Thus, we see that the distance between two points on opposite sides of the origin may also be found by subtracting their coordinates.

If we subtract coordinates in the opposite order, we obtain $21 - 29$, or -8, which is the negative of the distance between points A and B in Fig. 1-4. A useful device in describing distances on a line is the *absolute value* of a number. This allows us to subtract the coordinates of two points in either order in finding the distance between them.

Definition of absolute value

The absolute value of a number x is denoted by $|x|$ and is defined by

$$|x| = x \text{ if } x \geq 0$$
$$|x| = -x \text{ if } x < 0.$$

For example,

$$|3| = 3 \text{ because } 3 \geq 0.$$
$$|0| = 0 \text{ because } 0 \geq 0.$$
$$|-7| = -(-7) = 7 \text{ because } -7 < 0.$$

Keep in mind: *the absolute value of every nonzero number is a positive number.* Given a nonzero number x, either x or $-x$ is a positive number; the one that is positive is the absolute value of x.

If points A and B on a number line have coordinates a and b, respectively, then the *distance* between A and B is denoted by AB and is given by

$$AB = |a - b|.$$

Since $-(a - b) = b - a$, AB equals either $a - b$ or $b - a$, whichever is nonnegative.

We find distances between various points on the line in Fig. 1-6 as follows:

FIGURE 1-6

$$AB = |-4 - 5| = |-9| = 9$$
$$BC = |5 - (-1)| = |6| = 6$$
$$DE = |2 - (-5)| = |7| = 7$$
$$EB = |-5 - 5| = |-10| = 10$$
$$OB = |0 - 5| = |-5| = 5$$
$$AO = |-4 - 0| = |-4| = 4.$$

Exercises

Tell which of the following statements are true and which are false. Correct the statements that you marked false.

1. (a) $|3 - \pi| = 3 - \pi$ (b) $|3 - 5| = 5 - 3$

2. (a) $-5 \cdot 3 = -(|-5| \cdot |3|)$ (b) $(6)(-3) = |-6| \cdot |-3|$

3. (a) $|2 - \sqrt{3}| = -(\sqrt{3} + 2)$ (b) $\dfrac{1}{\sqrt{3}} \geq \dfrac{\sqrt{3}}{3}$

4. (a) $|-7| > |-4|$ (b) $|2| \geq |-8|$

Express each of the following numbers without using absolute-value signs.

5. (a) $|-5 - (-6)|$ (b) $|-5| - |-6|$

6. (a) $|-2| + |-4|$ (b) $|-2 + -4|$

7. (a) $|\sqrt{2} - 1.41|$ (b) $|\sqrt{15} - 4|$

8. (a) $|\tfrac{1}{3} - .333|$ (b) $\left|\dfrac{3}{4} - \dfrac{\pi}{4}\right|$

9. (a) $|12 + (-9)|$ (b) $|12| + |-9|$

10. (a) $|-5 - (-5)|$ (b) $|10^{-6}|$

Find all integral values of x that make each of the statements true if the set is finite. Otherwise, find six such values.

11. (a) $|x| = 4$ (b) $|x| + 3 = 10$

12. (a) $|x + 1| = 3$ (b) $|x - 6| = 9$

13. (a) $|x| < 5$ (b) $|x| > 5$

14. (a) $|x - 1| < 6$ (b) $|x - 1| > 6$

15. (a) $|2x + 1| \leqq 21$ (b) $|2x + 1| > 21$

16. (a) $12 > x + 1 > 2$ (b) $12 > |x + 1| > 2$

17. (a) $|2 - x| \leqq 7$ (b) $|2 - x| > 7$

18. (a) $3 < x < 10$ (b) $3 < |x| < 10$

19.

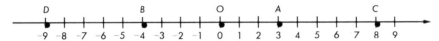

Refer to the figure above to find each of the following distances.

(a) OA (b) OC (c) OB (d) OD (e) CA (f) CB (g) CD (h) BD

20. Refer to the figure in Exercise 19 to find the coordinate of the point midway between each of the following pairs of points.

(a) O, C (b) O, B (c) A, C (d) B, C (e) D, B

21. If P is a point midway between points A and B on a number line, how can the coordinate of P be found using the coordinates of A and B? (Hint: see the results of Exercise 20.)

22. Draw a number line, and on it, indicate points O, A, B, C, D, E, and F which have respective coordinates 0, $-\frac{1}{2}$, -4, $\sqrt{2}$, $2\sqrt{3}$, -6, and 5. Find the following distances.

(a) OB (b) OC (c) AF (d) AB (e) DA (f) EC (g) FA (h) BA

23. For each of the following pairs of values of x and y, compare the value of $|x| \cdot |y|$ with that of $|x \cdot y|$.

(a) $5, 6$ (b) $-4, 3$

(c) $7, -8$ (d) $-2, -10$

(e) In general, is $|x| \cdot |y|$ greater than, equal to, or less than $|x \cdot y|$?

CHAPTER REVIEW

Find the sum of each of the following pairs of irrational numbers.

1. (a) $3\sqrt{5} + 2, 2\sqrt{5} - 4$ (b) $\sqrt{18} - \sqrt{2}, -2\sqrt{18} + 3\sqrt{2}$

2. (a) $4 - \sqrt{23}, 3 + 5\sqrt{23}$ (b) $7\sqrt{3}, 8 - 5\sqrt{3}$

Find the product of each of the following pairs of irrational numbers.

3. (a) $3 - \sqrt{2}, 3 + \sqrt{2}$ (b) $2\sqrt{7} - 5, 2\sqrt{7} + 5$

4. (a) $\sqrt{2} + \sqrt{3}, \sqrt{3} - \sqrt{2}$ (b) $\sqrt{11} + 2\sqrt{2}, \sqrt{11} - 2\sqrt{2}$

Find the following sums and differences.

5. $(2x + 4y - 2) + (-3x + 3y + 4)$

6. $(3a - 7b + 7) + (-4a + 9b + 3)$

7. $(4a + b + 5) - (2a + 5b - 3)$

8. $(14x - 7y + 12) - (17x + 4y - 8)$

Find the following products and quotients.

9. (a) $(4x^3y^4) \cdot (3xy^5)$ (b) $(x^4y^2) \cdot (3x^2y^4)$

10. (a) $(3ab^2c^3) \cdot (2a^3b^4c)$ (b) $(7a^3c^2) \cdot (-2a^4b^5)$

11. (a) $(2x^3y^5)^4$ (b) $(3x^{11}y^2)^3$

12. (a) $5x(2x + 3y)$ (b) $7y(3x - 2y)$

13. (a) $(x + 3y)(2x - 5y)$ (b) $(3x - 5y)(x + y)$

14. (a) $(8x^5y^2) \div (2x^3y)$ (b) $(4x^7yz^3) \div (3x^2yz^2)$

15. (a) $(3a^2b^4 - 2a^3b^5) \div (ab^4)$ (b) $(a^7 + 3a^4b^5) \div (3a^2)$

Find the following sums and differences.

16. (a) $\dfrac{3}{5} + \dfrac{7}{5}$ (b) $\dfrac{2}{3} - \dfrac{4}{3}$

17. (a) $\dfrac{3}{7} - \dfrac{2}{5}$ (b) $\dfrac{5}{8} + \dfrac{3}{4}$

18. (a) $\dfrac{x}{y^2} + \dfrac{3}{y}$ (b) $\dfrac{2y}{x} - \dfrac{4}{x^2}$

19. (a) $\dfrac{3}{a^2} - \dfrac{4}{a} + 2$ (b) $-5 + \dfrac{7}{a} - \dfrac{2}{a^2}$

Simplify.

20. (a) $3^3 \cdot 3^0$ (b) $2^7 \cdot 2^{-4}$

21. (a) $(3x^{-2}y^2) \cdot (2x^5y^{-4})$ (b) $(2^3x^4y^{-1}) \cdot (2^5x^{-2}y^3)$

22. (a) $(2a^{-4}b^2) \div (4a^3b^{-2})$ (b) $(a^7b^6) \div (a^8b^4)$

23. (a) $\left(\dfrac{2x^3y}{x^4y^2}\right)^4$ (b) $\left(\dfrac{x^{-2}y^2}{3xy^{-2}}\right)^{-3}$

24. (a) $\sqrt{27}$ (b) $\sqrt{150}$

25. (a) $\sqrt{18x^3y^2}$ (b) $\sqrt{8x^4y^3}$

26. (a) $\sqrt{\dfrac{9a^4}{b^3}}$ (b) $\sqrt{\dfrac{a^3}{8b^2}}$

Express each of the following numbers as a rational number times the square root of a square-free integer.

27. (a) $\sqrt{\dfrac{3}{50}}$ (b) $\sqrt{\dfrac{180}{7}}$ **28.** (a) $\sqrt{\dfrac{1000}{3}}$ (b) $\sqrt{\dfrac{512}{243}}$

Simplify.

29. (a) $\sqrt{4x^2y} + \sqrt{y^3}$ (b) $\sqrt{2x^3y^2} - \sqrt{18x}$

30. (a) $\sqrt{3ab^2} - \sqrt{12a^3}$ (b) $\sqrt{4a^5b^3} + \sqrt{ab^5}$

31. (a) $\sqrt{28} \cdot \sqrt{32}$ (b) $\sqrt{50} \cdot \sqrt{98}$

32. (a) $\sqrt{2a^3} \cdot \sqrt{18a}$ (b) $\sqrt{3a} \cdot \sqrt{2a^5}$

33. (a) $\dfrac{\sqrt{3x^3y}}{\sqrt{6xy^3}}$ (b) $\dfrac{\sqrt{x^4y^3}}{\sqrt{5xy^5}}$

Rationalize the denominator, and simplify.

34. (a) $\dfrac{2\sqrt{2}+3}{2\sqrt{2}-3}$ (b) $\dfrac{\sqrt{5}-2}{\sqrt{5}+1}$

35. (a) $\dfrac{\sqrt{5}+2\sqrt{3}}{2\sqrt{5}-\sqrt{3}}$ (b) $\dfrac{\sqrt{11}-2\sqrt{2}}{3\sqrt{11}+4\sqrt{2}}$

Simplify.

36. (a) $2^{1/3} \cdot 4^{2/3}$ (b) $3^{3/2} \cdot 27^{-5/2}$

37. (a) $(x^{2/3} \cdot y^{5/3})^6$ (b) $(x^{1/4} \cdot y^{3/2})^4$

Perform the indicated operation.

38. (a) $|5 - 7| - |7 - 5|$ (b) $|2 + 3| + |2 - 3|$

39. (a) $|10 - 14| + |3 - 5|$ (b) $|8 - 4| - |4 - 8|$

In Exercises 40–43, draw a number line and mark on it points O, R, S, T, P, Q having respective coordinates 0, 5, -3, 12, -4, 20. Find:

40. (a) $O\,Q$ (b) $S\,T$ **42.** (a) $Q\,R$ (b) $T\,P$

41. (a) $R\,P$ (b) $O\,S$ **43.** (a) $P\,O$ (b) $P\,Q$

Find all integral values of x for which each expression below is true.

44. (a) $|x + 7| = 9$ (b) $|x - 3| = 5$

45. (a) $|x - 3| \leq 7$ (b) $|x + 2| < 8$

Find:

46. (a) $\left| \dfrac{2}{21} - \dfrac{3}{28} \right|$ (b) $\left| \dfrac{7}{17} - \dfrac{9}{23} \right|$

47. (a) $\left| \dfrac{1}{4} - \dfrac{7}{27} \right|$ (b) $\left| \dfrac{11}{15} - \dfrac{18}{25} \right|$

2 · First-degree Equations and Inequalities

2–1   EQUATIONS IN ONE VARIABLE

Each of the algebraic expressions

$$3x - 7, \quad 11x + 33, \quad 4x, \quad -2, \quad 0$$

is called a linear form in the variable x. Thus, a *linear form in the variable x* is an algebraic expression of the type

$$ax + b,$$

where a and b are real numbers. Of course, there are linear forms in other variables. For example, $7y - 11$ is a linear form in the variable y.

If, in a linear form, we give the variable a value, the resulting number is called a *value* of the linear form. For example, the linear form $3x - 7$ has the value $(3 \cdot 5) - 7$, or 8, when $x = 5$.

If two linear forms in the same variable are connected by an equals sign, the resulting algebraic statement is called a *first-degree equation*, or *linear equation*, in that variable. For example,

$$3x - 7 = 11x + 33$$

is a first-degree equation in the variable x.

A number is called a *solution* of an equation in one variable if a true equation is obtained when we give the variable the value of the number. For example, 2 is a solution of the equation $3x - 1 = 7 - x$ since the equation obtained by letting $x = 2$ is true:

$$(3 \cdot 2) - 1 = 7 - 2, \quad \text{or } 5 = 5.$$

On the other hand, 3 is not a solution of this equation since the equation obtained by letting $x = 3$ is false:

$$(3 \cdot 3) - 1 = 7 - 3, \quad \text{or } 8 = 4.$$

If an equation has any solutions, then the set of all its solutions is called the *solution set of the equation.* If an equation has no solution, then its solution set is the empty set, ∅. When we *solve* an equation, we find its solution set.

Two or more equations in a variable are said to be *equivalent equations* if they have the same solution set. The process of solving an equation involves replacing the given equation by a succession of equivalent equations until we obtain an equation with an obvious solution set. For example, the given equation might be

$$2(x - 4) + 2x + 27 = 3(x + 7),$$

and the final equivalent one might be $x = 2$. Since $\{2\}$ is the solution set of the final equation, $\{2\}$ is also the solution set of the given equation.

We can use various axioms and properties, such as the additive and multiplicative axioms and the cancellation axioms of addition and multiplication, to derive equivalent equations from a given equation. Several of these axioms and properties are used in the following problems.

Problem 1. Solve the equation $3x - 7 = 11x + 33$.

Solution. Each of the following equations is equivalent to the preceding one for the reason given.

$$3x - 7 = 11x + 33$$
$$(3x - 7) + (-11x + 7) = (11x + 33) + (-11x + 7)$$
$$-8x = 40$$
$$(-\tfrac{1}{8})(-8x) = (-\tfrac{1}{8}) \cdot 40$$
$$x = -5$$

Thus, $\{-5\}$ is the solution set of the given equation.

Check.
$$[3 \cdot (-5)] - 7 \stackrel{?}{=} [11 \cdot (-5)] + 33$$
$$-15 - 7 \stackrel{?}{=} -55 + 33$$
$$-22 \stackrel{\checkmark}{=} -22$$

We check the solution to catch possible computational errors and to be certain that no errors have been made in forming each equivalent equation. If no errors have been made, the solution set of the final equation must be the solution set of the given equation.

Problem 2. Solve the equation $\frac{1}{3}y - 12 = 4 - \frac{3}{5}y$.

Solution. As before, we proceed by finding equivalent equations.

$$\frac{1}{3}y - 12 = 4 - \frac{3}{5}y$$

$$(\tfrac{1}{3}y - 12) + (\tfrac{3}{5}y + 12) = (4 - \tfrac{3}{5}y) + (\tfrac{3}{5}y + 12)$$

$$\tfrac{1}{3}y + \tfrac{3}{5}y = 4 + 12$$

$$(\tfrac{1}{3} + \tfrac{3}{5})y = 16$$

$$\tfrac{14}{15}y = 16$$

$$\tfrac{15}{14} \cdot \tfrac{14}{15}y = \tfrac{15}{14} \cdot 16$$

$$y = \tfrac{120}{7}$$

Thus, $\{17\frac{1}{7}\}$ is the solution set of the given equation.

Check.

$$(\tfrac{1}{3} \cdot \tfrac{120}{7}) - 12 \overset{?}{=} 4 - (\tfrac{3}{5} \cdot \tfrac{120}{7})$$

$$\tfrac{40}{7} - 12 \overset{?}{=} 4 - \tfrac{72}{7}$$

$$\frac{40 - 84}{7} \overset{?}{=} \frac{28 - 72}{7}$$

$$\frac{-44}{7} \overset{\checkmark}{=} \frac{-44}{7}$$

Exercises

In Exercises 1 and 2, test the solution of the second equation in the first equation to see whether or not the two equations are equivalent. If they are not equivalent, change the second equation to make it equivalent to the first.

1. (a) $\dfrac{x}{2} - \dfrac{x}{3} = 5$ (b) $\dfrac{x}{7} = 42$

      $3x - 2x = 30$ $x = 6$

2. (a) $5x - 6 = 17$ (b) $3x = 15$

      $5x = 11$ $x = 12$

Solve each of the following equations by writing a succession of equivalent equations, and check each solution.

3. (a) $3x + 4 = x + 12$ (b) $3 - 7x = 4x - 30$

4. (a) $5z + \frac{1}{3} = 2z - \frac{3}{2}$ (b) $\frac{1}{2}x - \frac{6}{5} = 12 - \frac{3}{2}x$

5. (a) $3(x - 3) = 7(2x + 1)$ (b) $2(3x + 2) - 12 = 3x - 11$

6. (a) $\frac{1}{5}(x + 1) = \frac{2}{3} + \frac{1}{9}(x - 1)$ (b) $\frac{1}{5}(x + 2) = \frac{2}{3} + \frac{1}{9}x$

7. (a) $.13y + 1.17 = 1.23y - .04$ (b) $6.1 - 5w = 4.6w + 3.22$

8. (a) $\dfrac{x - 13}{3} = \dfrac{78 - x}{10}$ (b) $\dfrac{x - 4}{3} = \dfrac{69 - x}{10}$

Tell whether or not the two equations of each given pair are equivalent. If not, change the second equation to make it equivalent to the first.

9. $\dfrac{x-3}{5} + \dfrac{3}{2} = 4 + \dfrac{5-x}{10}$, $2x - 6 + 15 = 40 + 5 - x$

10. $\dfrac{6x-1}{5} - 3x = \dfrac{12x-16}{15}$, $18x - 3 - 3x = 12x - 16$

11. $3(x-2) - 5 = 8 - 2(x-4)$, $3x - 6 - 5 = 8 - 2x - 8$

12. $4 - \dfrac{2x+1}{4} = \dfrac{1}{2} - \dfrac{9x+9}{8}$, $32 - 4x - 2 = 4 - 9x + 9$

Solve each of the following equations by writing a succession of equivalent equations, and check each solution.

13. $\dfrac{x+3}{5} - 2 = \dfrac{3x+2}{4} - 3$

14. $\dfrac{6y-1}{5} - 3y = \dfrac{12y-16}{15}$

15. $5\left(\dfrac{x+2}{3}\right) - x = \dfrac{20}{3}$

16. $5z - \tfrac{1}{5} = 3(z + \tfrac{13}{15})$

17. $t + 13 = 3 - 2(1 + t)$

18. $.6(1 - .8x) = .5 - .4(2 - 1.8x)$

19. $\tfrac{1}{3}(u + 8) - \tfrac{1}{4}(3 - 2u) = \tfrac{1}{6}$

20. $4 - \dfrac{2x-1}{4} = \dfrac{1}{2} - \dfrac{9x}{8}$

21. $\dfrac{w}{3} - \dfrac{4w+1}{2} = w - \dfrac{5}{6}$

22. $4 - \dfrac{2x+1}{4} = \dfrac{1}{2} - \dfrac{9x+9}{8}$

23. $2 + \dfrac{3w+1}{6} = \dfrac{4w-3}{2} - \dfrac{5w-9}{3}$

24. For what value of x does the linear form $3x + 7$ have the same value as the linear form $5x - 3$? Is there more than one such value?

25. (a) Compare the values of $6 - 2x$ and $-2(x - 3)$ for $x = 3, -3, 0, \tfrac{1}{2}$.
   (b) If two linear forms in x have the same value for more than one value of x, for how many values of x do you suspect that they will have the same value?

26. Are the equations $x = 3$ and $x^2 = 3x$ equivalent? Why?

2–2 WORD PROBLEMS

As the following examples show, we can use linear equations in one variable to solve many kinds of word problems.

Problem 1. It takes a man 2 hours to drive a distance of 100 miles. If he averages 60 miles per hour in the country and 30 miles per hour in each city he passes through, how great a part of the trip does he spend in the country?

Solution. If we let t designate the number of hours he spends driving in the country, then $2 - t$ is the number of hours he spends driving in cities. The formula relating distance, d, rate, r, and time, t, is

$$d = rt.$$

Thus, the man drives a distance of $30(2 - t)$ miles in cities and $60t$ miles in the country. It is given that the sum of these distances is 100 miles:

$$60t + 30(2 - t) = 100.$$

We can solve the problem by solving the above first-degree equation in t. Let us proceed as follows:

$$60t + 60 - 30t = 100,$$
$$30t + 60 = 100,$$
$$(30t + 60) - 60 = 100 - 60,$$
$$30t = 40,$$
$$t = \tfrac{4}{3}.$$

Thus, the man spends $\tfrac{4}{3}$ hours, or 1 hour and 20 minutes, driving in the country and $2 - \tfrac{4}{3}$ hours, or 40 minutes, driving in cities. He drives a distance of

$$60 \cdot \tfrac{4}{3}, \quad \text{or } 80,$$

miles in the country and $30 \cdot \tfrac{2}{3}$, or 20, miles in cities. Since

$$80 + 20 = 100,$$

these answers are correct.

An interesting type of problem involves the mixing of two substances in order to form a prescribed mixture. We can use first-degree equations to solve these problems also.

Problem 2. If a certain sample of sea water contains 8% salt, how much fresh water must we add to 40 pounds of the sea water so that the mixture contains only 5% salt?

Solution. In the 40 pounds of sea water, there are .08 × 40, or 3.2, pounds of salt. If we add N pounds of fresh water to the 40 pounds of sea water, we can obtain $N + 40$ pounds of water. We add only fresh water to the salt water. Therefore, the amount of salt in our mixture remains the same. Since we want 5% of the mixture to be salt, we must have

$$.05(N + 40) = 3.2.$$

We may solve the above first-degree equation in N as follows:

$$.05N + 2 = 3.2,$$
$$(.05N + 2) - 2 = 3.2 - 2,$$
$$.05N = 1.2,$$
$$N = \frac{1.2}{.05},$$
$$N = 24.$$

Thus, we must add 24 pounds of fresh water.

Check. $.05(24 + 40) \overset{?}{=} 3.2$
                                  $.05 \times 64 \overset{?}{\leq} 3.2$

Problem 3. Tickets at a theater sell for $5.50 on the main floor and $3.25 in the balcony. If $8550 is collected for 1800 tickets, how many of each kind are sold?

Solution. Let x denote the number of main floor tickets.
Then $1800 - x$ denotes the number of balcony tickets.

   $5.50x$ (the price per ticket times the number of tickets) denotes the money collected for main floor seats.

   $3.25(1800 - x)$ denotes money collected for balcony seats.

   $5.50x + 3.25(1800 - x)$ denotes total receipts for all tickets

Hence, from the information given in the problem, we know that

$$5.50x + 3.25(1800 - x) = 8550.$$

Solving this equation,

$$5.50x + (3.25)(1800) - 3.25x = 8550,$$
$$5.50x + 5850 - 3.25x = 8550,$$
$$5.50x - 3.25x + 5850 - 5850 = 8550 - 5850,$$
$$2.25x = 2700,$$
$$x = \frac{2700}{2.25} = 1200.$$

Thus, $1800 - x = 600$. There are 1200 tickets sold for the main floor and 600 tickets sold for the balcony.

$$1200(5.5) + 600(3.25) \overset{?}{=} 8550$$
$$6600 + 1950 \overset{\checkmark}{=} 8550$$

Exercises

Let x denote an arbitrary integer, and write an algebraic expression for each of the following phrases.

1. (a) The sum of four consecutive integers
   (b) The sum of five consecutive integers

2. (a) The sum of three consecutive odd integers
   (b) The sum of five consecutive even integers

Let x denote the number of 8¢ stamps in a collection that contains both 8¢ and 11¢ stamps. Write an algebraic expression for each of the following phrases.

3. (a) The cost of the 8¢ stamps
   (b) The cost of the 11¢ stamps if there are twice as many 11¢ as 8¢ stamps

4. (a) The number of 11¢ stamps if it is known that there are three times as many 11¢ as 8¢ stamps
   (b) The number of 11¢ stamps if there are 100 stamps in the collection

5. (a) The cost of the collection if there are 100 stamps in the collection
   (b) The cost of the collection if there are 60 stamps in the collection

Write an algebraic expression for each of the following phrases.

6. (a) The distance between two trains at the end of t hours if they left the same station at the same time, were headed in the same direction, and one was traveling at a rate of 50 miles per hour and the other at 70 miles per hour
   (b) The distance between the trains in part (a) if they were headed in opposite directions

7. (a) The distance separating two boys h hours after the first boy leaves camp, walking $2\frac{1}{2}$ miles per hour, if the second boy leaves camp three hours later, walking $3\frac{1}{2}$ miles per hour in the same direction
   (b) The distance between the two boys in part (a) if they were headed in opposite directions

Let x denote Jane's present age in years, and write an algebraic expression for each of the following phrases.

8. (a) Twice Jane's age next year
   (b) Four times Jane's age 3 years ago

9. (a) The present age of Jane's mother if her mother is now twice as old as Jane will be 3 years from now
   (b) The present age of Jane's father if his age is now 3 years less than 4 times Jane's age 7 years ago

Write an algebraic expression for each of the following phrases, and simplify it.

10. (a) The cost of 10 pounds of candy if some of it costs $1.69 a pound and the rest costs $1.98 a pound
   (b) The cost of 25 tickets to a football game if some of the tickets cost $3.00 and the rest cost $3.50.

11. (a) The amount of alcohol in a mixture after x ounces of a solution which is 65% alcohol is added to 15 ounces of a solution which is 75% alcohol
   (b) The income from two investments totaling $10,000 if part of it is invested at $4\frac{1}{2}$% simple interest and the rest is invested at $5\frac{3}{4}$% simple interest.

12. These early questions in algebra come from the Rhind papyrus, dated about 1600–1800 B.C. An Egyptian teacher put them to his pupil.
   (a) "Heap" and twice the "heap"; the total is 18. Tell me, my young friend, what is the "heap"?
   (b) "Heap" and one-fifth the "heap," take away three; the result is 21. What is the "heap"?

Write an equation for each of the following problems, and solve it. In each case, tell what is denoted by the variable that you use.

13. Find three consecutive even integers whose sum is 126.

14. Find four consecutive odd integers whose sum is 136.

15. If 3 times a number is added to 5 times the negative of the number, the sum is 12. Find the number.

16. There are 40 coins in a collection of nickels and quarters, and the collection is worth $5.40. How many nickels are there?

17. A newsboy collects $6.30 in nickels, dimes, and quarters. He has 4 more dimes than quarters and the number of nickels is 2 more than twice the number of dimes. How many coins of each type does he have?

18. In a local election, two-fifths of the eligible voters voted to retain Mayor Mills, three-eighths voted for his opponent, and the remaining 90 of those eligible did not vote. How many eligible voters were there in all?

19. Two years ago a man was 7 times as old as his son, but in 3 years he will only be 4 times as old as the boy. How old is each now?

20. Chuck's present age is $\frac{5}{8}$ that of John's age. In two years Chuck's age will be $\frac{2}{3}$ of John's. How old is Chuck now?

---

21. How many pounds of almonds which regularly sell for $1.10 per pound should be added to 10 pounds of peanuts which sell for 60¢ per pound if the resultant mixture should sell at 90¢ per pound?

22. Two men start at the same time from towns 19 miles apart and walk toward each other. One walks $2\frac{1}{2}$ miles per hour while the other covers $3\frac{1}{2}$ miles per hour. How long do they walk before meeting? How far has each man walked when they meet?

23. A man who walks $3\frac{1}{2}$ miles per hour sets out, from the same spot, to overtake a man who walks $2\frac{1}{2}$ miles per hour and who left $1\frac{1}{2}$ hours earlier. How long will it take the first walker to overtake the second one? How far has each man walked when the second one overtakes the first one?

24. What quantity of a solution which is to be 15% alcohol can be made from 7.5 quarts of pure alcohol?

25. How much water must be evaporated from 6 gallons of a 15%-salt solution if the residual solution is to contain 25% salt?

26. How much of the mixture in an 8-quart radiator should be drained and replaced with pure antifreeze if the mixture now consists of 75% antifreeze, and it is desired that the resultant mixture contain 90% antifreeze?

Preparation for Section 2–3

Give the reason that makes each of the following true.

1. If x is positive, then $3x > x$.   **2.** $-3 + a > -5 + a$

3. If x is negative, then $21x < 5x$.   **4.** If $7 > x$, then $10 > x$.

5. $-7 + x < 3 + x$

6. If $x < 2$, then $x < 12$.

2-3 INEQUALITIES IN ONE VARIABLE

A statement, such as

$$13x - 12 < 28 - 7x,$$

consisting of two linear forms in a variable connected by an order relation is called a *first-degree inequality*, or *linear inequality*, in the variable.

A number is called a solution of an inequality in one variable if a true statement is obtained when we give the variable the value of the number. The set of all solutions of an inequality is called the solution set of the inequality. If an inequality has no solution, its solution set is the empty set, $\emptyset$.

For example, let us determine which, if any, of the numbers $-2, 0, 2$, and 4 are solutions of the inequality above. If we let $x = -2$, we obtain

$$[13 \cdot (-2)] - 12 < 28 - [7 \cdot (-2)], \quad \text{or} \quad -38 < 42.$$

Since this is a true statement, -2 is in the solution set of the given inequality. If we let x equal 0, 2, and 4, in turn, we obtain the following statements:

$$(13 \cdot 0) - 12 < 28 - (7 \cdot 0), \quad \text{or} \quad -12 < 28,$$
$$(13 \cdot 2) - 12 < 28 - (7 \cdot 2), \quad \text{or} \quad 14 < 14,$$
$$(13 \cdot 4) - 12 < 28 - (7 \cdot 4), \quad \text{or} \quad 40 < 0.$$

Since the first statement is true and the last two are false, we conclude that 0 is in the solution set and that 2 and 4 are not in the solution set of the given inequality.

We solve an inequality as we solve an equation; that is, we find its solution set in a similar way. Two inequalities in a variable are said to be *equivalent* if they have the same solution set. Thus, we try to find an equivalent inequality with an obvious solution set. For example, if the inequalities

$$\tfrac{1}{2}(5x - 6) < \tfrac{1}{6}(108 - 3x)$$

and

$$x < 7$$

are equivalent, then we can tell from the second inequality that the solution set of both inequalities is the set of all real numbers less than 7.

In the solution of the following inequalities, we shall use several of the axioms and properties discussed in the appendix.

Problem 1. Solve the inequality $13x - 12 < 28 - 7x$.

Solution. Each of the following inequalities is equivalent to the preceding one.

$$13x - 12 < 28 - 7x$$
$$13x - 12 + (7x + 12) < 28 - 7x + (7x + 12)$$
$$(13x + 7x) + (12 - 12) < (28 + 12) + (7x - 7x)$$
$$20x + 0 < 40 + 0$$
$$20x < 40$$
$$\tfrac{1}{20} \cdot 20x < \tfrac{1}{20} \cdot 40$$
$$x < 2$$

We shall let you verify that the solution set of the given inequality is the set of all real numbers less than 2: $\{x \mid x < 2\}$.

The *graph* of an equation or inequality in one variable is the set of all points on a number line whose coordinates are solutions of the given equation or inequality. Since a first-degree equation in one variable usually has a single solution, its graph consists of a single point. On the other hand, the graph of an inequality often consists of more than one point.

For example, the graph of the inequality of Problem 1 is the set of all points on a number line having coordinates less than 2. This graph is an *open ray*, as indicated in Fig. 2–1. The hollow dot at 2 indicates that 2 is not part of the graph. The figure is incomplete, because the open ray extends infinitely far to the left.

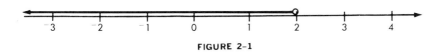

FIGURE 2-1

Problem 2. Solve the inequality $\tfrac{11}{3}x + 2 \geq \tfrac{7}{6}x - 8$.

Solution.
$$\tfrac{11}{3}x + 2 \geq \tfrac{7}{6}x - 8$$
$$\tfrac{11}{3}x + 2 + (-\tfrac{7}{6}x - 2) \geq \tfrac{7}{6}x - 8 + (-\tfrac{7}{6}x - 2)$$
$$\tfrac{11}{3}x + (-\tfrac{7}{6}x) \geq -8 - 2$$
$$\tfrac{15}{6}x \geq -10$$
$$\tfrac{6}{15} \cdot \tfrac{15}{6}x \geq \tfrac{6}{15} \cdot (-10)$$
$$x \geq -4$$

Thus, the set of all numbers greater than or equal to -4, designated by

$$\{x \mid x \geq -4\},$$

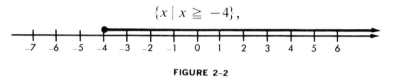

FIGURE 2-2

is the solution set of the given inequality. Its graph is the ray indicated in Fig. 2-2. The solid dot at -4 shows that -4 is part of the graph.

The graphs of the solution sets of two different inequalities may overlap, or intersect. For example, the solution set of the inequality $x + 1 < 4$ is the set of real numbers less than 3, or $\{x \mid x < 3\}$. The solution set of the inequality $2x > -4$ is the set of real numbers greater than -2, or $\{x \mid x > -2\}$. Those numbers which are greater than -2 and also less than 3, or $\{x \mid -2 < x < 3\}$, are in the solution set of both inequalities. The symbol $\cap$ is placed between two sets to indicate the set which is their *intersection*. Thus, we may write

$$\{x \mid x + 1 < 4\} \cap \{x \mid 2x > -4\} = \{x \mid -2 < x < 3\}.$$

The graph of the solution set of each of these two inequalities is an open ray, and the graph of the intersection of the two sets is an open interval, as shown in Fig. 2-3.

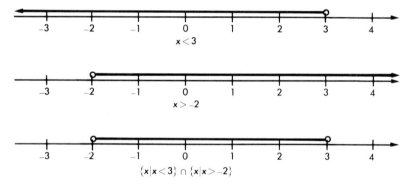

FIGURE 2-3

The *union* of two sets is the set consisting of all elements in either set. The symbol $\cup$ is used to denote the union of two sets. For example, the union of the closed intervals $\{x \mid -1 \leq x \leq 2\}$ and $\{x \mid 1 \leq x \leq 5\}$ is the closed interval $\{x \mid -1 \leq x \leq 5\}$:

$$\{x \mid -1 \leq x \leq 2\} \cup \{x \mid 1 \leq x \leq 5\} = \{x \mid -1 \leq x \leq 5\},$$

as shown in Fig. 2-4.

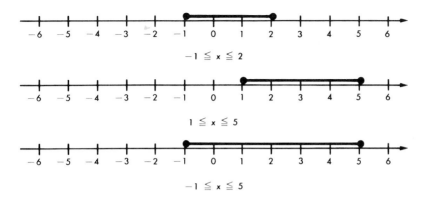

FIGURE 2-4

The *empty set*, denoted by 0, is the set having no elements. For example,

$$\{x \mid x \leq -2\} \cap \{x \mid x \geq 3\} = 0.$$

A bar drawn through a relation sign negates the relation. Thus,

$$x \neq y \quad \text{means} \quad x \text{ is not equal to } y,$$
$$x \not< y \quad \text{means} \quad x \text{ is not less than } y,$$
$$x \not\geq y \quad \text{means} \quad x \text{ is not greater than or equal to } y.$$

Exercises

1. Tell which of the numbers

$$-8, 8, -5, 3, 0, 1.5, -1.5, 10, 1.6$$

are in the solution set of the following inequalities.
(a) $2x - 5 > 7 - 6x$ (b) $2x - 5 \leq 7 - 6x$

Tell which of the numbers

$$0, -4, 5, -2, -3, 1, 3, -2.9, -3.1$$

are in the solution set of the inequalities in Exercises 2 and 3.
2. (a) $7 < 2x - 1$ (b) $2x - 1 < -7$
3. (a) $2x - 1 > 5$ (b) $2x - 1 < 5$
4. Tell which of the numbers

$$10, -2, 0, -1.5, -.5, 1, -1, 3$$

are in the solution set of the following inequalities.
(a) $4 - 5x \leq 7 - 2x$ (b) $4 - 5x > 7 - 2x$

Solve each of the following inequalities, and graph its solution set on a number line.

5. (a) $x + 3 > 2$ $\qquad\qquad$ (b) $x - 2 < 5$

6. (a) $x + 1 \geq -2$ $\qquad\qquad$ (b) $2x - 3 \leq 7$

7. (a) $4x + 7 \geq x - 11$ $\qquad$ (b) $\frac{1}{2}x + \frac{1}{3} \geq 3 - \frac{1}{6}x$

8. (a) $\frac{3}{5}x - \frac{1}{4} < \frac{49}{40} - \frac{7}{8}x$ $\qquad$ (b) $3(x + 1) \geq 2(5 - x)$

9. (a) $\frac{3}{2}x - 2 < 2x + \frac{1}{3}$ $\qquad$ (b) $-3(x + 2) > -9$

10. For each pair of inequalities, graph the two solution sets and show their intersection.

$\qquad$ (a) $x > -3,\ x < 5$ $\qquad\qquad$ (b) $x \geq -2,\ x \leq 2$

11. For each pair of inequalities, graph the two solution sets and describe the intersection of the two graphs.

$\qquad$ (a) $x > 3,\ x > -1$ $\qquad\qquad$ (b) $x < 5,\ x < -4$

12. Describe the intersections.

$\qquad$ (a) $\{x \mid x > 3\} \cap \{x \mid x < 1\}$ $\qquad$ (b) $\{x \mid x \leq 2\} \cap \{x \mid x > 2\}$

13. Graph each of the following sets.

$\qquad$ (a) $\{x \mid x > 1\} \cup \{x \mid x < -1\}$ $\quad$ (b) $\{x \mid x \geq 3\} \cup \{x \mid x \leq 1\}$

---

14. Graph sets A and B.

$$A = \{x \mid x + 3 > 0\} \cap \{x \mid x - 3 < 0\},\ B = \{x \mid |x| > 3\}.$$

Describe $A \cap B$ and $A \cup B$.

15. Graph sets C and D.

$$C = \{x \mid x \geq 3\} \cup \{x \mid x \leq -3\},\ D = \{x \mid |x| \geq 3\}.$$

Describe $C \cap D$ and $C \cup D$.

16. Determine which of the numbers $10, 8, 6, 4, 3, 2, 0, -4, -9, -10$ are in the solution set of the inequalities.

$\qquad$ (a) $x > 4$ $\qquad\qquad$ (b) $-2x > -8$

$\qquad$ (c) Describe $\{x \mid x > 4\} \cap \{x \mid -2x > -8\}$ and $\{x \mid x > 4\} \cup \{x \mid -2x > -8\}$.

17. (a) Graph each of the following inequalities. Then give four elements of each solution set.

$$x < 3,\quad 2x < -6,\quad -2x > -6$$

$\qquad$ (b) Are any of the inequalities in part (a) equivalent? If so, which?

Solve each inequality of the following pairs of inequalities, and find the intersection of the solution sets of each pair. For each pair, graph both solution sets and their intersection.

18. $2x + 1 < 7$ and $3x - 1 > 2$

19. $x + 1 < 2x - 4$ and $3x - 2 > 1$

20. $2x + 3 \geq 15 - 4x$ and $x - \frac{1}{3} > \frac{1}{6}x - 2$

21. $\frac{5}{4}x > 1 + x$ and $x + 2 < \frac{11}{5}$

22. (a) Write an inequality that has the same solution set as the inequality $x \nleq 6$.

(b) Write an inequality that has the same solution set as $x \nless -\frac{13}{5}$.

Two sets of real numbers are described below. Give three specific members of each set, and tell how the two sets are related to each other.

23. $A = \{x \mid x > -1\}$ and $B = \{x \mid x \nleq -1\}$

24. $A = \{x \mid 5x - 1 \nless 2\}$ and $B = \{x \mid 5x - 1 \nleq 2\}$

25. $A = \{x \mid 2x + 1 > 3\}$ and $B = \{x \mid 2x + 1 \nleq 3\}$

---

26. A football team has won 5 out of 7 games played. If there are 8 games remaining, how many more games must be won to give the team a season record of at least 60% games won out of all games played?

27. Johnny starts with the fraction $\frac{1}{2}$ and considers adding the same number x to both the numerator and the denominator. For what positive values of x will he obtain a number greater than or equal to $\frac{3}{4}$?

2–4   EQUATIONS IN TWO VARIABLES

An algebraic expression such as

$$3x - 2y + 4$$

is called a *linear form* in the two variables x and y. Every linear form in x and y is of the type

$$ax + by + c$$

for some real numbers a, b, and c. Note that

$$0x - 3y + 8, \quad \text{or} \quad -3y + 8,$$

may be considered to be a linear form in x and y although the variable x does not appear. Of course, $-3y + 8$ is also a linear form in the one variable y.

If values are given to the variables in a linear form, the resulting number is called a *value* of the linear form. For example, the linear form $3x - 2y + 4$ has the value

$$(3 \cdot 3) - 2 \cdot (-5) + 4, \quad \text{or } 23,$$

when $x = 3$ and $y = -5$. If we let $x = 17$ and $y = 3$ in the linear form $-3y + 8$, its value is $(-3 \cdot 3) + 8$, or -1. As long as we let $y = 3$, the value of this linear form is -1 for any value given to x.

A statement consisting of two linear forms in x and y connected by an equals sign is called a *first-degree equation, or linear equation,* in the variables x and y.
Consider

$$3x - 2y + 4 = -3y + 8$$

as an example of a first-degree equation in x and y. If we let $x = -1$ and $y = 7$ in this equation, we obtain the *true* equation

$$-3 - 14 + 4 = -21 + 8.$$

Therefore, the ordered pair $(-1, 7)$ is a *solution* of the given equation. On the other hand, the ordered pair $(3, 6)$ is *not a solution*, for if we let $x = 3$ and $y = 6$, we obtain the false equation

$$9 - 12 + 4 = -18 + 8.$$

An ordered pair (a, b) is called a solution of an equation in x and y if, and only if, a true equation results when we let $x = a$ and $y = b$. The set of all solutions of an equation in x and y is called the solution set of the equation. If an equation has no solution, its solution set is the empty set, 0.

We recall that a first-degree equation in one variable usually has only one solution. A first-degree equation in two variables, on the other hand, usually has an infinite number of solutions. A convenient method of finding solutions of a first-degree equation in two variables is to solve the given equation for one variable in terms of the other.

Problem. Solve the following equation for y in terms of x.

Solution.
$$3x - 2y + 4 = -3y + 8$$
$$(3y - 3x - 4) + 3x - 2y + 4 = -3y + 8 + (3y - 3x - 4)$$
$$y = -3x + 4$$

This final equation is equivalent to the given one. Hence, the solution set of the given equation may be described as follows:

$$\{(x, y) \mid y = -3x + 4\}.$$

By giving different values to x, we can find as many ordered pairs in the solution set of the given equation as we wish. For example, if we let $x = 3$, we obtain

$$y = (-3 \cdot 3) + 4, \text{ or } -5.$$

Thus, the ordered pair $(3, -5)$ is in the solution set. The following elements of the solution set were found in the same way.

$$(0, 4), \quad (1, 1), \quad (-1, 7), \quad (\tfrac{4}{3}, 0), \quad (2, -2), \quad (100, -296)$$

Exercises

1. (a) Tell which of the following ordered pairs are elements of the solution set of the equation $5x + 3y + 1 = 8x + 2y - 4$.

$$(\tfrac{1}{3}, -4), \ (3, 3), \ (0, -5), \ (\tfrac{1}{2}, \tfrac{7}{2}), \ (\tfrac{5}{3}, 0)$$

(b) Tell which of the following ordered pairs are elements of the solution set of the equation $4x + 2y + 20 = 3x + y + 15$.

$$(0, -5), \ (\tfrac{1}{2}, -4\tfrac{1}{2}), \ (-3, -2), \ (-1, -4), \ (4, 1)$$

2. Solve the equations for y in terms of x.
   (a) $3(2y - 1) - (x - 3) = 3x - y - 5$
   (b) $x - 3(x - 2y - 4) = 6 - (4x - y - 5)$

3. (a) Solve the equation in Exercise 2(a) for x in terms of y.
   (b) Solve the equation in Exercise 2(b) for x in terms of y.

Find five elements of the solution set of each of the following equations.

4. (a) $x + y + 8 = 0$ (b) $3x + y - 10 = 0$

5. (a) $x - 2y - 8 = 0$ (b) $\tfrac{1}{2}x + \tfrac{1}{4}y + 2 = 0$

Solve each of the following equations for y in terms of x. Find three ordered pairs that are elements of each solution set. Then check these solutions in the given equation.

6. (a) $3y - 2x + 4 = 8 - 3x$ (b) $5x - 6y - 9 = 2x + 4y - 3$

7. (a) $\dfrac{x}{5} - \dfrac{y}{6} + \dfrac{1}{2} = x + \dfrac{y}{3} - \dfrac{1}{10}$ (b) $\dfrac{1}{2}x + \dfrac{3}{10}y = \dfrac{4}{5}x + \dfrac{1}{5}y - \dfrac{1}{2}$

8. (a) Solve each equation in Exercises 6(a) and 7(a) for x in terms of y.
   (b) Solve each equation in Exercises 6(b) and 7(b) for x in terms of y.

9. Given the equation $x + y = 8$:
    (a) are there solutions with $x > 0$ and $y < 0$?
    (b) are there solutions with $x < 0$ and $y < 0$?

    In each case, if your answer is yes, find three solutions; if no, explain.

10. Are there solutions of the equation $2x + y + 10 = 0$ with:
    (a) $x < 0$ and $y > 0$?
    (b) $x > 0$ and $y > 0$?

    In each case, if your answer is yes, find three solutions; if no, explain.

___

11. Let sets R, S, and M be defined by

$$R = \{(x, y) \mid 2x - y = 1\},$$
$$S = \{(x, y) \mid 2x - y = -1\},$$
$$M = \{(x, y) \mid |2x - y| = 1\}.$$

    (a) Is $(3, 5)$ in R? S? M?
    (b) Is $(4, 9)$ in R? S? M?
    (c) Find two elements of R having $x < 0$. Do they also belong to S? M?
    (d) Find two elements of S having $x < 0$. Do they also belong to R? M?
    (e) How is set R related to set S?
    (f) What is the relationship of M to R and S?

12. Use the results of Exercise 11 to list two linear equations in x and y such that the union of their solution sets is the same as the solution set of the single equation $|x + y| = 3$.

13. List two linear equations in x and y such that the union of their solution sets is the same as the solution set of the single equation

$$|2x - 3y| = 10.$$

14. Find a single equation in x and y whose solution set is equal to the union of the solution sets described below.

$$\{(x, y) \mid 3y + 16 = 5y - x - 12\}, \quad \{(x, y) \mid 2x = 4y + 8\}$$

___

15. (a) What is the largest possible value for x in a solution of the equation $|x| + |y| = 2$? for y?
    (b) Give four solutions of the equation $|x| + |y| = 2$ with $x > 0$ and $y > 0$. What linear equation also has these solutions?
    (c) Give four solutions of $|x| + |y| = 2$ with $x < 0$ and $y < 0$. What linear equation also has these solutions?
    (d) Give four solutions of $|x| + |y| = 2$ with $x < 0$ and $y > 0$. What linear equation also has these solutions?

(e) Give four solutions of $|x| + |y| = 2$ with $x > 0$ and $y < 0$. What linear equation also has these solutions?

(f) Describe the solution set of the equation $|x| + |y| = 2$.

2–5 THE GRAPH OF A FIRST-DEGREE EQUATION IN TWO VARIABLES

If we wish to construct a rectangular *cartesian coordinate system* in a plane, we select two perpendicular lines in the plane. Then we put a number scale on each line, in each case placing the origin at the point of intersection of the lines. Unless we are given a statement to the contrary, we use the same unit of length on both lines. The two resulting number lines are customarily called the *x*-axis and the *y*-axis, and we usually place and direct them as shown in Fig. 2–5.

We assign to each point an ordered pair of real numbers; this ordered pair describes the position of the point relative to the axes. Conversely, each ordered pair is a pair of co-ordinates of some point in the plane. Some examples of points and their coordinates in the plane are given in Fig. 2–5. Since each ordered pair determines a point in the plane, a set of ordered pairs determines a set of points in the plane. This set of points is called the *graph of the set of ordered pairs*.

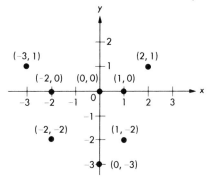

FIGURE 2-5

If the solution set of an equation in *x* and *y* is not the empty set, it is an example of a set of ordered pairs. The graph of the solution set is called the graph of the given equation. A first-degree equation in *x* and *y* has a straight line as its graph. In other words, its graph is the set of all the points on some straight line. It is for this reason that a first-degree equation in *x* and *y* is called a *linear equation*. Some examples of linear equations and their graphs are given in the following problems.

Problem 1. Graph the first-degree equation $3x - 2y + 4 = 0$.

Solution. When we solve the given equation for *y*, we obtain the equivalent equation

$$2y = 3x + 4,$$

or

$$y = \tfrac{3}{2}x + 2.$$

Thus,

$$\{(x, y) \mid y = \tfrac{3}{2}x + 2\}$$

is the solution set of the given equation. Several elements of the solution set are given below.

$(0, 2),\quad (2, 5),\quad (-1, \tfrac{1}{2}),\quad (-4, -4)$

These ordered pairs are graphed in Fig. 2-6. The straight line containing these points is the graph of the given equation.

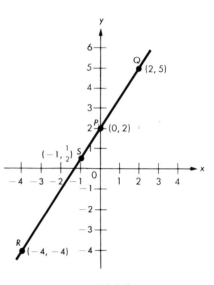

FIGURE 2-6

You might recall that each non-vertical straight line has a *slope* which we define as the ratio of the rise to the run of the line.

$$\text{slope} = \frac{\text{rise}}{\text{run}} \quad \text{or} \quad \frac{\text{change in ordinate}}{\text{change in abscissa}}$$

Any two points of the graph may be used to determine the slope. Thus, going from $P(0, 2)$ to $Q(2, 5)$,

$$\text{slope} = \frac{5 - 2}{2 - 0} \quad \text{or} \quad \frac{3}{2}.$$

Going from $S(-1, \tfrac{1}{2})$ to $P(0, 2)$,

$$\text{slope} = \frac{2 - \tfrac{1}{2}}{0 - (-1)} = \frac{\tfrac{3}{2}}{1} \quad \text{or} \quad \frac{3}{2}.$$

In both of these cases, rise and run are each positive, rise being "up" and run being "to the right." However, going from $Q(2, 5)$ to $S(-1, \tfrac{1}{2})$,

$$\text{slope} = \frac{\tfrac{1}{2} - 5}{-1 - 2} = \frac{-\tfrac{9}{2}}{-3} = \left(-\frac{9}{2}\right)\cdot\left(-\frac{1}{3}\right) \quad \text{or} \quad \frac{3}{2}.$$

Here, rise and run are both negative, rise being "down" and run being "to the left." In general, if $P(x_1, y_1)$ and $Q(x_2, y_2)$ are two points on a line, then we define

$$\text{slope} = \frac{y_2 - y_1}{x_2 - x_1} \quad \text{or} \quad \frac{y_1 - y_2}{x_1 - x_2}, \quad x_1 \neq x_2.$$

Notice that the slope of the line in Fig. 2-6 is $\frac{3}{2}$ and an equation of the line is $y = \frac{3}{2}x + 2$. It is not an accident that the coefficient of x is the same as the slope of the line. Whenever a first-degree equation in x and y is solved for y and written in the form

$$y = mx + b,$$

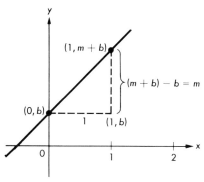

where m and b are real numbers, the coefficient of x (that is, m) is the slope of the straight line which is the graph of the equation. (See Fig. 2-7.) We can prove that m is the slope by noting that the points $(0, b)$ and $(1, m + b)$ are on the line, and that the rise is m and the run is 1 from $(0, b)$ to $(1, m + b)$.

FIGURE 2-7

Since b is the y-coordinate of the point where the line crosses the y-axis, b is called the y-*intercept* of the line.

Problem 2. Graph the first-degree equation

$$3x - 2y + 4 = -3y + 8.$$

Solution. In Section 2-4, we saw that this equation is equivalent to

$$y = -3x + 4$$

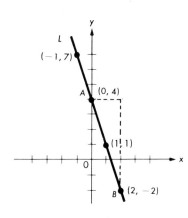

and that $(0, 4)$, $(1, 1)$, $(-1, 7)$, and $(2, -2)$ are points on the line. The line L is graphed in Fig. 2-8. From the point $(0, 4)$ to the point $(2, -2)$, the line has a rise of $-2 - 4$, or -6, and a run of $2 - 0$, or 2. Thus, its slope is $-\frac{6}{2}$, or -3. Of course, when we say that the line has a rise of -6, we actually mean that the line is *falling* six units from $(0, 4)$ to $(2, -2)$.

FIGURE 2-8

Using points $B(2, -2)$ and $A(0, 4)$, going from B to A,

$$\text{slope} = \frac{4 - (-2)}{0 - 2} = \frac{6}{-2} \quad \text{or } -3.$$

We could have predicted this from the equation $y = -3x + 4$ where -3 is the coefficient of x.

Problem 3. Consider $2x + 3 = 0$ as an equation in x and y, and $6y+$ [handwritten] draw its graph.

Solution. The given equation is equivalent to the equation $x = -\frac{3}{2}$. Thus, every ordered pair of the type $(-\frac{3}{2}, y)$ is in the solution set of the given equation. In other words, $\{(-\frac{3}{2}, y) \mid y$ a real number$\}$ is the solution set of this equation. The graph of the given equation is the vertical line drawn in Fig. 2-9. Some points on the graph are $(-\frac{3}{2}, 0)$, $(-\frac{3}{2}, 2)$, and $(-\frac{3}{2}, -1)$.

[handwritten] y is anything on y axis

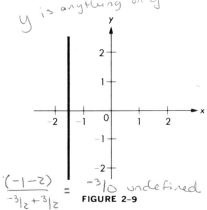

FIGURE 2-9

[handwritten] $\frac{(-1 - 2)}{-3|_2 + 3|_2} = \frac{-3|_0}{}$ undefined

Since there is no run from one point to another point on this line, the slope is not defined for this line.

[handwritten] if $2y + 3 = 0$ $y = -\frac{3}{2}$
then there is no rise & slope = 0
$\frac{(-3|_2 + 3|_2)}{(-1 - 2)} = \frac{0}{3}$ $m = 0$

Exercises

1. What is the slope of a line through the points
   (a) $(-2, -3)$ and $(7, 9)$?
   (b) $(-4, 5)$ and $(6, -3)$?

Plot each pair of points below, draw the straight line through them, and determine the slope of the line.

2. (a) $(-2, 3)$, $(5, -6)$
   (b) $(-4, -1)$, $(3, 5)$

3. (a) $(2, -1)$, $(-2, -4)$
   (b) $(6, 2)$, $(-3, -4)$

4. (a) What is the slope of a line through the points $(-1, 3)$ and $(5, 3)$?
   (b) What is the slope of any line parallel to the x-axis?   [handwritten] $y =$ × $= 0$

5. (a) Does the line through $(-1, 3)$ and $(-1, 5)$ have a slope? Why?
   (b) How can you describe the set of all lines for which the slope is not defined?

6. Graph each of the following linear equations on a cartesian coordinate system in a plane. Give the slope and the y-intercept of each line.
   (a) $x - y - 2 = 0$
   (b) $\frac{1}{2}x + y = 3$

In Exercises 7–10, graph each of the linear equations on a cartesian coordinate system in a plane. Give first the slope and then the y-intercept of each line (if they exist).

7. (a) $2x + 5y = 10$
   (b) $\frac{1}{2}x + \frac{1}{4}y = 1$

8. (a) $5y + 15 = 0$
   (b) $\frac{1}{5}y = 0$

9. (a) $3x + 6 = 0$
   (b) $2x = 0$

10. (a) $2x - \frac{1}{3}y = 0$
    (b) $2x + 3y = 0$

$slope = \dfrac{(y_2 - y_1)}{(x_2 - x_1)} = m$

$if\ x_2 = x_1\ then\ slope\ undefined$

$b/c\ \dfrac{(y_2 - y_1)}{0}\ is\ not\ possible$

$if\ m = \dfrac{+(y_2 - y_1)}{(x_2 - x_1)}\ then\ m = \dfrac{(y_1 - y_2)}{(x_1 - x_2)}$

---

11. (a) Graph each of the following equations on the same coordinate system.

$$y = 2x + 4, \quad y = 2x, \quad y = 2x - 3$$

   (b) What do the three graphs in part (a) have in common?
   (c) What do the three equations in part (a) have in common?

12. (a) Graph each of the following equations on the same coordinate system.

$$y = 2x + 4, \quad y = 4, \quad y = -x + 4, \quad y = \tfrac{1}{3}x + 4$$

   (b) What do the four graphs in part (a) have in common?
   (c) What do the four equations in part (a) have in common?

2-6 EQUATIONS OF THE LINE THROUGH TWO POINTS

Every linear equation has a straight line as its graph. It is true, conversely, that every straight line is the graph of some linear equation. For example, the line drawn through the points $A(-2, 3)$ and $B(4, -1)$ has

$$\text{slope} = \frac{3 - (-1)}{-2 - 4} = \frac{4}{-6} = -\frac{2}{3}.$$

A point $P(x, y)$ other than A is on this line if, and only if, the slope of the line drawn through A and P is $-\frac{2}{3}$; that is,

$$\frac{y - 3}{x - (-2)} = -\frac{2}{3}.$$

Simplifying this equation, we obtain $y - 3 = -\frac{2}{3}(x + 2)$, or

$$y = -\frac{2}{3}x + \frac{5}{3}. \tag{1}$$

This linear equation has the line drawn through the points A and B as its graph.

Check. Is $A(-2, 3)$ on the graph of this equation? Yes, if $x = -2$, $y = 3$ is a solution of equation (1):

$$3 \stackrel{?}{=} -\frac{2}{3}(-2) + \frac{5}{3}$$
$$3 \stackrel{\checkmark}{=} \frac{4}{3} + \frac{5}{3}$$

Is $B(4, -1)$ on the graph? That is, is $x = -2$, $y = 3$ a solution of (1)?

$$-1 \stackrel{?}{=} -\frac{2}{3}(4) + \frac{5}{3}$$
$$-1 \stackrel{\checkmark}{=} -\frac{8}{3} + \frac{5}{3}$$

More generally, if $A(x_1, y_1)$ and $B(x_2, y_2)$ are two points not lying on a vertical line (that is, if $x_1 \neq x_2$), then the line drawn through A and B has slope m given by

$$m = \frac{y_2 - y_1}{x_2 - x_1}$$

and equation

$$y - y_1 = m(x - x_1).$$

Problem 1. Find an equation of the line through $A(3, 4)$ and $B(-2, -6)$.

Solution. The slope of the line is given by

$$m = \frac{4 - (-6)}{3 - (-2)} = \frac{10}{5} = 2.$$

Letting $(3, 4) = (x_1, y_1)$, we have

$$y - 4 = 2(x - 3)$$

as an equation of the line. Simplifying,

$$y - 4 = 2x - 6,$$
$$y = 2x - 2.$$

We could just as easily have let $(-2, -6) = (x_1, y_1)$.   Then the equation would have been

$$y + 6 = 2(x + 2).$$

Simplifying, we get

$$y = 2x - 2$$

as before.

Problem 2.   Find an equation of the line with slope $-\frac{3}{2}$ and y-intercept 6.

Solution 1.   Since the y-intercept is 6, the point $(0, 6)$ is on the line. Using the form of the equation given above,

$$y - y_1 = m(x - x_1), \qquad \text{(where m is the slope and (x_1, y_1) is a point on the line)}$$

we have

$$y - 6 = -\tfrac{3}{2}(x - 0)$$

or

$$y = (-\tfrac{3}{2})x + 6$$

as an equation of the line.

Solution 2.   Using the slope-intercept form of the equation

$$y = mx + b, \qquad \text{(m is slope, b is y-intercept of the line)}$$

we have immediately

$$y = (-\tfrac{3}{2})x + 6$$

as an equation of the line.

Exercises

Find the slope and write an equation of the line through

1. $(-6, 5)$, $(-7, -2)$.   **2.** $(3, 1)$, $(7, -3)$.

Draw the line through the given point with the given slope m, and write an equation of the line.

3. $(-3, -2)$, $m = -\frac{1}{3}$

4. $(0, 4)$, $m = -\frac{2}{3}$

5. $(-2, 3)$, $m = 0$

6. $(4, 5)$, m undefined

7. Through the given point, draw the line with the given slope m.
  (a) $(1, -3)$, $m = \frac{1}{2}$ (b) $(1, -3)$, $m = -2$

Write an equation for each of the lines graphed below.

8. (a)

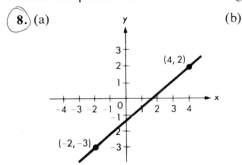

(b)

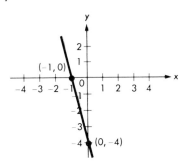

9. (a)

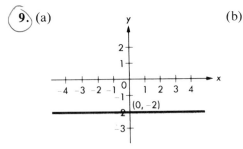

(b)

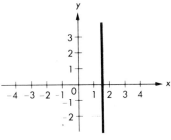

10. (a)

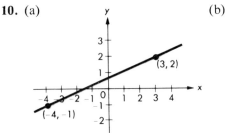

(b)

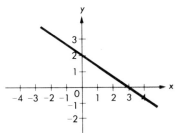

11. Show that three points

$$(4, 0), \ (8, -5), \ (0, 5)$$

are collinear (lie on the same line) by showing that the slope of the line drawn between any two of them is the same as the slope of the line drawn between any other two of them.

12. Are the following sets of points collinear? Why?

(a) $(2, -5), \ (4, 0), \ (7, 6)$

(b) $(0, 2), \ (3, 0), \ (1, 1)$

13. (a) Graph each of the following equations on the same set of axes.

$$\frac{x}{2} + \frac{y}{3} = 1, \quad \frac{x}{4} + \frac{y}{-6} = 1, \quad \frac{x}{-3} + \frac{y}{5} = 1$$

(b) Tell at what point each line graphed in part (a) cuts the x-axis and at what point it cuts the y-axis. Do the equations make these intercepts obvious?

(c) Give the x- and the y-intercept for the line with equation

$$\frac{x}{a} + \frac{y}{b} = 1.$$

(d) Write an equation of the line with x-intercept -2 and y-intercept 2.

---

14. (a) Graph $y = 3x - 1$ and $x = 3y - 1$ on the same cartesian coordinate system.

(b) How do you think the graphs of $y = rx + s$ and $x = ry + s$ will compare? In other words, find the slope and the y-intercept of the graph of each equation.

15. The equation $y = mx - 1$ represents a *family of lines*. Each value given m corresponds to a particular member of the family.

(a) Graph the member for which $m = 2$ (that is, $y = 2x - 1$).

(b) Graph the member for which $m = 3$.

(c) What do the members of the family of lines which have the equation $y = mx - 1$ have in common?

16. The equation $y = -x + b$ represents a *family of lines*. Each value given b corresponds to a particular member of the family.

(a) Graph the member for which $b = 2$ (that is, $y = -x + 2$).

(b) Graph the member for which $b = -2$.

(c) What do the members of the family of lines which have the equation $y = -x + b$ have in common? In what way do the members of this family differ?

17. (a) Draw three members of the family of lines represented by the equation

$$y + 1 = m(x + 1),$$

giving m the values -2, 4, and 0 in turn.

(b) Describe the family of lines which have the equation $y + 1 = m(x + 1)$, telling in what way they are alike and in what way different.

18. (a) Write an equation of the line with a slope of $\frac{1}{2}$ and a y-intercept of 3.

(b) Write an equation for the family of lines with a slope of $\frac{1}{2}$.

(c) Write an equation of the line passing through $(2, 3)$ with a slope of $\frac{1}{2}$.

19. (a) Write an equation of a family or set of lines with slope $\frac{3}{4}$.

(b) Write an equation of the line in this set that passes through the point $(-5, 2)$.

20. (a) Write an equation of a family or set of lines with y-intercept -5.

(b) Write an equation of the member of this family which passes through the point $(2, 7)$.

2–7   INEQUALITIES IN TWO VARIABLES

If two linear forms in x and y are connected by one of the order relations, the resulting statement is called a *first-degree inequality*, or *linear inequality*, in x and y. The solution set and graph of a linear inequality are defined as they were for a linear equation. To solve a linear inequality, we try to find an equivalent linear inequality with an obvious solution set.

Problem 1. Discuss the solution set and draw the graph of the inequality

$$2x - 2y + 9 > 3x - 3y + 8.$$

Solution. By adding $-2x + 3y - 9$ to each side of the given inequality, we obtain the equivalent inequality

$$y > x - 1.$$

Hence, the solution set of the given inequality is

$$\{(x, y) \mid y > x - 1\}.$$

To see what the graph of the inequality $y > x - 1$ is, sketch the graph of the *related equation* $y = x - 1$. The graph of this equation is the line L with slope $m = 1$ and y-intercept $b = -1$ shown in Fig. 2–10.

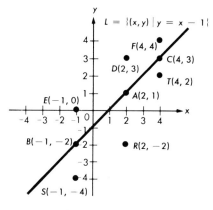

FIGURE 2-10

Any line divides a plane into three sets of points, those on the line and those on either side of the line. A point (x, y) is *on* the line L if, and only if, $y = x - 1$.

Thus,

> A $(2, 1)$ is on L, since $1 = 2 - 1$;
> B $(-1, -2)$ is on L, since $-2 = -1 - 1$;
> C $(4, 3)$ is on L, since $3 = 4 - 1$.

A point (x, y) is *above* the line L if, and only if, $y > x - 1$.

Thus,

> D $(2, 3)$ is above L, since $3 > 2 - 1$;
> E $(-1, 0)$ is above L, since $0 > -1 - 1$;
> F $(4, 4)$ is above L, since $4 > 4 - 1$.

Hence, the graph of the inequality $y > x - 1$ is the entire set of points *above* the line L. A portion of the graph is the shaded region in Fig. 2–11. Such a region is called a *half-plane*. The line L in the figure is broken to indicate that it is not part of the graph.

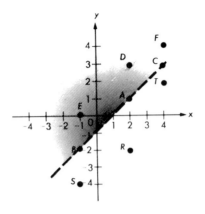

FIGURE 2-11

A point (x, y) is *below* the line L if, and only if, $y < x - 1$.

Thus,

$$R\,(2, -2) \text{ is below } L, \text{ since } -2 < 2 - 1;$$
$$S\,(-1, -4) \text{ is below } L, \text{ since } -4 < -1 - 1;$$
$$T\,(4, 2) \text{ is below } L, \text{ since } 2 < 4 - 1.$$

Hence, the graph of the inequality $y < x - 1$ is the half-plane below the line L. This region is infinite in extent. A portion of it is shaded in Fig. 2–12.

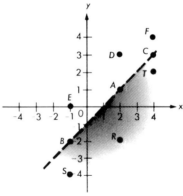

FIGURE 2-12

Problem 2. Discuss the solution set and draw the graph of the inequality

$$x - 2y - 3 < 0.$$

Solution. Upon adding $2y + 3$ to each side of the given inequality, we obtain the equivalent inequality

$$x < 2y + 3.$$

Hence,

$$\{(x, y) \mid x < 2y + 3\}$$

is the solution set of the given inequality.

To graph the inequality $x < 2y + 3$, first graph the related equation $x = 2y + 3$. The graph of $x = 2y + 3$ is the line K with slope $m = \frac{1}{2}$ and y-intercept $b = -\frac{3}{2}$ shown in Figure 2–13.

A point (x, y) is on K if, and only if, $x = 2y + 3$. For example, $A(5, 1)$ and $B(-1, -2)$ are on K.

A point (x, y) is *to the left* of K if, and only if, $x < 2y + 3$. For example,

C (2, 1) is to the left of K, since $2 < 2 \cdot 1 + 3$;
D $(-3, -2)$ is to the left of K, since $-3 < 2 \cdot (-2) + 3$.

In other words, the graph of the inequality $x < 2y + 3$ is the half-plane to the left of K, a portion of which is shaded in Figure 2–13.

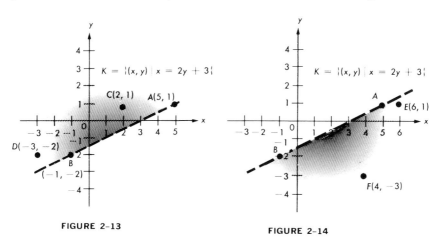

FIGURE 2-13

FIGURE 2-14

Similarly, you should see that the graph of the inequality $x > 2y + 3$ is the half-plane to the right of K, indicated in Figure 2–14.

Problem 3. Discuss the solution set and draw the graph of the inequality

$$2x + 3 \geqq 0.$$

Solution. Since the given inequality is equivalent to the inequality

$$x \geqq -\tfrac{3}{2},$$

the solution set is given by

$$\{(x, y) \mid x \geqq -\tfrac{3}{2}\}.$$

Clearly, the graph of this set is the shaded *half-plane and its edge,* as shown in Fig. 2–15. The line $x = -\tfrac{3}{2}$ is solid to indicate that it is part of the graph of the inequality.

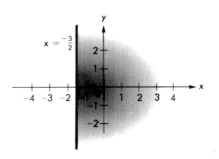

FIGURE 2-15

Exercises

Draw the graph of each inequality. If possible, give the slope and *y*-intercept of the line bounding each region.

1. (a) $y > 3$ (b) $y \leqq 1$

2. (a) $x < -2$ (b) $x \geqq 0$

3. (a) $y > -x + 2$ (b) $y < \tfrac{5}{2}x - 2$

4. (a) $x \geqq y + 2$ (b) $x < -y + 2$

Find the solution set of each inequality and draw the graph.

5. (a) $2x + y - 1 < 2y - x + 1$
   (b) $3x + 2y - 2 \leqq x - y - 8$

6. (a) $\dfrac{x}{2} - \dfrac{1}{3} \geqq \dfrac{x}{3} - y$

   (b) $\dfrac{x}{2} - 1 > \dfrac{y}{4} + \dfrac{x}{5}$

7. (a) $2x + 1 - y > x + 2y + 1$
   (b) $x + 1 < \tfrac{1}{2}(y + x + 1)$

Find an inequality whose solution set has the given graph. (Hint: First obtain an equation of the bounding line.)

8.

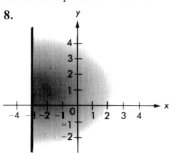

9.

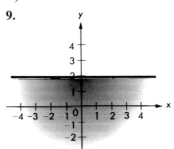

10.

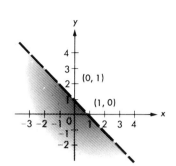

11.

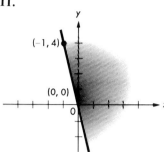

12. (a) Graph the inequality

$$y > -3x + 4.$$

(b) Which of the ordered pairs

$$(-1, \tfrac{1}{2}), \ (-1, 1), \ (-1, 2), \ (2, -1), \ (2, -2), \ (2, -3)$$

are elements of the solution set of the inequality $y > -3x + 4$?

(c) Which of the points in 10(b) are above and which are below the line $y = -3x + 4$?

13. (a) Graph the inequality

$$x < 2y + 3.$$

(b) Tell which of the points

$$(3, 0), \quad (2, 0), \quad (\tfrac{7}{2}, 0), \quad (6, 1), \quad (5, 1),$$
$$(4, 1), \quad (0, -2), \quad (-2, -2), \quad (-1, -2)$$

lie to the left of the line $x = 2y + 3$.

14. (a) Give the slope and y-intercept of the line bounding the graph of $y < 2x - 3$.

(b) Draw the graph of $y < 2x - 3$.

(c) Does the inequality $y < 2x - 3$, with $x > 0$ and $y < 0$, have a solution in which both variables are integers?

15. If $(-1, b)$ is in the solution set of $x \geq -3y + 6$, what is the smallest integral value possible for b?

16. Find a pair of positive integers a and b such that (a, b) is in the solution set of $x \geq -3y + 6$ and $a + b$ has the smallest possible value.

CHAPTER REVIEW

Solve each of the following equations and inequalities by writing a succession of equivalent ones. Check each solution.

1. $3m - 3 = 5 + m$

2. $2(p + 1) + 5 > 6$

3. $\dfrac{4(6 + x)}{3} < 4$

4. $4(3y + 5) + 1 = 1 + 8y$

5. $3(4x + 3) = 3x + 15$

6. $3(k + 5) > k - 3$

7. $2(9n - 3) + 4 = 2(n + 3) + 2$

8. $\dfrac{3m + 4}{2} < m + 3$

9. $\dfrac{3(2x + 1) - 4}{2} = -2$

10. $4t - 13 = 2(t + 13) - t$

11. $\dfrac{4(2y + 1)}{3} > y + 1$

12. $2(2x - 7) + 3 = 10 + x$

13. $4(n + 1) < n$

14. $2x - 6 = 3(2x + 6)$

15. $\dfrac{6k + 7}{2} > 5 - k$

16. $\dfrac{4(2m + 3)}{3} > \dfrac{80}{4}$

Using m for your variable, write an algebraic expression for each of the following phrases.

17. The product of two consecutive even integers

18. Three times Martin's age 4 years ago

19. The cost of a dozen candy bars when some cost 6¢ and the rest cost 12¢

20. The sum of three consecutive integers

Write an equation for each of the following problems and solve it to answer the questions.

21. Find four consecutive integers whose sum is 90.

22. Sue is three times as old as Mary was four years ago. Sue is two years older than Mary. How old are Sue and Mary?

23. There are 30 coins in a collection of nickels and dimes, and the value of the collection is $2.15. How many nickels and how many dimes are there?

Graph each of the following sets.

24. $\{x \mid x + 4 > 2\} \cap \{x \mid x - 3 < 0\}$

25. $\{x \mid x - 2 < 0\} \cap \{x \mid x + 5 \geq 0\}$

Solve each of the following equations for y in terms of x and then tell which of the ordered pairs are elements of the solution set for each.

26. $2(x + y) + 1 = 5x + y + 3$; $(0, 2)$, $(1, 0)$, $(3, 7)$, $(-2, -4)$

27. $5y + x = y + 2(x + 1)$; (4, 1), (2, 1), (−6, −1), (0, 0)
28. $3x + 3y = 2(x + y) + 5$; (3, 8), (1, 4), (−1, −4), (5, 0)
29. $3(x + y + 1) = 2(3x + y) − 1$; (1, −1), (0, 4), (2, 2), (−1, 1)
30. $x + 3y − 4 = 2(x + 7)$; (1, 7), (0, 6), (2, 8), (6, 8)

Graph each of the linear equations, giving the slope and y-intercept (if they exist).

31. (a) $y − 3x = 2$ (b) $2x + y = 3$
32. (a) $2y + 3 = 0$ (b) $y − 2 = 0$
33. (a) $3x − 1 = 0$ (b) $x + 2 = 0$
34. (a) $2x − 3y = 6$ (b) $3x + 2y − 4 = 0$

For each pair of points, draw the line which passes through them. Find the slope and equation of the line.

35. (a) (1, 1), (2, 3)   (b) (−2, 1), (0, 2)
36. (a) (4, −1), (2, −2)   (b) (−3, 1), (3, −1)
37. (a) (2, −2), (2, 3)   (b) (4, 1), (−2, 1)

Graph each inequality.

38. (a) $x > 1$ (b) $x < 2$
39. (a) $y \leqq 3$ (b) $y \geqq −1$
40. (a) $y \leqq 2x + 1$ (b) $y − x \geqq 3$
41. (a) $x − 2y > 3$ (b) $x + 3y < 3$

3 · Systems of Equations and Inequalities

3–1 SYSTEMS OF EQUATIONS IN TWO VARIABLES

Suppose we are asked how many boys and how many girls there are in a certain algebra class. Can we answer the question if all we know is that the total class size is 32? This is a problem involving two variables, say x boys and y girls, which our information says are related by the first-degree equation $x + y = 32$. Clearly, from the equation above we can only say that if $x = 15$, then $y = 17$; if $x = 20$, then $y = 12$, and so on. No single answer can be decided upon, and yet there is only one answer to the question "How many boys are in the algebra class?" With more information perhaps we can find a unique answer. For instance, suppose we learn that there are four more boys than girls. This tells us x and y are also related by another first-degree equation,

$$x = y + 4,$$

from which we conclude that if $y = 12$, then $x = 16$ and if $y = 17$, then $x = 21$; once again we have an infinite set of choices.

The single answer we seek can be found by solving the system of first-degree equations

$$\begin{cases} x + y = 32, \\ \quad\ x = y + 4. \end{cases}$$

The graphs of these two first-degree equations are nonparallel lines, and their point of intersection is the graph of the unique solution of the problem.

In Figure 3–1,

$$S = \{(x, y) \mid x + y = 32\},$$
$$T = \{(x, y) \mid x = y + 4\},$$

and $S \cap T$ consists of the point $P(18, 14)$. Hence, if $x = 18$ and $y = 14$, both statements

$$\begin{cases} x + y = 32, \\ \quad\;\; x = y + 4, \end{cases}$$

are true. We now know there are 18 boys and 14 girls in the class of 32 having four more boys than girls.

An ordered pair is a *solution* of a system of equations in x and y if it is a solution of *every* equation of the system. The set of all solutions of the system is again called the *solution set* of the system. Knowing the solution set of each equation of the system, we find the solution set of the system to be the *intersection* of the solution sets of the individual equations.

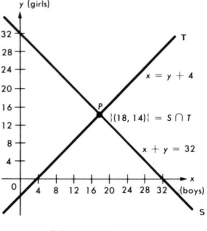

FIGURE 3–1

Problem 1. Solve the system of equations

$$\begin{cases} \quad\;\; x = 3, \\ 7x + 9y = -15. \end{cases}$$

Solution. The solution set is given by

$$\{(x, y) \mid x = 3\} \cap \{(x, y) \mid 7x + 9y = -15\}.$$

All elements of the first set are ordered pairs of the form $(3, y)$, and therefore, the intersection contains ordered pairs of this form. However, the ordered pair $(3, y)$ is in the second set if, and only if,

$$(7 \cdot 3) + 9y = -15.$$

We solve this first-degree equation in one variable as follows:

$$21 + 9y = -15,$$
$$9y = -36,$$
$$y = -4.$$

Hence,

$$\{(3, -4)\}$$

is the solution set of the given system. The graphs of the equations of the system and of the solution set of the system are shown in Fig. 3-2 .

Check. $3 \overset{\vee}{=} 3$ $(7 \cdot 3) + [9 \cdot (-4)] \overset{?}{=} -15$
$$21 - 36 \overset{\vee}{=} -15$$

We solve a system of two first-degree equations in two variables by reducing the system to an equivalent system of the type in Problem 1. Two systems are said to be *equivalent systems* if they have the same solution set. You probably learned several methods of reducing a system of equations in your previous algebra course. A very effective way is the *substitution method*, which we shall use in the next problem.

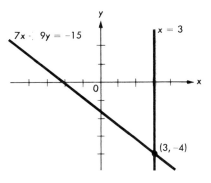

FIGURE 3-2

Problem 2. Solve the system of equations

$$\begin{cases} 3x - 2y = 19, \\ x + y = 23. \end{cases} \quad (1)$$

Solution. System (1) is equivalent to system (2) by the additive axiom.

$$\begin{cases} 3x - 2y = 19 \\ y = 23 - x \end{cases} \quad (2)$$

Upon substituting $23 - x$ for y in the first equation, we get system

$$\begin{cases} 3x - 2(23 - x) = 19, \\ y = 23 - x \end{cases} \quad (3)$$

which is equivalent to system (2).

The first equation of (3) is equivalent to each of the following equations:

$$3x - 46 + 2x = 19,$$
$$5x = 65,$$
$$x = 13.$$

Therefore, (3) is equivalent to the system

$$\begin{cases} x = 13, \\ y = 23 - x. \end{cases} \qquad (4)$$

The only solution of (4) is (13, 10). Hence,

$$\{(13, 10)\}$$

is the solution set of (1), the given system.

Check.
$$(3 \cdot 13) - (2 \cdot 10) \overset{?}{=} 19$$
$$39 - 20 \overset{\checkmark}{=} 19$$

$$13 + 10 \overset{\checkmark}{=} 23$$

A linear equation in x and y has a straight line graph. Two linear equations in x and y have two straight line graphs. This pair of lines may be parallel, having no point in common, so that the system of equations has an empty solution set. Such equations are called *inconsistent*. See Fig. 3–3.

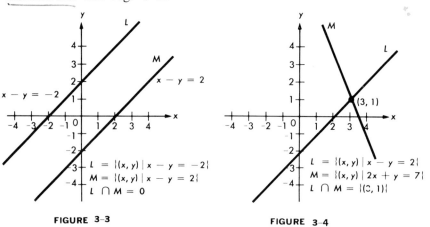

FIGURE 3-3   FIGURE 3-4

If the pair of lines intersect in one point, the solution set of the system has exactly one member, an ordered number pair. Such equations are called *independent* and *consistent*. See Fig. 3–4.

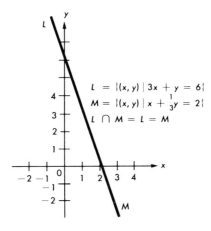

$L = \{(x, y) \mid 3x + y = 6\}$

$M = \{(x, y) \mid x + \frac{1}{3}y = 2\}$

$L \cap M = L = M$

FIGURE 3-5

If the graphs of the two equations coincide, then the solution set of the system is infinite. Such equations are called *dependent* but *consistent*. See Fig. 3-5.

Exercises   *Substitution*

Graph each equation in the following systems, and from your graph, find the solution set of each system.

1. (a) $\begin{cases} x - 3 = 0 \\ y - 4 = 0 \end{cases}$ (b) $\begin{cases} 2x + 5 = 0 \\ 3y + 6 = 0 \end{cases}$

2. (a) $\begin{cases} y = x \\ y + 2 = 0 \end{cases}$ (b) $\begin{cases} x + y = 0 \\ x + 3 = 0 \end{cases}$

3. (a) $\begin{cases} 2x + y = 1 \\ y - x = 4 \end{cases}$ (b) $\begin{cases} 2x - y + 6 = 0 \\ y + 2x = 0 \end{cases}$

Graph the systems, and tell if each system is dependent, independent, or inconsistent.

4. $\begin{cases} 3x - y = 6 \\ y = 3x + 2 \end{cases}$ 5. $\begin{cases} x - y - 1 = 0 \\ x - y + 2 = 0 \end{cases}$

6. $\begin{cases} -2x + 2y - 2 = 0 \\ x - y + 1 = 0 \end{cases}$ 7. $\begin{cases} 2x - 3y = 12 \\ 4 + y = \frac{2}{3}x \end{cases}$

8. $\begin{cases} x - y - 1 = 0 \\ 2x + y + 4 = 0 \end{cases}$ 9. $\begin{cases} y - 2x = 4 \\ 2x + y + 2 = 0 \end{cases}$

Use the substitution method to solve each of the following systems.

10. $\begin{cases} x + 2y = 8 \\ x = 10 - 4y \end{cases}$ 11. $\begin{cases} p = 5 + 4q \\ 3p + 2q = 17 \end{cases}$

12. $\begin{cases} x - y = 4 \\ 3x + 4y = 12 \end{cases}$

13. $\begin{cases} 4x - y = 3 \\ 2x + 7y = 9 \end{cases}$

14. $\begin{cases} y + x = 3 \\ 3x - y = 1 \end{cases}$

15. $\begin{cases} y - x = 5 \\ 4x - y = 10 \end{cases}$

16. $\begin{cases} u - 2v = 12 \\ v = 7u + 6 \end{cases}$

17. $\begin{cases} u - (v - 2) = 2 \\ v = 2u \end{cases}$

---

18. Try to solve the system

$$\begin{cases} 2x + 3y - 5 = 0, \\ 2x + 3y + 10 = 0 \end{cases}$$

(a) by the substitution method.
(b) by graphing.
(c) Explain what happend in part (a).

19. (a) Graph the system

$$\begin{cases} 2x + 3y + 1 = 0, \\ 2kx + 3ky + k = 0. \end{cases}$$
$$(k = 1, 2, 3, \ldots)$$

(b) Try to solve the system by substitution and explain what happens.

3–2   MORE ON SYSTEMS OF EQUATIONS

Before solving more systems of linear equations, let us make some general observations about equivalent systems. In the first place, two systems are equivalent if each equation of one system is equivalent to the corresponding equation of the other system. For example, the two systems

$$\begin{cases} 4x + y - 7 = 0, \\ 2x + 3y = 5 \end{cases} \quad \text{and} \quad \begin{cases} y = 7 - 4x, \\ 3y = 5 - 2x \end{cases}$$

are equivalent, because the first equations of each system are equivalent and the second equations are also equivalent.

Next, if a system has the form

$$\begin{cases} F_1 = G_1, \\ F_2 = G_2 \end{cases} \tag{1}$$

where F_1, G_1, F_2, and G_2 designate linear forms in x and y, then

$$\begin{cases} F_1 = G_1, \\ F_1 + F_2 = G_1 + G_2 \end{cases} \tag{2}$$

is an equivalent system. To see this, let L_1 and R_1 be the respective values of F_1 and G_1, and let L_2 and R_2 be the respective values of F_2 and G_2 when $x = a$ and $y = b$.

If (a, b) is a solution of system (1), so that

$$\begin{cases} L_1 = R_1, \\ L_2 = R_2 \end{cases}$$

are true equations, then

$$\begin{cases} L_1 = R_1, \\ L_1 + L_2 = R_1 + R_2 \end{cases}$$

are also true by the additive property of equals. Hence, (a, b) is a solution of system (2).

Conversely, if (a, b) is a solution of system (2), so that the two equations

$$\begin{cases} L_1 = R_1, \\ L_1 + L_2 = R_1 + R_2 \end{cases}$$

are true, then

$$\begin{cases} L_1 = R_1, \\ (L_1 + L_2) - L_1 = (R_1 + R_2) - R_1, \end{cases}$$

or

$$\begin{cases} L_1 = R_1, \\ L_2 = R_2, \end{cases}$$

are also true by the additive property of equals. Hence, (a, b) is also a solution of system (1). We conclude that systems (1) and (2) are equivalent.

The method described above for finding equivalent systems of equations is called the *addition method*. We illustrate its use in the following problems.

Problem 1. Solve the system of equations

$$\begin{cases} x - 2y = 13, & (L_1 = R_1) \\ 5x + 2y = 5. & (L_2 = R_2) \end{cases} \tag{1}$$

Solution. Note that the coefficients of y are negatives of each other in the two equations of (1). The first equation of system (2),

$$\begin{cases} x - 2y = 13, & (L_1 = R_1) \\ (x - 2y) + (5x + 2y) = 13 + 5, & (L_1 + L_2 = R_1 + R_2) \end{cases} \tag{2}$$

is the same as the first equation of (1), while the second equation of (2) is obtained from (1) by adding the corresponding sides of the two equations of (1). Hence, (2) is equivalent to (1) by the addition method described above. On simplifying the second equation of (2), we obtain the equivalent system

$$\begin{cases} x - 2y = 13, \\ 6x = 18. \end{cases} \tag{3}$$

Thus, $x = 3$ by the second equation, and

$$3 - 2y = 13, \quad -2y = 10, \quad y = -5$$

from the first equation. Hence,

$$\{(3, -5)\}$$

is the solution set of the given system.

Check.
$$3 - [2 \cdot (-5)] \overset{?}{=} 13$$
$$3 + 10 \overset{\checkmark}{=} 13$$

$$(5 \cdot 3) + [2 \cdot (-5)] \overset{?}{=} 5$$
$$15 + (-10) \overset{\checkmark}{=} 5$$

Problem 2. Solve the system of equations

$$\begin{cases} 2x - 5y = -6, \\ 3x + 2y = 29. \end{cases} \qquad \begin{matrix} (L_1 = R_1) \\ (L_2 = R_2) \end{matrix} \tag{1}$$

Solution. The coefficients of x (2 and 3) are not negatives of each other. The coefficients of y (-5 and 2) are not negatives. Hence, adding corresponding sides of the two equations would not eliminate either variable. If we decide to eliminate y, we can multiply each side of the first equation by 2 and each side of the second equation by 5, obtaining an equivalent system with the coefficients of y being additive inverses, -10 and 10. Thus,

$$\begin{cases} 4x - 10y = -12, \\ 15x + 10y = 145. \end{cases} \qquad \begin{matrix} (2L_1 = 2R_1) \\ (5L_2 = 5R_2) \end{matrix} \tag{2}$$

By the addition method, the system

$$\begin{cases} 4x - 10y = -12, \\ 19x = 133 \end{cases} \qquad \begin{matrix} (2L_1 = 2R_1) \\ (2L_1 + 5L_2 = 2R_1 + 5R_2) \end{matrix} \tag{3}$$

is equivalent to (2). From the second equation of (3), $x = 7$, and hence, from the first equation of (3),

$$(4 \cdot 7) - 10y = -12,$$
$$-10y = -40,$$
$$y = 4.$$

Therefore,

$$\{(7, 4)\}$$

is the solution set of system (1).

Check.
$$(2 \cdot 7) - (5 \cdot 4) \overset{?}{=} -6$$
$$14 - 20 \overset{\checkmark}{=} -6$$

$$(3 \cdot 7) + (2 \cdot 4) \overset{?}{=} 29$$
$$21 + 8 \overset{\checkmark}{=} 29$$

Exercises

Solve the given system of equations by the addition method and check each solution.

1. (a) $\begin{cases} 4x + y = 17 \\ 3x - y = 4 \end{cases}$ (b) $\begin{cases} x - 2y = 3 \\ x + 2y = -5 \end{cases}$

2. (a) $\begin{cases} 3x - y = 5 \\ 4x - y = 7 \end{cases}$ (b) $\begin{cases} 2x - y = 16 \\ x - y = 7 \end{cases}$

3. (a) $\begin{cases} 3m - 2n = -10 \\ 4m + n = 49 \end{cases}$ (b) $\begin{cases} u - v = -1 \\ 10u - 8v = -7 \end{cases}$

Start with the system of equations

$$\begin{cases} 2x - 5y = 9, \\ 3x + 4y = 8, \end{cases}$$

and write an equivalent system in which

4. (a) the coefficients of x are the same.
   (b) the coefficients of x are negatives, or additive inverses, of each other.
5. (a) the coefficients of y are negatives, or additive inverses, of each other.
   (b) the coefficients of y are the same.

Solve each system of equations by the addition method, and check each solution.

6. (a) $\begin{cases} 2x - 5y = 9 \\ 3x + 4y = 25 \end{cases}$ (b) $\begin{cases} x + 2y = 14 \\ 4x - 5y = 43 \end{cases}$

7. (a) $\begin{cases} y + 2x - 4 = 0 \\ \frac{5}{2}y = 13x + 10 \end{cases}$ **(b)** $\begin{cases} \frac{2}{7}x + \frac{1}{8}y = 0 \\ \frac{3}{4}x - \frac{1}{3}y = 0 \end{cases}$

8. (a) $\begin{cases} x + 3y = 11 \\ x - y = 17 \end{cases}$ **(b)** $\begin{cases} 8p + 4q = 3 \\ 2p - 8q = -3.75 \end{cases}$

Use any method to solve each of the following systems of equations.

9. (a) $\begin{cases} p + 3(1 - q) = 0 \\ 3q - 2(6 - p) = 0 \end{cases}$ **(b)** $\begin{cases} \dfrac{x + y}{4} + \dfrac{x - y}{2} = 1 \\ \dfrac{3x - y}{4} + \dfrac{4x + 2y}{11} = 3 \end{cases}$

10. (a) $\begin{cases} 3x - y = 6 + x + 2y \\ 3(y - 2) = 2(x + 1) - 10 \end{cases}$ **(b)** $\begin{cases} 2p + q + 14 = 7(p - 4q + 2) \\ 3(2p - 3q + 4) = 5p + 12 \end{cases}$

Addition Method

11. (a) $\begin{cases} x + 2y - 1 = \dfrac{x + y}{5} \\ 2x - y = \dfrac{5 - 2x}{6} \end{cases}$ **(b)** $\begin{cases} .07n - .04m = .01 \\ .2n - .05m = .035 \end{cases}$

12. Try to solve the system of equations

$$\begin{cases} 5x + 2y = 10, \\ 3 - 5x = 2y \end{cases}$$

by the addition method. What is your conclusion about the solution set of this system? What can you say about the graphs of these two equations?

3-3 APPLICATIONS

We can solve many word problems by writing and solving systems of linear equations. Consider, for example, the following problems.

Problem 1. A football game was attended by 4730 people, some paying $1.50 each for reserved seats and the rest paying 90¢ each for general admission. If the total receipts for the game were $5172, how many tickets of each kind were sold?

Solution. Let r designate the number of reserved-seat tickets and g the number of general-admission tickets sold. Since 4730 tickets were sold,

$$r + g = 4730.$$

The amount of money, in dollars, received from the sale of reserved-seat tickets was $1.50r$; that received from the sale of general-admission tickets was $.90g$. Since the total receipts were $5172,

$$1.50r + .90g = 5172.$$

Thus, the solution of the given problem is the solution of the system of equations

$$\begin{cases} r + g = 4730, \\ 1.50r + .90g = 5172. \end{cases} \tag{1}$$

Let us use the substitution method to solve system (1). If we solve the first equation for g in terms of r and substitute the result in the second equation, we obtain the equivalent system

$$\begin{cases} r + g = 4730, \\ 1.50r + .90(4730 - r) = 5172. \end{cases} \tag{2}$$

The second equation of (2) may be simplified as follows:

$$1.50r + 4257 - .90r = 5172,$$
$$.60r = 915,$$
$$r = 1525.$$

Thus, system (2) is equivalent to the system

$$\begin{cases} r + g = 4730, \\ r = 1525. \end{cases} \tag{3}$$

System (3) is easily solved, yielding

$$r = 1525, \quad g = 3205.$$

Check. $1525 + 3205 \overset{\checkmark}{=} 4730$ $(1.50 \cdot 1525) + (.90 \cdot 3205) \overset{?}{=} 5172$
$$2287.50 + 2884.50 \overset{\checkmark}{=} 5172$$

Problem 2. An airplane carries enough gas for 10 hours of flight. Suppose that its speed in still air is 530 miles per hour. If it flies against a wind of 30 miles per hour on its outbound trip and with a wind of 30 miles per hour on the return trip, how far can it fly without refueling?

Solution. The speed of the outbound plane is $530 - 30$, or 500, miles per hour, and the speed on the return flight is $530 + 30$, or 560, miles per hour. Let x denote the distance, in miles, the plane travels from its base, and t the time, in hours, it takes for the outbound journey. Since the product of rate and time is distance, our first equation is

$$500t = x.$$

Our second equation relating x and t describes the return flight. Since the total time of the flight is 10 hours, and the flight out takes t hours, the flight back takes $10 - t$ hours. We have found that the speed on the return trip was 560 miles per hour and since the distance out is the same as the distance back, the equation

$$560(10 - t) = x$$

describes the flight back.

The solution of the given problem is the same as the solution of the system of equations

$$\begin{cases} 500t = x, \\ 560(10 - t) = x. \end{cases}$$

You may easily verify that the following system is equivalent to the one above.

$$\begin{cases} 500t = x \\ t = \frac{280}{53} \end{cases}$$

Hence, the solution is
$$t = \frac{280}{53}, \quad x = \frac{140,000}{53}.$$

Thus, the airplane can fly approximately 2640 miles from its base and return without refueling. Does this answer check?

Exercises

1. How far can the airplane of Problem 2 fly without refueling
    (a) if there is no wind during the 10-hour flight?
    (b) if there is a wind of 50 miles per hour?

2. (a) Find two integers whose sum is 55 and whose difference is 9.
   (b) Find two numbers whose difference is 16 and whose sum is 73.

3. (a) A sum of money amounting to $4.15 consists of dimes and quarters. If there are 19 coins in all, how many quarters are there?
   (b) John's bank contains some quarters and 3 times as many dimes as nickels. If there are 26 coins totaling $3.90 in the bank, how many of each kind of coin does the bank contain?

4. (a) The initial investments of two partners in a business were $50,000 and $70,000. The partners agree to divide profits in the same ratio as their relative investments. How much does each partner receive if the first year's profits amount to $15,000?
   (b) A jet plane makes a 3000-mile trip to Europe in 5 hours, but takes 6 hours for the return trip. If the speed of the wind is constant throughout the trip, what is the speed of the wind and what is the average speed of the plane in still air?

5. (a) State the conditions on the integers d and s, given that there are two integers whose difference is d and whose sum is s.
   (b) The sum of the digits of a two-digit number is one-half the number. Show that this property characterizes the number completely because there is one, and only one, number with this property. (Hint: Recall

that in our decimal system an expression for the two-digit number with tens' digit, t, and units' digit, u, is $10t + u$.)

6. (a) The sum of the digits of a two-digit number is one-seventh the number. Find all numbers having this property.

   (b) Divide 240 into two parts such that the ratio of the larger to the smaller part is $17 : 13$. (Hint: The equation $x/y = 17/13$, or the equivalent linear equation $13x = 17y$, may be used to express the fact that x and y are in the ratio $17 : 13$.)

7. (a) A linear form

$$ax + by$$

is known to have value 21 when $x = 3$ and $y = 2$, and to have value 65 when $x = 7$ and $y = 10$. Find the coefficients a and b of this linear form.

   (b) A linear form

$$ax + by$$

is known to have value 2 when $x = 5$ and $y = 9$, and to have value 15 when $x = 3$ and $y = 10$. Find the coefficients a and b of this linear form.

---

8. Two machines A and B produce items at the constant rate of 50 and 40 items per hour, respectively. An order for 1000 items is to be filled.

   (a) If the total number of machine-hours of operation used is exactly 24, show that to fill the order, there is one, and only one, way of assigning a number of hours of operation to each machine.

   (b) If it costs $10 per hour to operate machine A and $7 per hour to operate machine B, what is the total cost of the production that satisfies the specifications in part (a)?

   (c) If the total number of machine-hours of operation used is to be *at most* 24 (instead of exactly 24), the entire order for 1000 items could be handled by machine A. Find the cost of production under such a scheme, and compare it with the cost of the production plan in part (a).

   (d) If the hourly costs are $10 for machine A and $9 for machine B, compare the production costs under the plan in part (a) with that of the plan in part (c).

===

Preparation for Section 3–4

Graph each of the following pairs of inequalities on the same coordinate plane

1. $x + 1 > 5, \; y < 0$
2. $x > 6, \; y \leq 3$
3. $x - 3 \leq 7, \; y + 4 \geq 0$
4. $x \leq 0, \; y - 5 > 1$

omit

3-4   SYSTEMS OF INEQUALITIES IN TWO VARIABLES

The solution set of a system of inequalities is the *intersection* of the
solution sets of the individual inequalities of the system.   For example, the system

$$\begin{cases} x > 0, \\ y > 0 \end{cases}$$

has as its solution the set of all number pairs (x, y) for which $x > 0$
and $y > 0$.   In set notation, the
solution set is given by

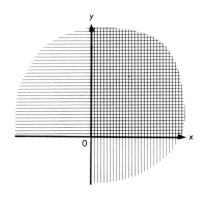

FIGURE 3-6

$$\{(x, y) \mid x > 0\} \cap \{(x, y) \mid y > 0\}.$$

The graph of this set is the set of all points in the first quadrant (the
hatched region of Fig. 3–6).

Problem 1. Describe the solution set and draw the graph of the system

$$\begin{cases} x - y - 2 < 0, \\ x + 2y - 8 > 0. \end{cases}$$

Solution. Each inequality of the system is simplified in the following
way.

$$x - y - 2 < 0$$
$$(x - y - 2) + y < y$$
$$x - 2 < y, \quad \text{or} \quad y > x - 2$$

$$x + 2y - 8 > 0$$
$$(x + 2y - 8) + (-x) + 8 > -x + 8$$
$$2y > -x + 8$$
$$y > -\tfrac{1}{2}x + 4$$

Thus, the given system is equivalent to the system

$$\begin{cases} y > x - 2, \\ y > -\tfrac{1}{2}x + 4, \end{cases}$$

and its solution set S is given by

$$S = \{(x, y) \mid y > x - 2\} \cap \{(x, y) \mid y > -\tfrac{1}{2}x + 4\}.$$

The line L of Fig. 3–7 is the graph of the equation $y = x - 2$. Therefore, the graph of the set $\{(x, y) \mid y > x - 2\}$ is the half-plane above L. In turn, the graph of the equation $y = -\frac{1}{2}x + 4$ is the line K of Fig. 3–7, and the graph of the set $\{(x, y) \mid y > -\frac{1}{2}x + 4\}$ is the half-plane above K. The intersection of these two half-planes is the graph of the solution set S. Thus, the graph of S is the hatched region of Fig. 3–7. Such a hatched region is called a *quarter-plane*.

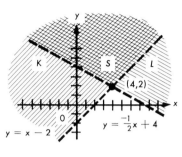

FIGURE 3-7

Problem 2. Describe the solution set and draw the graph of the system

$$\begin{cases} x - y - 2 < 0, \\ x + 2y - 8 > 0, \\ y < 7. \end{cases}$$

Solution. The solution set T consists of all points (x, y) of set S (in Problem 1) for which $y < 7$, that is,

$$T = S \cap \{(x, y) \mid y < 7\}.$$

The graph of T is the set of all points *inside* the triangle ABC (the triply hatched region of Fig. 3–8).

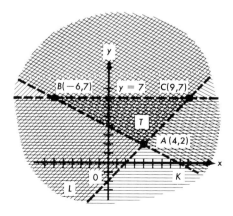

FIGURE 3-8

Problem 3. The shaded region of Fig. 3–9 lies between the two parallel lines with equations

$$x + y = 0,$$
$$x + y = 2.$$

Describe this shaded region as the graph of a system of inequalities.

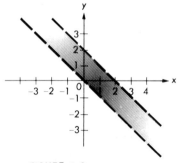

Solution. The shaded region is *above* the line with equation

$$x + y = 0, \quad \text{or } y = -x,$$

and *below* the line with equation

FIGURE 3-9

$$x + y = 2, \quad \text{or } y = -x + 2.$$

Thus, the shaded region is the graph of the set

$$\{(x, y) \mid y > -x\} \cap \{(x, y) \mid y < -x + 2\},$$

and hence of the system

$$\begin{cases} y > -x, \\ y < -x + 2. \end{cases}$$

Exercises

Describe the solution set and draw the graph of each of the following systems of inequalities.

1. (a) $\begin{cases} x < 0 \\ y < 0 \end{cases}$ (b) $\begin{cases} x \geq 0 \\ y \geq 0 \end{cases}$

2. (a) $\begin{cases} y < 2x \\ 2x + y < 12 \end{cases}$ (b) $\begin{cases} y > 3x \\ y < 5 - 3x \end{cases}$

3. (a) $\begin{cases} 2x + y > 3 \\ y < 5 - 2x \end{cases}$ (b) $\begin{cases} y < x + 2 \\ y > x - 4 \end{cases}$

4. (a) $\begin{cases} y < 2x \\ 2x + y < 12 \\ y > 2 \end{cases}$ (b) $\begin{cases} 3x + 4y \leq 12 \\ x \leq 4 \\ y \leq 3 \end{cases}$

Graph each of the following systems. In each case, list the positive integral solutions of the system.

5. (a) $\begin{cases} 3x + 4y \leq 12 \\ 4y \geq 3x \\ x \geq 0 \end{cases}$ (b) $\begin{cases} 50x + 40y \geq 1000 \\ x + y \leq 24 \\ y \geq 0 \end{cases}$

6. Give a system of inequalities for which the graph is the intersection of the half-planes below the graph of $x + y + 2 = 0$ and to the left of $2x - y = 4$. Draw the graph.

7. Give a system of inequalities for which the graph is the region which lies between the graphs of $x - 2y + 6 = 0$ and $x - 2y = 4$. Draw the graph.

Describe the region bounded by the graphs of each of the following systems of inequalities by giving its shape (triangle, pentagon, and so on) and the coordinates of the vertices of its boundary.

8. $\begin{cases} x > 0 \\ y > 0 \\ x < 5 \\ y < 7 \\ x + y \leq 8 \end{cases}$

9. $\begin{cases} x \geq 3 \\ x \leq 15 \\ y \geq 0 \\ y \leq 22 \\ x + y \leq 30 \end{cases}$

10. $\begin{cases} y \geq 0 \\ y \leq 3 \\ 2y - x \leq 0 \\ y \leq 16 - 2x \end{cases}$

11. $\begin{cases} 2x + y \geq 8 \\ x + 3y \geq 9 \\ 3x + 4y \geq 22 \\ x \leq 9 \\ y \leq 8 \end{cases}$

12. $\begin{cases} .9x + .6y \geq 1 \\ .1x + .4y \geq .4 \\ x \leq 4 \\ y \leq \frac{5}{3} \end{cases}$

13. $\begin{cases} 2x + y + 9 \geq 0 \\ -x + 3y + 6 \geq 0 \\ x + 2y - 3 \leq 0 \\ x + y \leq 0 \end{cases}$

14. Give a system of inequalities for which the graph is the intersection of the half-planes above the graph of $3x + 2y = 12$ and below the graph of $2x - 3y + 18 = 0$. Draw the graph.

15. Given that

$$A = \{(x, y) \mid 2x - y \leq 8\},$$
$$B = \{(x, y) \mid 2x + y \leq 4\},$$
$$C = \{(x, y) \mid x \geq 0\},$$

draw the graph of each of the following.
(a) $A \cap B$ (b) $A \cap C$ (c) $B \cap C$ (d) $A \cap B \cap C$
(e) Describe the region $A \cap B \cap C$ by naming its shape and giving the coordinates of the vertices of its boundary.
(f) List all the points of $A \cap B \cap C$ with integral coordinates.

16. Graph the following system of inequalities, and list the positive integral solutions of the system. Where are the corners of the graph?

$$\begin{cases} 2x - y \leq 6 \\ 2x + y \leq 4 \\ x \geq 0 \end{cases}$$

17. Describe the solution set and draw the graph of the system

$$\begin{cases} 5x - 3y - 9 < 0, \\ 2x + 3y - 12 > 0. \end{cases}$$

Is there a point where y is least? Why?

---

18. The following table gives percentages of protein and fat contained in one gram of each of two foods.

	Protein	Fat
Bread	8%	1%
Butter	2%	80%

(a) Write a system of inequalities involving the two unknowns x and y (number of grams of bread and of butter, respectively) which expresses the fact that these two foods together are to supply daily at least 82 grams of protein and 90 grams of fat.
(b) Graph the solution set of your system in the region $x \geq 0$ and $y \geq 0$, and give the coordinates of the corner points.
(c) Give at least three solutions to the problem of meeting the daily minimum requirements of protein and fat.

CHAPTER REVIEW

Solve each of the following systems of linear equations. Tell which, if any, are inconsistent.

1. (a) $\begin{cases} y + x = 4 \\ \quad\; x = 2 \end{cases}$ (b) $\begin{cases} 3x + y = 5 \\ \qquad y = 8 \end{cases}$

2. (a) $\begin{cases} 3y + 2x = 6 \\ 2y - 2x = 9 \end{cases}$ (b) $\begin{cases} \quad\; y - 2x = 4 \\ -y + 3x = 5 \end{cases}$

3. (a) $\begin{cases} 2y + 3x = 5 \\ 4y + 6x = 7 \end{cases}$ (b) $\begin{cases} \;x = y + 3 \\ 2y = 2x - 1 \end{cases}$

4. (a) $\begin{cases} \;x + 2y = 9 \\ 4x - y = 0 \end{cases}$ (b) $\begin{cases} 2x - 5y = 6 \\ 3x + 4y = 32 \end{cases}$

Describe the solution set of each of the following systems of inequalities, and draw its graph.

5. (a) $\begin{cases} x > 2 \\ y < 1 \end{cases}$ (b) $\begin{cases} x \leq 0 \\ y \geq -1 \end{cases}$

6. (a) $\begin{cases} y \leq -x \\ 2y \geq x \end{cases}$ (b) $\begin{cases} x < 3y \\ y > 2x \end{cases}$

7. (a) $\begin{cases} x > -2 \\ x < 2 \\ x > y \end{cases}$ (b) $\begin{cases} y \leq 1 \\ y \geq 0 \\ y \leq x \end{cases}$

8. (a) $\begin{cases} x + y < 2 \\ x > 0 \\ y > 0 \end{cases}$ (b) $\begin{cases} y > x + 1 \\ x < -1 \\ 3y - x < 7 \end{cases}$

9. A newsboy has three times as many dimes as quarters. If the dimes and quarters total $7.15, how many of each does he have?

10. Mr. Smith spent 4 hours driving from his home to his cabin on the lake, while he spent only 3 hours and 20 minutes returning. If his speed on the return trip was 10 miles per hour faster than his speed going, what is the distance, in miles, from his home to his cabin?

11. Joe earns $30 a week less than twice what Jane earns. What is the minimum amount each can earn if they want to meet their combined weekly budget of $150? What is the least each could earn to meet a budget of $210 a week?

12. John has a collection of nickels and dimes, with the dimes numbering three more than twice the number of nickels. If he has at least $2 and at most $3, what possible combinations of dimes and nickels could he have?

4 · Functions

4–1 DEFINITION OF A FUNCTION

Every person in North America has a surname. If we consider one set consisting of all people in North America and a second set consisting of all of their surnames, then there is a definite correspondence between these two sets that associates with each person his or her surname. Such a correspondence between two sets is an example of a *function*. The set of people in North America is called the *domain*, and the set of surnames is called the *range* of this function.

A map of Mexico contains numerous dots, each of which is accompanied by the name of a city. Thus, on the one hand, we have a set of dots on a piece of paper and, on the other hand, a set of cities in Mexico. There is a definite correspondence between these two sets that associates with each dot in the one set a city in the other set. Again, this correspondence is an example of a function whose domain is the set of dots on the map of Mexico and whose range is the set of cities in Mexico.

The formula $A = s^2$ gives the area A of a square in terms of the length s of a side. For example, if $s = 6$, then $A = 36$, and if $s = \sqrt{2}$, then $A = 2$. This formula associates a positive number A with each positive number s, and hence, defines a function whose domain and range are the set P of positive numbers.

These examples suggest the following definition.

Definition of function, domain, image, and range

A function is a correspondence between two sets that associates with each element of the first set a unique element of the second set. The first set is called the domain of the function. For each element x of the domain, the corresponding element y of the second set is called the image of x under the function. The set of all images of the elements of the domain is called the range of the function.

The examples already given illustrate different ways of defining functions. Some functions are defined by equations, others by verbal statements.

The area function defined by $A = s^2$ has domain $D = \{s \mid s > 0\}$ and range $R = \{s^2 \mid s > 0\}$. Obviously, $D = R$ in this example. The distance an automobile travels at a rate of 50 miles per hour is 50 times the number of hours spent traveling. This verbal statement defines a function in which the set of positive real numbers is both the range and the domain of the function. This distance function can also be defined by the following formula.

$$d = 50t \quad \text{if } t > 0$$

A precise statement of the range of a function is not important. As long as we know the domain and have directions for finding the image of each element of the domain, we have a complete definition of the function. Often the domain of a function defined by an equation or verbal statement is not given explicitly. In such a case, the domain is assumed to be the set of all numbers for which the equation or verbal statement makes sense.

We can also consider a function as a *set of ordered pairs* in which no two different pairs have the same first element. The set of all first elements is the *domain*, and the set of all second elements is the *range* of the function. Thus, there is associated with each element x in the domain a unique element y in the range.

An example of a set of ordered pairs is

$$S = \{(x, |x|) \mid x \text{ a real number}\}.$$

In this set, no two different pairs have the same first element. Set S is the *absolute-value function*, which associates with each real number x its absolute value, $|x|$.

Exercises

Each of the following formulas defines a function. State the domain of each function.

1. (a) $C = 10n$; n representing the number of articles, and C the total cost of n articles if each costs 10¢.
   (b) $d = 50t$; t representing the time, in hours, spent, and d the distance, in miles, covered by a car traveling at a constant speed of 50 miles per hour.

2. (a) $p = 4s$; s the side and p the perimeter of a square.

(b) $d = s\sqrt{2}$; s the side and d the diagonal of a square.

3. (a) $s = 64 - 16t^2$; t representing the time, in seconds, elapsed after an object is dropped from a height of 64 feet, and s the distance, in feet, of the object above the ground at time t.

(b) $C = 1.25 + .045(n - 15)$; n representing the number of words in a telegram having at least 15 words, and C the cost of the telegram.

Each of the following tables defines a function. Using set notation, describe the domain and range of each function.

4. (a)

x	2	3	4
y	4	9	16

(b)

x	7	8	9
y	9	10	11

5. (a)

x	7	8	9
y	-3	2	0

(b)

x	1	2	3	4
y	2	1	2	1

6. (a)

x	1	2	3	4
y	1	1	1	1

(b)

x	2	5	7	9
y	$\frac{1}{2}$	$\frac{1}{5}$	$\frac{1}{7}$	$\frac{1}{9}$

7. (a) (i) Solve the linear equation $5x + 2y = 10$ for y in terms of x.

(ii) Does the resulting equation in part (i) define y as a function of x?

(iii) Solve the linear equation in part (i) for x in terms of y.

(iv) Does the resulting equation in part (iii) define x as a function of y?

(b) (i) Solve the linear equation $4x + 3y = 12$ for y in terms of x.

(ii) Does the resulting equation in part (i) define a function of x?

(iii) Solve the linear equation in part (i) for x in terms of y.

(iv) Does the resulting equation in part (iii) define a function of y?

8. (a) Take any number between 0 and 10; multiply this number by 5, then add 11. Express the answer A as a function of the number x first chosen. What is the domain of this function?

(b) Take any number between 0 and 10; add 20 to this number, then divide by 5. Express the answer A as a function of the number x first chosen. What is the domain of this function?

9. (a) Why is the following set of ordered pairs *not* a function?

$$\{(1, 3,) (2, 3), (2, 4), (3, 1)\}$$

(b) Why is the following set of ordered pairs *not* a function?

$$\{(1, 1), (1, 2), (2, 3), (3, 4)\}.$$

10. The following table gives the distance a car travels for various car speeds before a driver's reactions cause him to apply his brakes. (This information is based on the assumption that the average driver takes three-fourths of a second to apply his brakes.)

Speed (in mph)	20	30	40	50	60
Distance (in ft)	22	33	44	55	66

(a) Use set notation to give the domain and the range of the function defined by this set of ordered pairs.

(b) Let d denote distance in feet and s the speed in miles per hour. Find a formula in which d is expressed as a function of s and for which the values in the table form a partial list of ordered pairs.

11. For parking a car, a garage charges 50¢ for the first half-hour or any part of the half-hour and 25¢ per half-hour or any part of a half-hour thereafter. The minimum charge is 50¢, and the maximum amount of time a car may park in one day is 16 hours.

(a) Describe the domain of the function.

(b) Describe the range of the function.

12. (a) Solve the equation $4y - 8x^2 = 12$ for y in terms of x.

(b) Does the resulting equation in part (a) define a function of x?

(c) Solve the equation in part (a) for x in terms of y.

(d) Does the resulting equation in part (c) define a function of y?

13. Each rectangle in a set of rectangles has one side 3 units longer than the other. Write a formula which expresses the area function A of a rectangle in this set in terms of the shorter side x. Give the domain and range of A.

14. A square piece of tin is 10 inches on each side. A small square is cut from each corner and the tin folded to form an open box. (See the figure.) Find a formula which expresses the volume function V of the open box in terms of x, the side of a cut-out square. Give the domain and range of V.

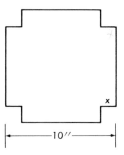

15. Each rectangle in a set of rectangles has an area of 100 square units. Write a formula expressing the base function B for a rectangle in this set in terms of the height h. Give the domain and range of B.

16. Exactly 50 yards of fencing is available for enclosing a rectangular garden. Write a formula for the area function A in terms of one of the sides of the rectangle. Give the domain and range of A.

17. A page with dimensions 12 inches by 14 inches has a border of uniform width x surrounding the printed part of the page. Write a formula for the area function A of the printed part in terms of the width of the border x. Give the domain and range of A.

18. A rectangle y inches long and x inches wide has a perimeter of 10 inches.
   (a) Express y as a function of x.
   (b) Express the area of the rectangle as a function of x.

4-2 FUNCTIONAL NOTATION

An important feature of algebra is its symbolic language. For example, we can use the symbols

$$x + y = 37$$

to express the following sentence:

The sum of two numbers is thirty-seven.

Just as we use letters to designate variables, we shall use letters such as f, g, and A to designate functions. When we use the letter f to designate a function, then for each x in the domain of f,

$$f(x)$$

denotes the *image of x* under f. The symbol $f(x)$ is read "f of x." Therefore, if $x = 2$, we denote the image of 2 as $f(2)$.

Let us consider the *squaring function* f having the set P of positive real numbers as its domain D. The image $f(x)$ of each x in P is the square of x, that is,

$$f(x) = x^2 \quad \text{for each } x \text{ in } P.$$

For example, the numbers 3, $\sqrt{2}$, and 10 are in the domain of f, and their images in the range of f are as follows:

$$f(3) = 3^2, \text{ or } 9; \quad f(\sqrt{2}) = (\sqrt{2})^2, \text{ or } 2; \quad f(10) = 10^2, \text{ or } 100.$$

This function f has geometric significance: It is the *area function* of a square. Thus, if the length of a side of a square is 3 inches, the area of the square is $f(3)$, or 9 square inches. We could just as well denote this function by A and define it by the formula

$$A(s) = s^2 \quad \text{for each positive real number } s.$$

These two functions f and A are equal; that is, they have the same domain P and $f(a) = A(a)$ for each number a in P. On the other hand, the function g, defined by

$$g(x) = x^2 \quad \text{for every real number } x,$$

is not equal to f, although the equation defining g is the same as the equation defining f. They are different because the domain of g is the set of all real numbers, but the domain of f is the set of all *positive* real numbers. For example,

$$g(-3) = (-3)^2, \quad \text{or } 9,$$

but $f(-3)$ is not defined since -3 is not in the domain of f.

As a second example, let us consider function s and its domain D, defined in the following manner.

$$s(t) = 64 - 16t^2, \quad D = \{t \mid 0 \leq t \leq 2\}.$$

Some images of elements of D under s are

$$s(0) = 64 - (16 \cdot 0^2), \quad \text{or } 64;$$
$$s(\tfrac{1}{2}) = 64 - [16 \cdot (\tfrac{1}{2})^2], \quad \text{or } 60;$$
$$s(1) = 64 - [16 \cdot 1^2], \quad \text{or } 48;$$
$$s(\tfrac{3}{2}) = 64 - [16 \cdot (\tfrac{3}{2})^2], \quad \text{or } 28;$$
$$s(2) = 64 - [16 \cdot 2^2], \quad \text{or } 0.$$

The function s has physical significance as a *distance function*. If an object is dropped from a point 64 feet above the ground, then the distance of the object from the ground t seconds after it is dropped is $s(t)$ feet. For example, 1 second after the object is dropped, it is 48 feet above the ground. Since $s(2) = 0$, it takes the object 2 seconds to reach the ground.

As a third example, consider the function C which has the set of positive integers as its domain and is defined in the following way.

$$C(n) = \begin{cases} 1.25 \text{ if } 0 < n \leq 15 \\ 1.25 + .045(n - 15) \text{ if } n > 15 \end{cases}$$

Note that two equations are used to define C. From the first equation, we know that each of the following is equal to 1.25.

$$C(1), \ C(2), \ \ldots, \ C(15)$$

From the second equation, we know that

$$C(25) = 1.25 + .045 \cdot (25 - 15)$$
$$= 1.25 + .45, \quad \text{or } 1.70.$$

This function might describe the cost, in dollars, of sending a telegram having n words. Thus, a 25-word telegram would cost $1.70.

If we want a formula such as $f(x) = 7/(x - 3)$ to give the image of each real number x in the domain of the function f, then we must exclude the value $x = 3$. In this case, it is customary to write the complete description of f as

$$f(x) = \frac{7}{x - 3}, \quad x \text{ real and } x \neq 3.$$

Exercises

1. (a) Let the function f be defined as follows: The domain of f is the set of all real numbers and the image of each real number is given by the formula

$$f(x) = 2x^2 + 5x - 3.$$

Find $f(-3)$, $f(-\sqrt{2})$, $f(-\frac{5}{4})$, and $f(0)$.

(b) Let the function f be defined as follows: The domain of f is the set of all real numbers and the image of each real number is given by the formula

$$f(x) = 3x^2 - 4x + 1.$$

Find $f(-1)$, $f(5)$, $f(0)$, $f(-\frac{1}{2})$.

2. (a) If $g(x) = 4/(x^2 - 1)$ gives the image of a real number x under the function g, what real numbers must be excluded from the domain of g? Write a complete description of the function g.
Find $g(2)$, $g(-2)$, $g(3)$, $g(-3)$, $g(4)$, and $g(-4)$.
For the real number k, $k \neq \pm 1$, how does $g(k)$ compare with $g(-k)$?

(b) If $g(x) = \dfrac{3}{x + 2}$ gives the image of a real number x under the function g, what number must be excluded from the domain of g? Find $g(-1)$, $g(0)$, $g(\frac{1}{3})$, $g(-\frac{5}{2})$, $g(-\frac{3}{2})$.

Give the restrictions, if any, on the domain of each of the following functions.

3. (a) $f(x) = \dfrac{5}{x + 4}$ (b) $f(x) = 1 + \dfrac{1}{x}$

4. (a) $f(x) = \sqrt{x^2 - 1}$ (b) $f(x) = -5$

5. (a) $f(x) = \dfrac{3}{x - 2}$ (b) $f(x) = x + \dfrac{1}{x}$

6. (a) $f(x) = 4$ (b) $f(x) = \sqrt{16 - x^2}$

7. (a) For each of the functions defined in Exercises 3(a), 4(a), 5(a), and 6(a), find $f(2)$, $f(-1)$, and $f(\frac{3}{2})$.

   (b) For each of the functions defined in Exercises 3(b), 4(b), 5(b), and 6(b), find $f(3)$, $f(-3)$, and $f(\frac{1}{3})$.

8. (a) A function g is defined by the equation $g(x) = 3$, and the domain of g is the set of all real numbers. This type of function is called a *constant function.*
   Find $g(-7)$, $g(-3)$, and $g(0)$.
   What is the range of g?

   (b) A function f is defined by the equation $f(x) = \sqrt{9 - x^2}$.
   Find $f(1)$, $f(-1)$, $f(9)$, $f(-9)$, and $f(0)$.
   Use set notation to describe the domain of f.
   Use set notation to describe the range of f.

9. (a) A function f whose domain is the set of real numbers is defined by the equation

$$f(x) = \sqrt{x^2 + 1}.$$

   Find $f(2\sqrt{2})$, $f(\sqrt{15})$, $f(0)$, and $f(-1)$.

   Use set notation to describe the range of f.

   (b) If $g(x) = -\sqrt{x^2 + 1}$ and the domain of g is the set of real numbers, use set notation to describe the range of the function g.

---

10. Given that $g(x) = x^2$, with the domain of g the set of all real numbers,
    (a) find $g(3)$, $g(4)$, $g(7)$, and compare $g(7)$ with $g(3) + g(4)$.
    (b) find $g(-2)$, $g(5)$, $g(3)$, and compare $g(3)$ with $g(-2) + g(5)$.
    (c) do you think that the equation $g(a) + g(b) = g(a + b)$ will be true for any pair a, b of real numbers? Explain your answer.

11. Given that $g(x) = x^2$, with the domain of g the set of all real numbers,
    (a) find $g(3)$, $g(5)$, $g(15)$, and compare the number $g(15)$ with the product $g(3) \cdot g(5)$.
    (b) find $g(-2)$, $g(6)$, $g(-12)$, and compare $g(-12)$ with $g(-2) \cdot g(6)$.
    (c) find $\dfrac{g(28)}{g(7) \cdot g(4)}$.

12. The weight W of an object varies directly with its volume V, that is, $W = kV$ for some constant of proportionality k.
   (a) An object weighs 14 grams and has a volume of 10 cubic centimeters. Find the constant of proportionality.
   (b) Use functional notation to write an expression for this weight function W. What is its domain?
   (c) Find $W(20)$ and $W(15)$.

13. The number N of articles purchased varies inversely with the price p per article, that is, $N = k/p$ for some constant k.
   (a) If 11 articles at 12¢ per article can be bought with available money, find the constant of proportionality.
   (b) Using functional notation, write an expression for the function N. What is the domain of N?
   (c) Find $N(11)$, $N(6)$, and $N(4)$.

---

14. The function N whose domain is the set of real numbers is defined in the following way.

$$N(x) = \begin{cases} x & \text{if } x \text{ is a nonnegative real number} \\ -x & \text{if } x \text{ is a negative real number} \end{cases}$$

   (a) Find $N(2)$, $N(\sqrt{3})$, $N(1 - \sqrt{2})$, $N(-2)$, $N(-\sqrt{3})$, $N(\sqrt{2} - 1)$, and $N(0)$.
   (b) Describe this function and write a single equation defining $N(x)$.

15. The operation of multiplying each real number by 7 defines a certain function. If we designate this function by O, then $O(x) = 7x$ for each real number x. Similarly, each of the following operations defines a function which you may designate by O. Assume that the domain of each function O is the largest possible set of real numbers, and define each function O by an equation.
   (a) Each number x is multiplied by 10.
   (b) Each number x is added to 7.
   (c) Each number x is divided by -3.
   (d) Each number x is multiplied by 1.
   (e) Each number x is replaced by 1.

16. (a) Show that the function f defined by the two equations

$$f(x) = \begin{cases} \dfrac{x - 9}{\sqrt{x} - 3}, & x \neq 9 \text{ and } x \geq 0, \\ 6 \text{ if } x = 9 \end{cases}$$

   can be defined by one equation whose domain x is the set of non-negative numbers.
   (b) Find $f(4)$, $f(16)$, $f(25)$, and $f(100)$.

17. The function g is given by the following two equations. Find one equation which defines this function.

$$\begin{cases} g(x) = \dfrac{\sqrt{x} - 2}{x - 4}, & x \neq 4 \text{ and } x > 0, \\ g(4) = \frac{1}{4} \end{cases}$$

18. (a) The two functions g, h are defined below. Are they equal functions?

$$g(x) = \frac{\sqrt{x^2 + 16} - 5}{x^2 - 9}, \quad x \neq \pm 3,$$

$$h(x) = \frac{1}{\sqrt{x^2 + 16} + 5}$$

(b) For what values of x does $g(x) = h(x)$?

Preparation for Section 4–3

1. Graph the equation $y = 2x - 3$.
(a) What is the slope of this line? What is the y-intercept?
(b) Find the x-intercept of this line.
(c) Which of the following points are on this line?

$$(1, -1), \ (2, 5), \ (-\tfrac{1}{2}, -4), \ (0, -3), \ (4, 4), \ (x, 2x - 3)$$

2. Graph the equation $y = x^2$.
3. Graph the equation $y = x^2 + x + 1$.

4–3 THE GRAPH OF A FUNCTION

If both the domain and the range of a function are sets of real numbers, then the function may be displayed by a graph in a cartesian coordinate system. The graph of a function is defined in the following way.

Definition of graph of a function

The graph of a function f having domain D is the graph of the set

$$\{(x, f(x)) \mid x \text{ in } D\}.$$

A function L of the form

$$L(x) = mx + b,$$

where m and b are given real numbers, is called a *linear function*. Its graph is a straight line. The following problem is an example of the linear function.

Problem 1. Graph the linear function L defined by

$$L(x) = 2x - 3, \quad D = \{x \mid x \text{ real}\}.$$

Solution. We are asked to graph the set

$$\{(x, 2x - 3) \mid x \text{ in } D\},$$

which is the same as the set

$$\{(x, y) \mid y = 2x - 3\}.$$

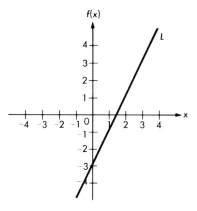

The graph of the latter set is the straight line of Fig. 4–1. This line has slope 2 and y-intercept -3. What is its x-intercept?
    A function P defined by

$$P(x) = x^n,$$

FIGURE 4-1

for some number n, is called the *power function with exponent n*. Its domain is the set of all real numbers having an nth power.

Problem 2. Graph the following power function with exponent 3.

$$P(x) = x^3, \quad D = \{x \mid x \text{ real}\}$$

Solution. The graph of P is the graph of the set

$$\{(x, y) \mid y = x^3\}.$$

The following table of values will help us to draw this graph (shown in Fig. 4–2).

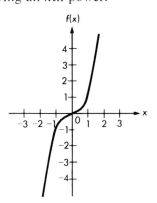

FIGURE 4-2

x	-3	-2	-1.5	-1	$-.5$	0	$.5$	1	1.5	2	3
$P(x)$	-27	-8	-3.375	-1	$-.125$	0	$.125$	1	3.375	8	27

The part of the graph close to the origin is very flat, but the part of the graph away from the origin is quite steep.

Problem 3. The *greatest-integer function F* is defined in the following way. For each real number x, $F(x)$ is the largest integer that is less than or equal to x.   Graph the function F.

Solution. By definition,

$$
\begin{aligned}
F(x) &= -2 \quad \text{if} \quad -2 \le x < -1, \\
F(x) &= -1 \quad \text{if} \quad -1 \le x < 0, \\
F(x) &= 0 \quad\ \text{if} \quad\ \ 0 \le x < 1, \\
F(x) &= 1 \quad\ \ \text{if} \quad\ \ 1 \le x < 2, \\
F(x) &= 2 \quad\ \ \text{if} \quad\ \ 2 \le x < 3,
\end{aligned}
$$

and so on.   Thus, the graph consists of an infinite number of line segments, or steps, as shown in Fig. 4–3.   Each step includes its left-hand endpoint, indicated by the solid dot, and does not include its right-hand endpoint, indicated by the hollow dot.

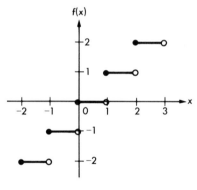

FIGURE 4-3

Exercises

1. (a) Graph the function defined by $f(x) = |x|$.
   (b) Graph the function defined by $f(x) = |x - 1|$.
2. (a) Graph on the same axes the functions defined below.

$$f(x) = x, \quad g(x) = x^2, \quad h(x) = x^3, \quad k(x) = x^4$$

   Compare and contrast the graphs.
   (b) Graph the functions defined below on the same axes.

$$f(x) = x^2, \quad g(x) = x^2 + 4, \quad h(x) = x^2 - 1, \quad k(x) = 3x^2$$

   Compare and contrast the graphs.

3. (a) Graph the quadratic function $f(x) = x^2 + 2x + 3$.
   (b) Graph the quadratic function $f(x) = x^2 - 2x + 4$.

4. (a) What is the domain of the function f defined by the equation

$$f(x) = \sqrt{9 - x^2}?$$

Graph the function f.
How does your graph compare with the graph of the equation $x^2 + y^2 = 9$?
Write another function g whose graph is the remaining portion of the graph defined by the above equation. Graph g.

(b) What is the domain of the function f defined by the equation

$$f(x) = -\sqrt{4 - x^2}?$$

Graph the function f.
How does your graph compare with the graph of the equation $x^2 + y^2 = 4$?
Write another function g whose graph is the remaining portion of the graph defined by the above equation. Graph g.

5. (a) The shipping charges of a mail-order company are 25¢ for the first pound or fraction thereof, an additional 25¢ for orders weighing more than 1 pound but not more than 2 pounds, and so on, for each additional pound or fraction thereof.
   Graph this shipping function, F. What is its domain? Describe the range of F.

   (b) Given that $f(x) = 2^x$ for x a nonnegative *integer*, graph this function.

---

6. The figure shows the graph of a function f whose domain is the interval $\{x \mid -2 \leq x \leq 3\}$ and whose range is the interval $\{y \mid -1 \leq y \leq 1\}$. Sketch the graph of each of the following equations, carefully labeling your scale on each axis.

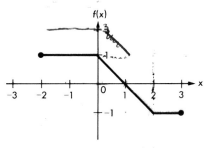

(a) $y = f(x) + 2$ (b) $y = 2f(x)$
(c) $y = -f(x)$ (d) $y = |f(x)|$

$y = -y$ $y = |y|$
                                  $|f(x)| = f(x)$

7. We can define four functions by solving each of the following equations first for y and then for x. In each case, give the definitions of the functions, and show how their graphs are related to the graph of the given equation.
   (a) $x^2 + y^2 = 4$
   (b) $x^2 - y^2 = 1$
   (c) $9x^2 + 25y^2 = 225$
   (d) $x^2 + 4y^2 = 4$

8. The function f, defined by the equation $f(x) = 3/(x - 2)$, has domain $D = \{x \mid x \neq 2\}$. The graph of this function is sketched below. Although we can find no points with abscissa 2, we can find points with abscissas as close to 2 as we wish. Complete the following table to see the behavior of the curve near $x = 2$ and then for $|x|$ very large.

x	1	1.5	1.75	1.9	3	2.5	2.25	2.1	12	102	1002	-8	-98	-998
$f(x)$	?	?	?	?	?	?	?	?	?	?	?	?	?	?

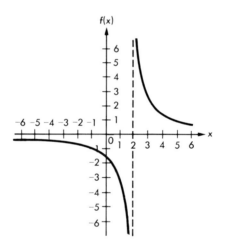

Graph the following functions, paying particular attention to points whose abscissas are close to numbers excluded from the domain of the function. Draw dashed vertical lines at the excluded numbers. (See Exercise 8.)

9. $f(x) = x + \dfrac{1}{x}$

10. $g(x) = \dfrac{3}{(x + 2)^2}$

11. $f(x) = \dfrac{x - 2}{x - 3}$

12. $f(x) = 1 + \dfrac{1}{x - 3}$

13. $g(x) = \dfrac{4}{x^2 - 4}$

14. $h(x) = \dfrac{4x}{x^2 - 4}$

Preparation for Section 4–4

1. Simplify.

$$2^{-3},\ 2^{-1},\ 25^{-\frac{1}{2}},\ (\tfrac{1}{27})^{-\frac{1}{3}},\ 36^{\frac{3}{2}},\ 4^{-2.5},\ 4^{1.5}$$

2. Using a table of square roots, give 2-decimal approximations for the following.

$$2^{-2.5},\ 2^{-1.5},\ 2^{-.5},\ 2^{.5},\ 2^{1.5},\ 2^{2.5}$$

3. Simplify.

$$16^{\frac{1}{8}},\ 9^{\frac{1}{4}},\ 27^{-\frac{1}{9}}$$

4–4   EXPONENTIAL FUNCTIONS

So far, we have defined the rth power of each positive real number a for every rational number r. Thus, for each positive real number a and each rational number r, there is defined a unique positive real number a^r. You may wonder whether it is possible to define a^r in a sensible way for an irrational exponent r. For example, can one formulate a reasonable definition of $2^{\sqrt{3}}$? Actually, it is possible to do so in a way that we shall describe in this section.

Consider, for example, the equation

$$y = 2^x.$$

We know that for every rational value of x, there is a unique real value of y which makes this equation true. We can get some idea of the shape of the graph by plotting points from the values given in the table.

x	-3	-2.5	-2	-1.5	-1	$-.5$	0	$.5$	1	1.5	2	2.5	3	3.5	4
y	.125	.18	.25	.35	.5	.71	1	1.41	2	2.83	4	5.66	8	11.31	16

The points we have plotted seem to lie on a smooth curve. If we were to take many more rational values of x and plot the points corresponding to them, we would obtain a better picture of this curve. In fact, we could plot so many points, say between $x = 0$ and $x = 1$, that we would not be able to distinguish between our set of points and a curve showing no breaks for irrational values of x. It would then seem reasonable to define 2^x, for x irrational, as the y-coordinate of the curve through these points. Thus, let us make the reasonable assumption that to each real number x there corresponds a unique positive number y such that the point (x, y) is on the smooth curve

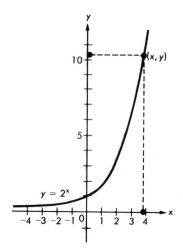

FIGURE 4-4

indicated in Fig. 4–4. Using this assumption, we can say that for each real number x, there is a unique positive number y such that the equation $y = 2^x$ is true.

A number such as $2^{\sqrt{3}}$ can be approximated in the following way. Since $1 < \sqrt{3} < 2$ and since the curve in Fig. 4–4 is rising, we must have $2^1 < 2^{\sqrt{3}} < 2^2$, that is, $2 < 2^{\sqrt{3}} < 4$. A better approximation of $2^{\sqrt{3}}$ can be obtained by taking a better approximation of $\sqrt{3}$. Thus, $1.7 < \sqrt{3} < 1.8$ and therefore,

$$2^{1.7} < 2^{\sqrt{3}} < 2^{1.8}.$$

Note that $2^{1.7}$ and $2^{1.8}$ are rational powers of 2 and hence, have been previously defined. Thus, $1.7 = \frac{17}{10}$ and $2^{1.7} = \sqrt[10]{2^{17}}$; similarly, $2^{1.8} = \sqrt[5]{2^9}$. It can be shown that $2^{1.7} \doteq 3.2$ and $2^{1.8} \doteq 3.5$ and therefore, that $3.2 < 2^{\sqrt{3}} < 3.5$.

We can now define the function E:

$$E(x) = 2^x.$$

From our discussion, we know that the domain of E is the set of all real numbers. We call E the *exponential function with base* 2. The graph of E is sketched in Fig. 4–4.

For each positive real number b not equal to 1, we may similarly define the exponential function E with base b.

Definition of the exponential function

$$E(x) = b^x, \quad \textit{domain of } E = \{x \mid x \textit{ real}\}$$

If $b > 1$, the graph of the exponential function with base b is similar to that in Fig. 4–4. If $b = 1$, the function E, defined by

$$E(x) = 1^x,$$

is simply the constant function

$$E(x) = 1,$$

and this case is usually excluded from consideration as an exponential function.

If $0 < b < 1$, then b^x gets smaller and smaller as x assumes larger and larger positive values, and b^x increases as x assumes smaller and smaller negative values. For example, if E is the exponential function with base $\frac{1}{2}$,

$$E(x) = (\tfrac{1}{2})^x.$$

Then

$$E(x) = 2^{-x},$$

and the graph of E (in Fig. 4–5) is the mirror image in the y-axis of Fig. 4–4.

Exponential functions have many applications in the sciences. If ideal conditions for growth and reproduction prevail, then the growth curve of a population is exponential in nature. For example, the number of bacteria in a culture might be given by the exponential function

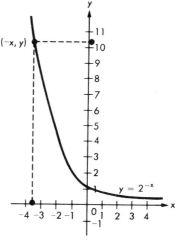

FIGURE 4-5

$$E(t) = 1000 \cdot 3^t.$$

Thus, initially, there are 1000 bacteria, that is, $E(0) = 1000$. Then

$$1 \text{ hour later, } E(1) = 3^1 \times 1000 = 3000;$$
$$2 \text{ hours later, } E(2) = 3^2 \times 1000 = 9000;$$
$$3 \text{ hours later, } E(3) = 3^3 \times 1000 = 27{,}000;$$

and so on.

Exercises

1. Graph each of the following groups of exponential functions on the same set of axes. Compare and contrast the graphs of each group.
   (a) $E(x) = 3^x$, $E(x) = 3^{-x}$, $E(x) = 3^x + 2$
   (b) $E(x) = 3^x + 1$, $E(x) = 3^{\frac{x}{2}}$, $E(x) = 3^{x+1}$

2. (a) Consider the following exponential function which describes the growth of bacteria. In this function, t is time measured in hours and $E(t)$ is the number, in thousands, of bacteria in a culture.

$$E(t) = 100 \times 16^t$$

What is the initial number of bacteria?
After $\frac{1}{4}$ hour, how many bacteria are there?
After $\frac{1}{2}$ hour, how many bacteria are there?
After 1 hour, how many bacteria are there?
Verify that $E(t) = 100\sqrt{2}$ when $t = \frac{1}{8}$.

   (b) The following exponential function describes the growth of bacteria.

$$E(t) = 3 \times 16^t$$

What is the initial number of bacteria?
After $\frac{1}{4}$ hour, how many bacteria are there?
After $\frac{1}{2}$ hour, how many bacteria are there?
After 1 hour, how many bacteria are there?
Verify that $E(t) = 3\sqrt{2}$ when $t = \frac{1}{8}$.

3. (a) The decay curve of a radioactive element is exponential. If the initial quantity of an element is a, then the quantity present after t units of time is given by the function

$$E(t) = a \times b^{-t}.$$

The base b will depend on the element and also on the choice of units for time. Consider the specific law of decay

$$E(t) = 150 \times 2^{-.002t},$$

where t is the time, in years, and $E(t)$ is the amount, in milligrams, of a radioactive substance present at time t.

What is the initial quantity?
How much is left after 1000 years?
How long does it take for the initial quantity to decay to $\frac{1}{8}$ the original amount?
Will the amount present ever vanish completely?

(b) A culture of bacteria, which contains 2000 bacteria, has a count of 18,000 bacteria after 2 hours. Assuming the exponential law of growth, show that the following function fits the above conditions:

$$E(t) = 2 \times 3^t.$$

Here $E(t)$ is the number of thousands of bacteria present after t hours. Find the number of bacteria present after 1 hour.

4. Graph each of the following exponential equations. You will find it convenient to choose different scales for the two axes.
(a) $y = 10^x$ (b) $y = 10^{-x}$

$E(t) = a \times b^{t+t}$

5. A culture with an initial count of 1000 bacteria contains 8000 bacteria $1000 \times 8^{t/3}$ 3 hours later. Assuming exponential growth, find the growth formula. How long does it take this culture to double in size?

6. Sometimes the population growth of a town approximately follows an exponential law for the limited period of time. Assuming this type of growth, find the estimated population in 1970 for a hypothetical town, given the following data.

1950 population   5000
1960 population   7070

7. The half-life of radium is known to be approximately 1600 years, since it takes 1600 years for a given quantity of radium to decay to one-half its initial mass. Start with 300 milligrams of radium, and verify that the law of decay is given by

$$E(t) = 300 \times 2^{-\frac{t}{1600}}.$$

Find the quantity present at the end of the first 800 years.

8. A radioactive element has a law of decay given by

$$E(t) = 400 \times 4^{-\frac{t}{1000}}.$$

Determine its half-life by finding the time at which the amount present is one-half the original amount.

9. When $b > 1$, the graph of $E(x) = b^x$ rises steadily, that is

$$b^{x_1} > b^{x_2} \quad \text{if, and only if,} \quad x_1 > x_2.$$

We may use this property of the exponential function to solve such inequalities as $2^x > 32$, since $32 = 2^5$ and $2^x > 2^5$ if, and only if, $x > 5$. In other words, the solution set of this inequality is

$$\{x \mid x > 5\}.$$

Solve each of the following inequalities.

(a) $3^x \leq 81$ (b) $3^{2x} > 27$

(c) $4^x < 8$ (d) $2^x > 1$

10. Inequalities such as $(\frac{1}{3})^x > \frac{1}{81}$ involve the exponential function with a base less than 1. Such inequalities can be solved by the use of the property stated in Exercise 9 since $(\frac{1}{3})^x = 3^{-x}$ and $\frac{1}{81} = 3^{-4}$. Thus, $3^{-x} > 3^{-4}$ if, and only if, $-x > -4$ or $x < 4$. Solve each of the following inequalities.

(a) $(\frac{1}{32})^{2x} < \frac{1}{64}$ (b) $(\frac{4}{9})^{3x} < \frac{32}{243}$

(c) $128^{-x} \geq 16$ (d) $(\frac{1}{2})^x > 64$

CHAPTER REVIEW

1. The number of degrees centigrade, C, is related to the number of degrees Fahrenheit, F, by the formula $C = \frac{5}{9}(F - 32)$.

    (a) Solve this equation for F and express the resulting formula in functional notation.

    (b) Find F(0), F(100), and F(−40).

    (c) What type of function is F?

2. Boyle's law states that the volume V of a gas kept at constant temperature varies inversely with the pressure P. For a particular gas kept at a certain temperature, a volume of 300 cubic inches is formed under a pressure of 15 pounds per square inch. Write an expression for the volume function V and use it to find $V(20)$.

3. Graph each of the following functions and give the domain.

    (a) $f(x) = \dfrac{1}{3x + 6}$ (b) $f(x) = \sqrt{16 - x^2}$

    (c) $f(x) = 2^x$ (d) $f(x) = x^{\frac{1}{4}}$

4. (a) If a function f is defined by the equation

    $$f(x) = \frac{3}{x^2} - 4,$$

    what real numbers must be excluded from the domain of f?

    (b) For the function f in part (a), find

    $$f(0), \quad f(\tfrac{1}{2}), \quad f(-\tfrac{1}{2}), \quad f(1), \quad f(-1), \quad f(3), \quad f(-3), \quad f(\tfrac{3}{2}), \quad f(6).$$

    (c) Graph the function f.

5. If the domain of the function f is $\{x \mid -2 \leq x \leq 4\}$ and $f(x) = x - 1$, graph each of the following equations.

    (a) $y = f(x)$ (b) $y = f(-x)$

    (c) $y = f(|x|)$ (d) $y = f(x + 2)$

6. Graph the function defined by the equation

$$f(x) = \left[\frac{x}{2}\right].$$

Remember that the notation for greatest integer in x is $[x]$.

7. The function g whose domain is the set of real numbers is defined as follows:

$$g(x) = \begin{cases} 0 & \text{if } x \text{ is a negative number,} \\ x & \text{if } x \text{ is a nonnegative number.} \end{cases}$$

Find $g(-3)$, $g(-2)$, $g(0)$, $g(\frac{7}{4})$, $g(\sqrt{5})$, $g(6)$, and $g(\pi)$.

8. Graph each of the following functions on the same set of axes.
(a) $f(x) = x - 3$ (b) $g(x) = (x - 3)^2$
(c) $h(x) = (x - 3)^3$ (d) $k(x) = (x - 3)^4$

9. The law of decay of a radioactive element is given by

$$A = 700 \times 8^{-\frac{t}{1500}}.$$

Determine the half-life of the element by finding the time at which the amount present is one-half the original amount.

5 · Polynomials

5–1 WORKING WITH POLYNOMIALS

The function

$$f(x) = 4x^3 - 3x^2 + 2x + 1$$

is an example of a *polynomial function*. The expression

$$4x^3 - 3x^2 + 2x + 1$$

is called a polynomial in the variable x. Thus, a *polynomial in x* is an expression of the form

$$a_n x^n + a_{n-1} x^{n-1} + \cdots + a_2 x^2 + a_1 x + a_0, \ n \text{ a nonnegative integer.}$$

The real numbers $a_0, a_1, a_2, \ldots, a_{n-1}, a_n$ are called the *coefficients* of the polynomial; a_n, which is assumed to be nonzero, is called the *leading coefficient* and $a_n x^n$ the *leading* term; a_0 is called the *constant term*. For the polynomial

$$4x^3 - 3x^2 + 2x + 1$$

$4, -3, 2, 1$ are the coefficients, 4 is the leading coefficient, $4x^3$ the leading term, and 1 the constant term.

A polynomial with leading coefficient $a_n x^n$ is said to have *degree n*. For example,

$4x^3 - 3x^2 + 2x + 1$	has degree 3	(*cubic* polynomial)
$7x^2 + 1$	has degree 2	(*quadratic* polynomial)
$-4x + 5$	has degree 1	(*linear* polynomial)
11	has degree 0	(*constant* polynomial)

The constant polynomial 0 doesn't have a degree.

Any two polynomials in x can be added, subtracted, or multiplied, the result being another polynomial. For example, the sum of two polynomials is found as follows:

$$(2x^3 - 7x + 3) + (5x^3 + 4x^2 + 6x - 8)$$
$$= (2x^3 + 5x^3) + 4x^2 + (-7x + 6x) + (3 - 8)$$
$$= 7x^3 + 4x^2 - x - 5$$

The difference is as follows:

$$(7x^2 + 2x - 2) - (4x^2 + 2x + 5)$$
$$= (7x^2 - 4x^2) + (2x - 2x) + (-2 - 5)$$
$$= 3x^2 + 0x - 7, \text{ or } 3x^2 - 7$$

The product of two polynomials is found by multiplying every term of the first polynomial by every term of the second, and then adding the resulting terms. For example,

$$(x^2 - 3x + 4) \cdot (2x^2 + 2x - 1)$$
$$= x^2 \cdot 2x^2 + x^2 \cdot 2x + x^2 \cdot (-1) + (-3x) \cdot 2x^2$$
$$+ (-3x) \cdot 2x + (-3x) \cdot (-1) + 4 \cdot 2x^2$$
$$+ 4 \cdot 2x + 4 \cdot (-1)$$
$$= 2x^4 + 2x^3 - x^2 - 6x^3 - 6x^2 + 3x + 8x^2 + 8x - 4$$
$$= 2x^4 - 4x^3 + x^2 + 11x - 4$$

The product may be obtained by the vertical method used in multiplying numbers. For example, let us find the product

$$(7x^2 + 5x - 6) \cdot (3x + 4)$$

by the vertical method.

$$
\begin{array}{r}
7x^2 + 5x - 6 \\
\times \quad 3x + 4 \\
\hline
21x^3 + 15x^2 - 18x \quad [= 3x \cdot 7x^2 + 3x \cdot 5x + 3x \cdot (-6)] \\
+ 28x^2 + 20x - 24 \quad [= 4 \cdot 7x^2 + 4 \cdot 5x + 4 \cdot (-6)] \\
\hline
21x^3 + 33x^2 + 2x - 24
\end{array}
$$

This is the product!

By looking at the two examples above, we see that the degree of the product of two polynomials can be predicted.

The degree of the product of two polynomials is the sum of their degree.

Exercises

Perform the indicated operations with polynomials.

1. (a) $(x^2 + 3x + 5) + (2x - 2)$
   (b) $(2x^2 - 3x + 5) + (x^3 - x + 7)$

2. (a) $(3x^3 - 5x + 7) - (7 + 3x^3 - 5x)$
   (b) $(x^5 - 5x + 7) + (-x^5 + 5x - 7)$

3. (a) $(4x^2 - 3x + 5) - (x^3 - 3x + 7)$
   (b) $(7x^3 - 4x^2 + 2x - 4) - (7x^3 - 4x^2 - 4)$

4. (a) $(4x^3 - x^2 + 3x - 2) + (-3x^3 + 7x)$
   (b) $(x^4 + 3x) + (12x^3 - 2x^2 + 5)$

5. (a) $(5x^2 + 7x + 9) - (x^3 + 7x + 3)$
   (b) $(x + 4) + (x^3 - 3x^2 + 2x + 1)$

6. (a) $(x^3 - x^2 + x + 1) - (x^2 - x - 1)$
   (b) $(x^4 - 3x^2 + 5) + (2x^4 + 3x^2 - 5)$

7. (a) $(x^2 + 11x - 4) + (2x^2 - 7x + 4)$
   (b) $(5x^3 - 9x + 8) - (5x^3 - 9x + 8)$

8. (a) $(3x + 13) - (2x^2 + 3x + 11)$
   (b) $(x^6 - 4x^3 + 4) + (4x^3 - 4)$

9. (a) $(2x + 1)(x^2 + 3x - 2)$ (b) $(x - 4)(2x^2 - x + 2)$

10. (a) $(x^2 + 2)(x^2 - 5x + 4)$ (b) $(2x^2 + x)(3x^2 - 5x - 6)$

11. (a) $(x^2 + x + 1)(x^2 - x + 1)$ (b) $(3x^2 + 2x - 1)(3x^2 + 2x + 1)$

12. (a) $(x^3 - 2x)(x^2 + 5x + 1)$ (b) $(x^4 - 1)(x^8 + x^4 + 1)$

13. (a) $(-5x^3 + x^2 - 1)(x^3 - 2x + 4)$
    (b) $(x^3 - x^2 + x - 1)(x^2 + 1)$

14. (a) $0 \cdot (5x^2 + 7x + 3)$ (b) $(8x^4 - 3x^2 + 5) \cdot 0$

15. (a) $(x^2 - \frac{1}{2})(x^4 + \frac{1}{2}x^2 + \frac{1}{4})$ (b) $(x^3 + \frac{1}{2}x - \frac{1}{3})(x^3 + \frac{1}{2}x + \frac{1}{3})$

16. (a) $(x^4 - x^3 + x^2 - 1)(x^4 + x^3 + x^2 + 1)$
    (b) $(x - 1)(x^5 + x^4 + x^3 + x^2 + x + 1)$

5–2 DIVISION OF POLYNOMIALS

It is possible to divide one polynomial by another, obtaining an algebraic expression such as

$$\frac{x^2 + 3x - 2}{x + 7}.$$

Such a quotient is called a *rational expression*. Remember, a quotient of two integers is called a rational number.

One integer can be divided by a smaller integer yielding a quotient and a remainder. For example,

$$
\begin{array}{r}
72 \\
12\overline{)871} \\
84 \\
\hline
31 \\
24 \\
\hline
7
\end{array}
$$

871 divided by 12 yields a quotient of 72 and a remainder of 7. The remainder is always smaller than the divisor (12).

This may be written

$$\frac{871}{12} = 72 + \frac{7}{12}$$

or

$$871 = 12 \times 72 + 7.$$

In a similar manner, any polynomial can be divided by another of the same or lower degree.

$$
\begin{array}{r}
x - 4 \\
x + 7\overline{)x^2 + 3x - 2} \\
x^2 + 7x \\
\hline
-4x - 2 \\
-4x - 28 \\
\hline
26
\end{array}
$$

$x^2 + 3x - 2$ divided by $x + 7$ yields a *quotient* of $x - 4$ and a *remainder* of 26. The remainder is always smaller than the divisor $(x + 7)$.

This may be written

$$\frac{x^2 + 3x - 2}{x + 7} = x - 4 + \frac{26}{x + 7}$$

or

$$x^2 + 3x - 2 = (x + 7)(x - 4) + 26.$$

The justification of this division process is essentially the same as the justification of the division process for integers.

The quotient and remainder obtained when one integer is divided by another are unique. Symbolically, this means that if a and b are integers, with $b > 0$, then there is one, and only one, integer q and one, and only one, integer r such that

$$\frac{a}{b} = q + \frac{r}{b} \quad \text{or} \quad a = qb + r$$

and

$$0 \leqq r < b.$$

The integer q is the quotient and r is the remainder when a is divided by b.

Similarly, the quotient and remainder obtained by dividing one polynomial by another are unique. Thus, if A and B are polynomials in x, with $B \neq 0$, then there exist unique polynomials Q and R such that

$$\frac{A}{B} = Q + \frac{R}{B} \quad \text{or} \quad A = (Q \cdot B) + R$$

with $R = 0$ or the degree of R less than the degree of B.

If the remainder $R = 0$, then $A = (Q \cdot B)$ and B is called a *divisor*, or *factor*, of A. We also say that A is a *multiple* of B. Of course, if the remainder $R \neq 0$, then B is not a divisor of A and A is not a multiple of B. In practice, on dividing one polynomial by another, we find the quotient and remainder by division, as illustrated in the following problems. (Note that both divisor and dividend are arranged so that the exponents of x are in decreasing order.)

Problem 1. Find the quotient and remainder on dividing the polynomial $3x^4 - 7x^2 + 2x$ by $x^2 + x - 3$.

Solution.

$$
\require{enclose}
\begin{array}{r}
3x^2 - 3x + 5 \\
x^2 + x - 3 \enclose{longdiv}{3x^4 - 7x^2 + 2x} \\
\underline{3x^4 + 3x^3 - 9x^2 } \\
-3x^3 + 2x^2 + 2x \\
\underline{-3x^3 - 3x^2 + 9x} \\
5x^2 - 7x \\
\underline{5x^2 + 5x - 15} \\
-12x + 15
\end{array}
$$

In the division above, $3x^2 - 3x + 5$ is the quotient and $-12x + 15$ is the remainder when $3x^4 - 7x^2 + 2x$ is divided by $x^2 + x - 3$. Note that we left space for the missing term of degree 3 and also for the missing constant term. We may express the results of this division process as follows:

$$3x^4 - 7x^2 + 2x = (3x^2 - 3x + 5)(x^2 + x - 3) + (-12x + 15).$$

Note that the degree of the remainder is 1, which is less than 2, the degree of the divisor.

Problem 2. Find the quotient and remainder on dividing the polynomial $x^4 + x^3 - 7x^2 + 17x - 12$ by $x^2 - 2x + 3$.

Solution.

$$
\begin{array}{r}
x^2 + 3x - 4 \\
x^2 - 2x + 3\overline{)x^4 + x^3 - 7x^2 + 17x - 12} \\
\underline{x^4 - 2x^3 + 3x^2} \\
3x^3 - 10x^2 + 17x \\
\underline{3x^3 - 6x^2 + 9x} \\
-4x^2 + 8x - 12 \\
\underline{-4x^2 + 8x - 12} \\
0
\end{array}
$$

The quotient is $x^2 + 3x - 4$ and the remainder is 0:

$$\frac{x^4 + x^3 - 7x^2 + 17x - 12}{x^2 - 2x + 3} = x^2 + 3x - 4 + \frac{0}{x^2 - 2x + 3}$$

or,

$$x^4 + x^3 - 7x^2 + 17x - 12 = (x^2 - 2x + 3)(x^2 + 3x - 4).$$

This means that $x^2 - 2x + 3$ is a divisor, or factor, of $x^4 + x^3 - 7x^2 + 17x - 12$.

Problem 3. Find the quotient and remainder on dividing the polynomial $2x^3 - 5x^2 + x - 1$ by $x - 3$.

Solution.

$$
\begin{array}{r}
2x^2 + x + 4 \qquad \text{(quotient)} \\
x - 3\overline{)2x^3 - 5x^2 + x - 1} \\
\underline{2x^3 - 6x^2} \\
x^2 + x - 1 \\
\underline{x^2 - 3x} \\
4x - 1 \\
\underline{4x - 12} \\
11 \qquad \text{(remainder)}
\end{array}
$$

Thus,

$$\frac{2x^3 - 5x^2 + x - 1}{x - 3} = 2x^2 + x + 4 + \frac{11}{x - 3}$$

or, $2x^3 - 5x^2 + x - 1 = (2x^2 + x + 4)(x - 3) + 11.$

Exercises

In each of the following exercises, find the quotient and remainder on dividing the first polynomial A by the second polynomial B. Then express the first polynomial A in the form $A = (Q \cdot B) + R$, with $R = 0$ or the degree of R less than the degree of B.

1. (a) $4x^3 - 5x^2 + 3x - 2$ by $x + 1$
   (b) $4x^3 - 5x^2 + 3x - 2$ by $x + 2$
2. (a) $3x^3 - 5x^2 + 2x - 1$ by $x^2 - 3x + 1$
   (b) x^3 by $x^2 + 7x - 11$
3. (a) $x^2 - 2x + 3$ by $x^2 + x - 2$
   (b) $4x^2 - 9$ by $2x^2 - 7$
4. (a) $3x + 5$ by $6x - 1$
   (b) $3x + 1$ by $2x - 5$
5. (a) $5x^4 - 3x + 8$ by $x^3 - 5x^2 + 2x - 1$
   (b) $5x^4 - 3x + 8$ by $x^3 - x - 1$
6. (a) $2x^3 - 8x^2 + 9x - 2$ by $2x^2 - 4x + 1$
   (b) $x^4 + 4$ by $x^2 - 2x + 2$
7. (a) $1 - x^2 + x^4$ by $1 - x$
   (b) $1 - x^2 + x^4$ by $1 + x$

---

8. Write $x^3 + x^2 - 4x - 4$ as a product of three linear factors by first dividing by $x - 2$ and then factoring the quotient.
9. Use the fact that

$$x^4 + 2x^3 + 5x^2 + 8x + 4$$

   is divisible by $x^2 + 4$ to write the fourth-degree polynomial as a product of three polynomials.
10. Factor $x^4 - 6x^2 + 5$ by first dividing by $x^2 - 5$.
11. Factor $x^3 + 5x^2 + 8x + 4$ by first dividing by $x + 1$.
12. Factor $x^4 - 2x^3 - 3x^2 + 4x + 4$ by first dividing by $(x + 1)^2$.

13. Use the fact that

$$x^5 + 6x^4 + 9x^3 + 8x^2 + 48x + 72$$

is divisible by $x^3 + 8$ to write the fifth-degree polynomial as a product of four polynomials.

14. Factor $x^5 + 2x^4 - 4x^3 - 8x^2$ by first dividing by $x^2(x - 2)$.

---

15. (a) Divide $4x^3 - 5x^2 + 3x - 2$ by $x - 1$ and record the remainder R.
   (b) Evaluate $4x^3 - 5x^2 + 3x - 2$ for $x = 1$, and compare this value with R found in 15(a).

16. (a) Divide $2x^3 - 3x^2 + 5x - 7$ by $x - 2$ and record the remainder R.
   (b) Evaluate $2x^3 - 3x^2 + 5x - 7$ for $x = 2$ and compare this value with R found in 16(a).

17. (a) Evaluate $2x^3 - 5x^2 + x - 1$ for $x = 3$.
   (b) Compare the value in 17(a) with the remainder R in Problem 3, page 250.

5-3 SYNTHETIC DIVISION

The division process can be considerably shortened if the divisor is a linear polynomial of the form $x - a$. For example, the solution of Problem 3 on page 125 can be shortened in the following way.

$$
\require{enclose}
\begin{array}{r}
2x^2 + x + 4 \\
x - 3 \enclose{longdiv}{2x^3 - 5x^2 + x - 1} \\
\underline{-6x^2} \\
x^2 \\
\underline{-3x} \\
4x \\
\underline{-12} \\
11
\end{array}
$$

We can shorten the division process by moving terms up under the dividend. The resulting array is shown below.

$$
\require{enclose}
\begin{array}{r}
2x^2 + x + 4 \\
x - 3 \enclose{longdiv}{2x^3 - 5x^2 + x - 1} \\
\underline{-6x^2 - 3x - 12} \\
2x^3 \qquad x^2 \quad 4x \quad 11
\end{array}
$$

Note that in this latter array we have also put the leading term of the divisor, $2x^3$, on the bottom line. Next, we observe that the quotient $2x^2 + x + 4$ is repeated on the lower line, except that each term has been multiplied by x. Thus, we can omit the top line if we remember how it is obtained from the bottom line. We may also omit all powers of x, leaving the following array of coefficients.

$$\begin{array}{r|rrrr} -3 & 2 & -5 & 1 & -1 \\ & & -6 & -3 & -12 \\ \hline & 2 & 1 & 4 & 11 \end{array} \quad \text{(subtract)}$$

The top row of the array consists of -3, which comes from the polynomial $x - 3$, and the numbers 2, -5, 1, and -1, which are the coefficients (arranged in descending order) of the given polynomial, $2x^3 - 5x^2 + x - 1$.

Each number in the last row is obtained by subtracting the number in the middle row from the number in the top row. Each number in the middle row is obtained by multiplying the number preceding it in the bottom row by -3. The bottom row of the array contains both the quotient and the remainder. Thus, 2, 1, and 4 are the coefficients (in descending order) of the quotient $2x^2 + x + 4$, and the last number, 11, is the remainder.

One final simplification can be made when we realize that if we multiply by 3, and add, instead of multiplying by -3, and subtracting, we obtain the same result. This new array is shown below.

$$\begin{array}{r|rrrr} 3 & 2 & -5 & 1 & -1 \\ & & 6 & 3 & 12 \\ \hline & 2 & 1 & 4 & 11 \end{array} \quad \text{(add)}$$

The process described above for dividing a polynomial by $x - a$ is called *synthetic division*. Some further illustrations of its use are given below.

Problem 1. Find the quotient and remainder on dividing the polynomial $3x^4 - 11x^3 - 21x^2 + 3x + 17$ by $x - 5$.

Solution. We first write the coefficients of the dividend in order of decreasing powers of x. Then we write the number 5, from $x - 5$, as shown below.

$$\begin{array}{r|rrrrr} 5 & 3 & -11 & -21 & 3 & 17 \end{array}$$

Next, the leading coefficient, 3, is brought down to the bottom line, and the product of 3 and 5 is placed under the second term, -11.

$$\begin{array}{c|ccccc} 5 & 3 & -11 & -21 & 3 & 17 \\ & & 15 & & & \\ \hline & 3 & & & & \end{array}$$

We now *add* 15 to -11 and place the sum on the bottom line. Continuing, we have the following.

$$\begin{array}{c|ccccc} 5 & 3 & -11 & -21 & 3 & 17 \\ & & 15 & 20 & -5 & -10 \\ \hline & 3 & 4 & -1 & -2 & 7 \end{array}$$

The numbers 3, 4, -1, and -2 in the bottom line are the coefficients of the powers of x (given in descending order) in the quotient; the last number, 7, is the remainder. Since the dividend is a polynomial of degree 4 and the divisor of degree 1, the quotient is a polynomial of degree 3. Thus,

$$3x^3 + 4x^2 - x - 2$$

is the quotient and 7 is the remainder. We can express this result by the equation

$$3x^4 - 11x^3 - 21x^2 + 3x + 17 = (3x^3 + 4x^2 - x - 2)(x - 5) + 7.$$

Problem 2. Find the quotient and remainder on dividing the polynomial $-5x^3 + 14x - 7$ by $x + 2$.

Solution. We note that the coefficient of x^2 in the dividend is zero, and that $x + 2 = x - (-2)$. The synthetic division for this problem is shown below.

$$\begin{array}{c|cccc} -2 & -5 & 0 & 14 & -7 \\ & & 10 & -20 & 12 \\ \hline & -5 & 10 & -6 & 5 \end{array}$$

Therefore, $-5x^2 + 10x - 6$ is the quotient and 5 is the remainder.

$$-5x^3 + 14x - 7 = (-5x^2 + 10x - 6)(x + 2) + 5.$$

Exercises

Use synthetic division to find the quotient and remainder on dividing the first polynomial A by the second polynomial B. Express the results in the form $A = (Q \cdot B) + R$, with $R = 0$ or the degree of R less than the degree of B.

1. (a) $(2x^3 - x^2 + 4x - 5) \div (x + 2)$
   (b) $(3x^4 - x^2 + 5) \div (x - 3)$

2. (a) $4x^2 - 3x + 7$ by $x - 2$
   (b) $2x^2 + 5x - 3$ by $x - 3$

3. (a) $x^3 - 3x^2 + 4x + 8$ by $x + 1$
   (b) $-2x^4 + 3x^3 - x^2 + 2x - 4$ by $x + 3$

4. (a) $x^4 + x^2 + 1$ by $x + 3$
   (b) $x^5 - 3x^3 + 4x - 7$ by $x - 1$

5. (a) $x^5 + 1$ by $x - 1$
   (b) $x^5 + 32$ by $x + 2$

6. (a) $3x^4 - 4x$ by $x + 2$
   (b) $-3x^5 + 2x^2 - 2$ by $x - 2$

7. (a) $3x^4 - 4x^3 + x^2 + 6x + 17$ by $x - \frac{1}{3}$
   (b) $-4x^3 + 3x + 5$ by $x + \frac{1}{2}$

---

8. Determine k so that when $2x^3 - x^2 + 3x + k$ is divided by $x - 1$, the remainder is zero.

9. Determine a and b so that when $x^4 + x^3 - 7x^2 + ax + b$ is divided by $(x - 1)(x + 2)$, the remainder is zero.

10. The integer 185 may be divided by 12 as follows: First divide 185 by 4 to obtain $185 = (46 \cdot 4) + 1$, and then divide the quotient, 46, by 3 to obtain $185 = [(15 \cdot 3) + 1]4 + 1$, or $185 = (15 \cdot 3 \cdot 4) + (1 \cdot 4) + 1$, or $185 = (15 \cdot 12) + 5$. Use such a procedure to find the quotient and remainder on dividing the following integers.
    (a) 833 by 15   (b) 479 by 28

11. The procedure of Exercise 10 can be applied to the division of polynomials, but synthetic division should be employed where the divisors are of the form $x - a$. Use this combination of procedures to perform each of the following divisions.
    (a) $x^2 - 4x + 2$ by $(x - 1)(x - 2)$
    (b) $2x^3 - 5x^2 + 4x - 7$ by $(x + 2)(x - 3)$
    (c) $x^5 - 5x^3 + 12x^2 - 10$ by $x^2 - 1$

Preparation for Section 5–4

Find $f(2)$, $f(-2)$, $f(\sqrt{3})$, $f(-1)$, and $f(\frac{1}{2})$ for each of the following.

1. $f(x) = x - 6$
2. $f(x) = 3x + 7$
3. $f(x) = x^2 - 1$
4. $f(x) = x^2 + 3x + 7$
5. $f(x) = 5x^2 + 3x - 8$
6. $f(x) = 2x^2 - \sqrt{2}x + 17$
7. $f(x) = x^3 + 4x^2 + x + 5$
8. $f(x) = x^4 - 3x^3 + 5x - 3$

5–4 REMAINDER THEOREM AND FACTOR THEOREM

Synthetic division may be used to evaluate a polynomial function. Consider, for example, the polynomial function

$$f(x) = x^3 + x^2 - x - 10.$$

We divide $f(x)$ by $x - 3$,

$$
\begin{array}{r|rrrr}
3 & 1 & 1 & -1 & -10 \\
  &   & 3 & 12 & 33 \\
\hline
  & 1 & 4 & 11 & 23
\end{array}
$$

getting a quotient of $x^2 + 4x + 11$ and a remainder of 23. Thus,

$$f(x) = (x - 3)(x^2 + 4x + 11) + 23.$$

Now evaluate $f(x)$ when $x = 3$:

$$
\begin{aligned}
f(3) &= (3 - 3)(3^2 + 4\cdot3 + 11) + 23 \\
&= 0\cdot32 - 23 \\
&= 23
\end{aligned}
$$

Observe that $f(3)$ is simply the remainder on dividing $f(x)$ by $(x - 3)$! This illustrates the following theorem.

REMAINDER THEOREM

If the polynomial f(x) is divided by x − r, the remainder is f(r).

The proof of this theorem is indicated in the example shown above. If the polynomial $f(x)$ is divided by $x - r$, the quotient will be some polynomial $q(x)$, and the remainder R a polynomial that is either zero or of lower degree than $x - r$. Since $x - r$ has degree 1, the remainder R either 0 or of degree 0. In either case, R is a constant polynomial.

$$f(x) = q(x)(x - r) + R$$

When we assign to x the value r, we get

$$f(r) = q(r)(r - r) + R = (q(r) \cdot 0) + R = 0 + R, \quad \text{or } R.$$

This proves the theorem.

The remainder theorem provides us with a convenient method of computing values of a polynomial function. It is frequently easier to divide synthetically by $x - r$ than to let $x = r$ in $f(x)$ when we wish to compute $f(r)$. Thus, to find $f(r)$, we need find only the remainder on dividing $f(x)$ by $x - r$. The remainder may be computed by synthetic division, as shown in the following problem.

Problem 1. If $f(x) = x^4 - 2x^2 - 7x + 6$, find $f(-2)$, $f(1)$, $f(2)$, and $f(5)$.

Solution. To obtain $f(-2)$, we find the remainder on dividing $f(x)$ by $x - (-2)$, as shown below. The other values of f are also computed below.

```
-2 | 1   0  -2  -7    6          1 | 1   0  -2  -7    6
         -2   4  -4   22                  1   1  -1  -8
      ─────────────────────             ─────────────────────
      1  -2   2 -11   28              1   1  -1  -8  -2
         Thus, f(-2) = 28.              Thus, f(1) = -2.


 2 | 1   0  -2  -7    6          5 | 1   0  -2   -7     6
          2   4   4  -6                  5  25  115   540
      ─────────────────────             ─────────────────────
      1   2   2  -3    0              1   5  23  108   546
         Thus, f(2) = 0.                Thus, f(5) = 546.
```

A number r is called a zero of the polynomial $f(x)$ if $f(r) = 0$; that is, r is a zero of $f(x)$ if r is a solution of the polynomial equation

$$f(x) = 0.$$

For example, in Problem 1, a zero of the polynomial $f(x)$ is 2 since it was shown that $f(2) = 0$.

According to the remainder theorem, if we divide the polynomial $f(x)$ by $x - r$, we obtain a quotient $q(x)$ and a remainder $f(r)$, that is,

$$f(x) = q(x)(x - r) + f(r).$$

Given that r is a zero of $f(x)$, then $f(r) = 0$ and

$$f(x) = q(x)(x - r) + 0,$$

or

$$f(x) = q(x)(x - r).$$

Hence, $x - r$ is a *divisor*, or *factor*, of $f(x)$ if $f(r) = 0$. Conversely, if $x - r$ is a divisor of $f(x)$, then the remainder obtained on dividing $f(x)$ by $x - r$ must be 0. This remainder is $f(r)$ by the remainder theorem; hence, $f(r) = 0$, and we have proved the following theorem.

FACTOR THEOREM

The polynomial $x - r$ is a divisor, or factor, of the polynomial $f(x)$ if, and only if, r is a zero of $f(x)$.

Problem 2. Which of the polynomials $x - 1$, $x + 1$, $x - \frac{1}{2}$, $x - 2$, and $x + 3$ are divisors of the polynomial

$$f(x) = 4x^3 + 16x^2 + 9x - 9?$$

Solution. We know that $x - 1$ will be a factor of $f(x)$ if 1 is a zero of $f(x)$. Since

$$f(1) = 4 + 16 + 9 - 9, \quad \text{or } 20,$$

1 is not a zero of $f(x)$. Hence, $x - 1$ is not a divisor of $f(x)$. Also,

$$f(-1) = -4 + 16 - 9 - 9, \quad \text{or } -6,$$

and -1 is not a zero of $f(x)$. Therefore, $x - (-1)$, or $x + 1$, is not a divisor of $f(x)$. Let us compute $f(\frac{1}{2})$, $f(2)$, and $f(-3)$ by synthetic division.

$$\frac{1}{2} \begin{array}{|rrrr} 4 & 16 & 9 & -9 \\ & 2 & 9 & 9 \\ \hline 4 & 18 & 18 & 0 \end{array}$$

Thus, $f(\frac{1}{2}) = 0$.

$$2 \begin{array}{|rrrr} 4 & 16 & 9 & -9 \\ & 8 & 48 & 114 \\ \hline 4 & 24 & 57 & 105 \end{array}$$

Thus, $f(2) = 105$.

$$-3 \begin{array}{|rrrr} 4 & 16 & 9 & -9 \\ & -12 & -12 & 9 \\ \hline 4 & 4 & -3 & 0 \end{array}$$

Thus, $f(-3) = 0$.

Clearly, $\frac{1}{2}$ and -3 are zeros of $f(x)$, so that $x - \frac{1}{2}$ and $x + 3$ are divisors of $f(x)$. Since $f(2) \neq 0$, $x - 2$ is not a divisor of $f(x)$.

Exercises

1. (a) Given that $f(x) = 2x^3 - 3x^2 + 4x - 3$, find $f(0)$, $f(-2)$, $f(5)$, and $f(-4)$.
   (b) Given that $q(y) = 12y^3 + 7y^2 - 14y + 3$, find $q(-2)$, $q(-3)$, $q(3)$, and $q(5)$.
2. (a) Given that $g(x) = x^4 - 7x^3 + 4x^2 + 5x$, find $g(0)$, $g(3)$, $g(-3)$, and $g(6)$.
   (b) Given that $p(y) = y^5 - y + 3$, find $p(10)$, $p(-3)$, $p(1)$, and $p(2)$.

In Exercises 3–6, use synthetic division or substitution to find which, if any, of the numbers -3, -2, -1, 0, 1, 2, and 3 are zeros of the polynomials.

3. (a) $x - x^3$ (b) $x^3 - 7x + 6$
4. (a) $3x^3 + 8x^2 - 2x + 3$ (b) $3x^4 + 8x^3 + 6x^2 + 3x - 2$
5. (a) $x^3 + 3x^2 - x - 3$ (b) $y^3 + y + 1$
6. (a) $x^3 - 4x^2 + x + 6$ (b) $x^4 + x^3 - 3x^2 - 4x - 4$

Which of the polynomials $(x - 1)$, $(x + 1)$, $(x - 4)$, and $(x + 3)$ are divisors, or factors, of the following polynomials?

7. (a) $x^3 - 2x^2 - 11x + 12$ (b) $2x^3 + 3x^2 - 23x - 12$
8. (a) $2x^4 + x^3 + x^2 - x - 3$ (b) $x^4 + x^3 - 19x^2 + x - 20$

Use substitution to find which, if any, of the numbers $\sqrt{2}$, $\sqrt{3}$, $-\sqrt{2}$, and $-\sqrt{3}$ are zeros of the following polynomials.

9. (a) $x^3 + 3x^2 - 2x - 6$ (b) $x^4 - 5x^2 + 6$

10. (a) $x^3 + (\sqrt{6} - \sqrt{2} - \sqrt{3})x^2 + (\sqrt{6} - 3\sqrt{2} - 2\sqrt{3})x + 6$
    (b) $x^3 - \sqrt{2}\,x^2 - 3x + 3\sqrt{2}$

If $f(-r) = f(r)$ for every r in the domain of f, the function is said to be an *even function*. If $f(-r) = -f(r)$ for every r in the domain of f, the function is said to be an *odd function*. For each of the following functions, find $f(1)$ and $f(-1)$, $f(2)$ and $f(-2)$, $f(k)$ and $f(-k)$, and then tell which are odd, which are even, and which are neither.

11. (a) $f(x) = x^4 + 3x^2 + 4$ (b) $f(x) = 2x^3 - 3x$
12. (a) $f(x) = 3x^4 - 2x^2 + x$ (b) $f(x) = x^6 + 3x^4 - 8$
13. (a) $f(x) = 2x^5 - x^2$ (b) $f(x) = 1 - x^2 - x^4$

14. (a) If all the exponents in a polynomial are even, is the polynomial an even function?
    (b) If all the exponents in a polynomial are odd, is the polynomial an odd function?

15. (a) Is every polynomial function either odd or even? Illustrate your answer with an example.
    (b) Is there any polynomial which is both odd and even?

---

16. Which, if any, of the numbers $2 + \sqrt{3}$, $3 + \sqrt{2}$, -3, $2 - \sqrt{3}$, and $3 - \sqrt{2}$ are zeros of the following polynomials?
    (a) $x^3 - x^2 - 11x + 3$
    (b) $x^4 - 10x^3 + 32x^2 - 34x + 7$
    (c) $x^3 - 5x^2 + x + 7$
    (d) $x^3 + (\sqrt{2} - \sqrt{3} - 5)x^2 + (6 + 3\sqrt{3} - 2\sqrt{2} - \sqrt{6})x$

17. If all the coefficients of a polynomial are integers and if the constant term is an odd integer, can an even integer be a zero of the polynomial? Can an odd integer be a zero? Justify your answers with specific illustrations.

---

18. Consider a third-degree polynomial of the form

$$p(x) = a_3x^3 + a_2x^2 + a_1x + a_0$$

with a_3, a_2, a_1, a_0 all integers.
    (a) Given that a_3, a_2, a_1, a_0 are all positive integers, what is the sign of each real zero of $p(x)$?

(b) Given that a_3, a_2, a_1, a_0 are all negative integers, what is the sign of each real zero of $p(x)$?

(c) Given that $a_0 = 1$ and r is an integral zero of $p(x)$, show that either $r = 1$ or $r = -1$.

5-5 INTEGRAL POLYNOMIALS

If we want to find the zeros of a given polynomial, we can try to guess one zero, apply the factor theorem using synthetic division, and if we are successful in finding such a zero, use the quotient polynomial to proceed with attempts to find further zeros, etc. When all the coefficients of a polynomial are integers, there are some simple rules which make our "guesswork" more efficient.

A polynomial all of whose coefficients are integers is called an *integral polynomial*. For example,

$$2x^3 - 3x + 1 \qquad \text{and} \qquad 7x - 5$$

are integral polynomials. We also use the term *integral zero* for any integer r that is a zero of polynomial $f(x)$. We first consider the problem of finding all the *integral zeros* of integral polynomials.

We first make the following remark.

If

$$f(x) = a_n x^n + a_{n-1} x^{n-1} + \cdots + a_1 x + a_0$$

is an integral polynomial and r is an integer, then $f(r) = a_n r^n + a_{n-1} r^{n-1} + \cdots + a_1 r + a_0$ is an integer. This is a consequence of the closure properties of addition and multiplication of integers.

Problem 1. Find all the integral zeros of the integral polynomial

$$f(x) = 2x^3 - 5x^2 - 27x + 10.$$

Solution. If r is an integral zero of the polynomial f, we have

$$f(r) = 2r^3 - 5r^2 - 27r + 10 = 0.$$

That is,

$$r(2r^2 - 5r - 27) = -10.$$

But then, we have on the left-hand side a product of two integers r and $2r^2 - 5r - 27$. We have thus written -10 as a product of two integers, one of which is r, showing that r divides 10.

This means that in our search, we need only try the integers ± 1, ± 2, ± 5, ± 10 as candidates for integral zeros of f.
We have

$$f(1) = 2 - 5 - 27 + 10, \quad \text{or} \quad -20$$
$$f(-1) = 2(-1)^3 - 5(-1)^2 - 27(-1) + 10$$
$$= -2 - 5 + 27 + 10, \quad \text{or} \quad 30.$$

So that 1 and -1 are not zeros of f.

Using synthetic division, we check other possibilities,

2	2	-5	-27	10		-2	2	-5	-27	10
		4	-2	-58				-4	18	18
	2	-1	-29	-48			2	-9	-9	28
5	2	-5	-27	10		-5	2	-5	-27	10
		10	25	-10				-10	75	-240
	2	5	-2	0			2	-15	48	-230

Since $f(10) = 2 \cdot 10^3 - 5 \cdot 10^2 - 27 \cdot 10 + 10$ and the first term, $2 \cdot 10^3$, is much larger than the sum of the other three we see that the sum of the four terms of $f(10)$ cannot be zero. Therefore, 10 is not a zero of f. Similarly, -10 is not a zero of f.

In only one case above, when $x = 5$, is the remainder 0. Hence, 5 is the only integral zero of f.

It is evident at a glance whether or not 0 is a zero of a polynomial; 0 is a zero if, and only if, the constant term of the polynomial is 0. Although we are not able to determine at a glance all the integral zeros of an integral polynomial, we can follow the procedure indicated in Problem 1 to determine the *possible* integral zeros. Thus, if

$$f(x) = a_n x^n + a_{n-1} x^{n-1} + \cdots + a_1 x + a_0$$

is an integral polynomial and r is an integral zero of f, then

$$f(r) = a_n r^n + a_{n-1} r^{n-1} + \cdots + a_1 r + a_0 = 0$$
$$r(a_n r^{n-1} + a_{n-1} r^{n-2} + \cdots + a_1) = -a_0.$$

Therefore, r must be a divisor of $-a_0$ or alternatively of a_0. This proves the following theorem.

INTEGRAL ZERO THEOREM

An integer is a zero of an integral polynomial only if it is a divisor of the constant term of the polynomial.

We note that this theorem does *not* claim that every divisor, or even any divisor, of the constant term is a zero of the polynomial. For example, the only possible integral zeros of the integral polynomial $f(x) = x^2 + x + 1$ are $+1$ and -1 but since $f(1) = 3$ and $f(-1) = 1$, neither of these is a zero of f. Consequently, the polynomial $x^2 + x + 1$ has no integral zeros.

Problem 2. Find the integral zeros of the integral polynomial

$$f(x) = x^3 + 2x^2 - 5x - 6.$$

Solution. By the integral zero theorem, the possible integral zeros are the divisors of the constant term -6:

$$\pm 1, \ \pm 2, \ \pm 3, \ \pm 6$$

since $f(1) = -8$, 1 is not a zero of f.

Using synthetic division, we see that -1 is a zero of the polynomial

$$
\begin{array}{r|rrrr}
-1 & 1 & +2 & -5 & -6 \\
   &   & -1 & -1 & 6 \\
\hline
   & 1 & 1 & -6 & 0
\end{array}
\qquad -1 + 2 + 5 = 6.
$$

The synthetic division tells us that

$$x^3 + 2x^2 - 5x - 6 = (x + 1)(x^2 + x - 6).$$

Factoring $x^2 + x - 6$, we see that

$$x^3 + 2x^2 - 5x - 6 = (x + 1)(x + 3)(x - 2).$$

Hence -3 and 2 are also zeros of the given polynomial and we have found the complete set of integral zeros to be $\{-3, -1, 2\}$.

A proof similar to that used to obtain the integral zero theorem yields the following as an extension of that theorem.

RATIONAL ZERO THEOREM

A rational number p/q, $q > 0$, expressed in lowest form, is a zero of the integral polynomial

$$g(x) = a_n x^n + a_{n-1} x^{n-1} + \cdots + a_1 x + a_0$$

only if p is a divisor of the constant term a_0 and q is a divisor of the leading coefficient a_n.

Note that, since an integer r may be written as the rational number $r/1$, and since the integer 1 surely divides any integer a_n as leading coefficient, the rational zero theorem includes as a special case the integral zero theorem.

We shall illustrate the argument for the proof of the rational zero theorem with an example.

Problem 3.   Find all the rational zeros of the integral polynomial

$$g(x) = 6x^3 - x^2 - 2x - 15.$$

Solution.   According to the integral zero theorem, the possible integral zeros are the divisors of -15.

$$\pm 1, \ \pm 3, \ \pm 5, \ \pm 15$$

You may readily verify that not one of these eight integers is a zero of $g(x)$.

On the other hand, the synthetic division

$$
\begin{array}{r|rrrr}
\frac{3}{2} & 6 & -1 & -2 & -15 \\
 &   & 9 & 12 & 15 \\
\hline
 & 6 & 8 & 10 & 0
\end{array}
$$

shows that $\frac{3}{2}$ is a zero of $g(x)$.

Any rational number p/q, $q > 0$, expressed in lowest form is a zero of $g(x)$ if, and only if,

$$6\left(\frac{p}{q}\right)^3 - \left(\frac{p}{q}\right)^2 - 2\left(\frac{p}{q}\right) - 15 = 0,$$

or

$$6p^3 - p^2 q - 2pq^2 - 15q^3 = 0. \tag{1}$$

Following the pattern we used in the integral zero theorem, we write this as

$$p(6p^2 - pq - 2q^2) = 15q^3.$$

The left side is a product of two integers, one of which is p, and the product equals the integer $15q^3$. Hence, the integer p is a divisor of the integer $15q^3$. But we had assumed that p and q had no common factors so that p must divide 15 and hence it divides -15, the constant term of the polynomial $g(x)$.

If we now return to equation (1) and rewrite it as

$$6p^3 = p^2q + 2pq^2 + 15q^3$$
$$= (p^2 + 2pq + 15q^2)q,$$

we have on the right side of the equation the product of two integers, one of which is q, and this product equals the integer $6p^3$. That is, q is a divisor of $6p^3$ and again, since q and p have no common factors, the integer q must divide 6, the coefficient of the leading term of the polynomial $g(x)$.

Thus we have shown that if the rational number p/q expressed in lowest form, with $q > 0$, is a zero of the given $g(x)$, then p must be a divisor of the constant term -15 and q a divisor of the leading coefficient, 6.

The possible values of p are ± 1, ± 3, ± 5, ± 15; those for q are 1, 2, 3, and 6. Hence the possible rational zeros of $g(x)$, other than integers, are

$$\pm\tfrac{1}{2}, \pm\tfrac{1}{3}, \pm\tfrac{1}{6}, \pm\tfrac{3}{2}, \pm\tfrac{5}{2}, \pm\tfrac{5}{3}, \pm\tfrac{5}{6}, \pm\tfrac{15}{2}.$$

We used synthetic division to show that $\tfrac{3}{2}$ is a zero of $g(x)$. This synthetic division enables us to factor the given cubic $g(x)$ as follows:

$$6x^3 - x^2 - 2x - 15 = (x - \tfrac{3}{2})(6x^2 + 8x + 10) \quad \text{or,}$$
$$= (x - \tfrac{3}{2}) \cdot 2(3x^2 + 4x + 5)$$
$$= (2x - 3)(3x^2 + 4x + 5).$$

Any number other than $\tfrac{3}{2}$ which is a zero of $g(x)$ must be a zero of $3x^2 + 4x + 5$. If we apply the rational zero theorem now to this quadratic, we see that the rational zero candidate list has shrunk to the set: $\pm\tfrac{1}{3}$, $\pm\tfrac{5}{3}$ and synthetic division shows none of these to be zeros of the quadratic. That is, $\tfrac{3}{2}$ is the only rational zero of $6x^3 - x^2 - 2x - 15$. (Alternatively, if you recall the quadratic formula which is presented again in Chapter 9 of this text in a more general setting, you could use it to show that the quadratic $3x^2 + 4x + 5$ has no real zeros, so that in fact, the given cubic has $\frac{3}{2}$ as its only real zero.)

Problem 4. Find the rational zeros of the integral polynomial

$$g(x) = 10x^3 - 17x^2 - 7x + 2.$$

Solution. According to the rational zero theorem, the possible zeros have the form p/q where p is a divisor of 2 and q a divisor of 10. Thus, possible candidates are

$$\pm 1, \ \pm\tfrac{1}{2}, \ \pm\tfrac{1}{5}, \ \pm\tfrac{1}{10}, \ \pm 2, \ \pm\tfrac{2}{5}.$$

By direct substitution, $g(1) = -12$ and $g(-1) = -18$ so that neither 1 nor -1 is a zero of $g(x)$.

Upon synthetic division by 2, one of the other possible integer candidates, we are lucky:

$$
\begin{array}{r|rrrr}
2 & 10 & -17 & -7 & 2 \\
  &   & 20 & 6 & -2 \\
\hline
  & 10 & 3   & -1 & 0
\end{array}
$$

Hence,

$$
\begin{aligned}
10x^3 - 10x^2 - 7x + 2 &= (x - 2)(10x^2 + 3x - 1) \\
&= (x - 2)(5x - 1)(2x + 1).
\end{aligned}
$$

We were again lucky in having the quadratic quotient polynomial factor easily. We find the rational zeros, by the factor theorem, to be $2, \frac{1}{5}, -\frac{1}{2}$.

Problem 5. Find the rational zeros of the integral polynomial

$$f(x) = 3x^3 + x - 5.$$

Solution. The set of possible rational zeros is

$$\{\pm 1, \ \pm 5, \ \pm\tfrac{1}{3}, \ \pm\tfrac{5}{3}\}.$$

Again, by inspection, 1 and -1 are not zeros of f, and it is easy to see that 5 and -5 also fail to qualify. We try synthetic division for the other candidates.

$$
\begin{array}{r|rrrr}
\tfrac{1}{3} & 3 & 0 & 1 & -5 \\
 & & 1 & \tfrac{1}{3} & \\
\hline
 & 3 & 1 & \tfrac{4}{3} &
\end{array}
\qquad
\begin{array}{r|rrrr}
-\tfrac{1}{3} & 3 & 0 & 1 & -5 \\
 & & -1 & \tfrac{1}{3} & \\
\hline
 & 3 & -1 & \tfrac{4}{3} &
\end{array}
$$

$$
\begin{array}{r|rrrr}
\tfrac{5}{3} & 3 & 0 & 1 & -5 \\
 & & 5 & \tfrac{25}{3} & \\
\hline
 & 3 & 5 & &
\end{array}
\qquad
\begin{array}{r|rrrr}
-\tfrac{5}{3} & 3 & 0 & 1 & -5 \\
 & & -5 & \tfrac{25}{3} & \\
\hline
 & 3 & -5 & &
\end{array}
$$

You will note that we did not complete some of the divisions above but stopped as soon as a nonintegral rational number appeared in the bottom row or was about to appear. Any further multiplication of this number and succeeding numbers by the rational number at the side will not yield an integer, and hence the final remainder at the end of the row cannot be zero.

We have shown that the polynomial $3x^3 + x - 5$ has no rational zero.

We conclude this section by remarking that the methods discussed can be applied to find the rational zeros of a polynomial which has rational (not necessarily integral) coefficients by first writing such a polynomial as a constant times an integral polynomial. For example, the polynomial

$$f(x) = \tfrac{1}{3}x^2 - \tfrac{3}{2}x + \tfrac{5}{6}$$

may be written as

$$f(x) = \tfrac{1}{6}(2x^2 - 9x + 5).$$

(Note that 6 is the least common multiple of the set of rational coefficients.)

Having done this, it is clear that r is a zero of f if, and only if, it is a zero of the integral polynomial $2x^2 - 9x + 5$.

Exercises

In Exercises 1–4, list the possible rational zeros of each integral polynomial. Then find which are actually zeros of the polynomial.

1. (a) $2x^3 - x^2 - 2x + 1$ (b) $x^3 - 3x^2 + 3x - 2$
2. (a) $3x^3 + 20x^2 + 15x + 2$ (b) $6x^3 + x^2 - 4x + 1$
3. (a) $2x^4 + 5x^3 + 3x^2 + x - 2$ (b) $5x^3 - 17x^2 + 16x - 4$
4. (a) $2x^4 - 5x^2 + 2$ (b) $2x^3 + x^2 + x - 1$

Find all the rational zeros of each of the following polynomials.

5. (a) $2x^3 + x^2 - 4x - 2$ (b) $x^3 + 4x^2 + 8x + 5$
6. (a) $x^3 - 6x^2 + 11x - 6$ (b) $3x^3 - 2x^2 - 8x - 3$
7. (a) $2x^3 + x^2 + x - 1$ (b) $3x^3 + 5x^2 + 4x - 2$
8. (a) $2x^3 - 13x^2 - 13x - 15$ (b) $2x^4 + 7x^3 + 4x^2 - 7x - 6$
9. (a) $x^4 - 4x^2 - 5$ (b) $6x^3 - 11x^2 + 7x - 6$
10. (a) $x^4 + x^3 - x^2 - 2x - 2$
    (b) $10x^4 + 19x^3 - 5x^2 + 19x - 15$

11. If the integral polynomial $f(x)$ has leading coefficient 1, show that all the rational zeros of $f(x)$ must be integers.

Find all the integral zeros of each of the following polynomials.

12. $x^3 - 2x^2 - 4x + 8$ 13. $x^3 - 9x^2 + 26x - 24$
14. $x^4 + 6x^3 + 10x^2 - 3x - 14$
15. $x^5 - 5x^4 + 4x^3 - 20x^2 + 3x - 15$

Find the rational zeros of each of the following polynomials and write each polynomial as a product of the factors you have found.

16. $10x^3 + 21x^2 - 25x + 6$ 17. $9x^3 - 19x - 10$
18. $12x^4 - 4x^3 + 31x^2 - 12x - 15$ 19. $7x^4 + 22x^3 + 38x^2 + 5x$
20. $20x^4 + x^3 + 19x^2 + x - 1$ 21. $30x^4 + 11x^3 + 6x^2 - 24x - 5$
22. (a) Find the zeros of $2x^3 + 5x^2 - x - 6$.
    (b) Find the zeros of $2 + 5x - x^2 - 6x^3$.
    (c) Compare the zeros of the polynomials in parts (a) and (b).
    (d) If the zeros of $4x^2 - 16x - 12$ are -2, $-\frac{3}{4}$, and 2, what do you expect the zeros of $4 + 3x - 16x^2 - 12x^3$ will be? Check to determine whether your answers are correct.

23. What relation do you think the zeros of $a_n x^n + a_{n-1} x^{n-1} + \cdots + a_1 x + a_0$ have to the zeros of $a_n + a_{n-1} x + \cdots + a_1 x^{n-1} + a_0 x^n$? (Hint: Think about Exercise 20.)

24. Prove the rational zero theorem for $p(x) = a_3 x^3 + a_2 x^2 + a_1 x + a_0$.

25. The rational zero theorem may be used to prove that certain numbers are irrational. For example, since $(\sqrt{3})^2 - 3 = 0$, the number $\sqrt{3}$ is a zero of the integral polynomial $x^2 - 3$. According to the rational zero theorem, the only possible *rational* zeros of this polynomial are ± 1 and ± 3. By substitution, we see that not one of these four numbers is a zero of $x^2 - 3$. Therefore, the polynomial $x^2 - 3$ has no rational zero. Hence, if $x^2 - 3$ does have real zeros they must be irrational numbers. That is, the real number $\sqrt{3}$ which is a zero of this polynomial must be irrational.

Use the method above to prove that the following numbers are irrational.
(a) $\sqrt{2}$ (b) $\sqrt{5}$ (c) $\sqrt[3]{4}$
(First find an integral polynomial with the given number as a zero.)

26. (a) Find an integral polynomial of degree three having zeros $\{2, 3, 5\}$ and write answer in polynomial form.
(b) Find a rational polynomial of degree three having zeros $\{\frac{1}{2}, \frac{1}{3}, \frac{1}{5}\}$. Leave answer in factored form.
(c) Find an *integral* polynomial of degree three having the set of zeros of part (b). Give answer in polynomial form.
(d) How are the polynomials of (a) and (c) related?

CHAPTER REVIEW

In Exercises 1–3 perform the indicated operations with polynomials.

1. $(x^3 + 3x^2 + 5x + 5) + (2x - 4)$

2. $(x^4 + x^2 + x)(x^4 + x^2 - x)$

3. $(x^3 - x^2 + 5) \div (x^2 + 1)$

4. Use synthetic division to find the quotient and remainder when $4x^3 - 5x + 1$ is divided by each of the following.

(a) $x - 2$ (b) $x + 3$ (c) $x - \frac{1}{2}$

5. If $p(x) = 2x^3 - x^2 + 3x - 4$, find $p(-2)$, $p(1)$, $p(3)$, and $p(4)$.

6. Determine k so that when $4x^3 - 2x^2 + 6x + 2k$ is divided by $2x - 2$ the remainder is 0.
Which of the polynomials $(2x - 2)$, $(2x + 2)$, $(2x - 8)$, and $(2x + 6)$ are divisors of the following polynomials?

7. $2x^3 - 4x^2 - 22x + 24$

8. $4x^4 + 2x^3 + 2x^2 - 2x - 6$

9. $4x^3 + 6x^2 - 46x - 24$

10. $2x^4 + 2x^3 - 38x^2 + 2x - 40$

Find an integral polynomial of degree 4 for each of the following sets of zeros.

11. $\{1, 2, 4, -7\}$ **12.** $\{0, 1, -2, 3\}$

13. $\{1, 0, -1, \frac{1}{3}\}$ **14.** $\{\frac{1}{2}, -\frac{1}{2}, 1\}$

Find the rational zeros of each of the following polynomials.

15. $20x^3 - 34x^2 - 14x + 4$ **16.** $2x^4 - \frac{3}{2}x^3 + 6x^2 + x + \frac{3}{2}$

17. $2x^3 - 7x^2 - 7x + 30$ **18.** $2x^5 - 11x^4 + 65x^2 + 31x$

19. $2x^4 - 3x^3 - 11x^2 + 3x + 9$

Factor each of the following into a product of as many integral polynomials as possible.

20. $x^4 + 2x^3 - 25x^2 - 26x + 120$

21. $x^4 - 3x^2 + 2$

22. $x^4 + 3x - 2$

23. $6x^3 - x^2 - 12x - 5$

24. Prove that $\sqrt{2}/\sqrt{3}$ is irrational.

6 · Logarithms

6-1   LOGARITHMS

Let us consider an exponential function E, defined by

$$E(x) = b^x,$$

$$\text{where } b > 0 \text{ and } b \neq 1.$$

The domain of E is the set of all real numbers, and the range of E is the set of *positive* real numbers. Thus, for each real number r, there exists a unique positive real number s such that $s = b^r$.

If we draw the graph of E, as shown in Fig. 6-1, then another property of the function can be seen: For each positive number s, the line $y = s$ intersects the graph of E in one, and only one, point, (r, s). This means that the range of E is the set of all positive real numbers, and that for each positive real number s, there exists a *unique* real number r such that $b^r = s$.

The remarks above lead us to define the logarithm function to the base b, denoted by $\log_b$, in the following manner.

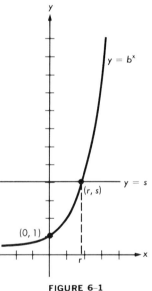

FIGURE 6-1

Definition of the Logarithm Function

For every positive number s,

$$\log_b s = r,$$

where r is the number such that $b^r = s$ (assuming $b > 0$ and $b \neq 1$).

145

According to this definition, the function $\log_b$ has the set of all positive real numbers as its domain. Also,

$\log_b s$ is the power to which b must be raised to give s.

To illustrate the definition, let us find each of the following logarithms.

$\log_2 16$. If we let $r = \log_2 16$, then $2^r = 16$. Since $16 = 2^4$, we conclude that $r = 4$. Thus,

$$\log_2 16 = 4.$$

$\log_2 \sqrt[3]{2}$. If we let $r = \log_2 \sqrt[3]{2}$, then $2^r = \sqrt[3]{2}$. Since $\sqrt[3]{2} = 2^{\frac{1}{3}}$, we conclude that $2^r = 2^{\frac{1}{3}}$ and $r = \frac{1}{3}$. Thus,

$$\log_2 \sqrt[3]{2} = \tfrac{1}{3}.$$

$\log_2 \frac{1}{4}$ If we let $r = \log_2 \frac{1}{4}$, then $2^r = \frac{1}{4}$. Since $\frac{1}{4} = 2^{-2}$, we conclude that $r = -2$. Thus,

$$\log_2 \tfrac{1}{4} = -2.$$

$\log_5 5$. If we let $r = \log_5 5$, then $5^r = 5$. Since $5^1 = 5$, we conclude that $r = 1$ and

$$\log_5 5 = 1.$$

$\log_8 16$. If we let $r = \log_8 16$, then $8^r = 16$. To find the power of 8 that is equal to 16, we replace 8 by 2^3, obtaining the equation $(2^3)^r = 16$ or, equivalently, $2^{3r} = 16$. Since $16 = 2^4$, we conclude that $2^{3r} = 2^4$ and $3r = 4$. Thus, $r = \frac{4}{3}$ and

$$\log_8 16 = \tfrac{4}{3}.$$

$\log_{\frac{1}{10}} 1000$. If we let $r = \log_{\frac{1}{10}} 1000$, then $(\frac{1}{10})^r = 1000$. Since $\frac{1}{10} = 10^{-1}$, we conclude that $(10^{-1})^r = 1000$, or

$$10^{-r} = 1000.$$

Now $1000 = 10^3$, and, therefore, $-r = 3$ or $r = -3$. Thus,

$$\log_{\frac{1}{10}} 1000 = -3.$$

Each problem above is solved by using the fact that the two equations

$$y = \log_b x \quad and \quad b^y = x$$

are equivalent, that is, that they have the same solution set.

Problem. Solve each of the following equations.

(a) $4 = \log_5 x$ (b) $y = \log_4 32$ (c) $\frac{2}{3} = \log_b 9$

Solution.

(a) The equation $4 = \log_5 x$ is equivalent to the equation $5^4 = x$. Hence, $x = 625$ is the solution.

(b) The equation $y = \log_4 32$ is equivalent to the equation $4^y = 32$. Since $4 = 2^2$ and $32 = 2^5$, another equivalent equation is $(2^2)^y = 2^5$, or $2^{2y} = 2^5$. Hence, $2y = 5$ and $y = \frac{5}{2}$.

(c) The equation $\frac{2}{3} = \log_b 9$ is equivalent to the equation $b^{\frac{2}{3}} = 9$. In turn, this latter equation is equivalent to the equation $(b^{\frac{2}{3}})^{\frac{3}{2}} = 9^{\frac{3}{2}}$, or $b = 9^{\frac{3}{2}}$. Hence, $b = 27$ is the solution. Although it is true that $(-27)^{\frac{2}{3}} = (\sqrt[3]{-27})^2$, or 9, so that $b = -27$ is a solution of the equation $b^{\frac{2}{3}} = 9$, no negative number can be a base for logarithms. Thus, $b = 27$ is the only solution of the given equation.

The following properties of logarithms follow from the definition of a logarithm.

$$\log_b 1 = 0 \quad since \quad b^0 = 1$$
$$\log_b b = 1 \quad since \quad b^1 = b$$
$$\log_b b^r = r \quad since \quad b^r = b^r$$

$$\log_{\frac{1}{b}} x = -\log_b x \quad since \quad \left(\frac{1}{b}\right)^r = b^{-r}$$

In view of the last property, we might as well restrict the base b to be greater than 1, for if $0 < b < 1$, then $1/b > 1$, and each logarithm to the base b is easily expressed in terms of a logarithm to the base $1/b$. For example,

$$\log_{\frac{1}{2}} 4 = -\log_2 4, \quad or \quad -2,$$
$$\log_{\frac{1}{10}} .001 = -\log_{10} .001, \quad or \quad -(-3), \quad or \quad 3.$$

1-30

Exercises

Write the logarithmic equation that corresponds to each of the following exponential equations.

1. (a) $2^5 = 32$ (b) $3^{-2} = \frac{1}{9}$

2. (a) $7^0 = 1$ (b) $25^{\frac{3}{2}} = 125$

3. (a) $16^{-\frac{3}{2}} = \frac{1}{64}$ (b) $10^0 = 1$

4. (a) $16^{-\frac{3}{4}} = .125$ (b) $(\frac{1}{3})^{-2} = 9$

Write the exponential equation that corresponds to each of the following logarithmic equations.

5. (a) $\log_{10} 100 = 2$ (b) $\log_8 4 = \frac{2}{3}$

6. (a) $\log_{\frac{1}{3}} 81 = -4$ (b) $\log_{25} \frac{1}{125} = -\frac{3}{2}$

7. (a) $\log_8 1 = 0$ (b) $\log_a y = x$

8. (a) $\log_n 256 = 2$ (b) $\log_{16} 8 = \frac{3}{4}$

9. (a) $\log_n 9 = .4$ (b) $\log_{\frac{1}{8}} 4 = -\frac{2}{3}$

Find the value of each of the following logarithms.

10. (a) $\log_{10} 10^2$ (b) $\log_2 2^{10}$

11. (a) $\log_b b^4$ (b) $\log_b b$

12. (a) $\log_7 \sqrt[3]{7}$ (b) $\log_2 8\sqrt{32}$

13. (a) $\log_7 \frac{1}{49}$ (b) $\log_3 \sqrt[5]{81}$

14. (a) $\log_{10} \sqrt[3]{100}$ (b) $\log_{27} 81$

15. (a) $\log_{\frac{1}{10}} 100$ (b) $\log_{100} .001$

Solve each of the following equations for n.

16. $\log_{10} .0001 = n$ **17.** $\log_{36} n = -\frac{3}{2}$ **18.** $\log_n 125 = -\frac{3}{4}$

19. $\log_7 7^{-3} = n$ **20.** $\log_{49} n = \frac{3}{2}$ **21.** $\log_n 1000 = 1.5$

22. $\log_{16} 8 = n$ **23.** $\log_{64} n = \frac{7}{6}$ **24.** $\log_n (\frac{1}{81}) = -2$

===

In Exercises 25–30, solve each of the equations for x.

25. $\log_{10} 1 = x$ **26.** $\log_x 1 = 0$ **27.** $\log_4 x = -3$

28. $\log_x 3 = \frac{1}{4}$ **29.** $x = \log_{36} 216$ **30.** $x = \log_2 2$

6–2 LOGARITHMIC GRAPHS

The graph of the function $\log_b$ is simply the graph of the equation

$$y = \log_b x.$$

The particular graph of $\log_2$ is sketched in Fig. 6–2 from the following table of values.

x	$\frac{1}{8}$	$\frac{1}{4}$	$\frac{1}{2}$	1	2	4	8	16
y	-3	-2	-1	0	1	2	3	4

This graph is very similar to the exponential graph with base 2 sketched in Fig. 6–1. In fact, the two graphs can be made to coincide by turning over the piece of paper on which one is drawn and placing the positive x-axis of the logarithmic graph along the positive y-axis of the exponential graph. This is so because the two equations $y = \log_2 x$ and $2^y = x$ are equivalent.

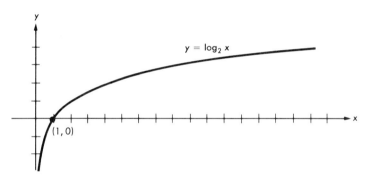

FIGURE 6-2

The logarithmic graph with base $b > 1$ has the following important properties, which are illustrated in Fig. 6–2.

1. *The entire graph is to the right of the y-axis.*
2. *The graph has x-intercept 1.*
3. *The graph is rising as we traverse it from left to right. In other words,*

$$\log_b x_1 > \log_b x_2 \quad \textit{if, and only if,} \quad x_1 > x_2.$$

The first property is true because $\log_b x$ is defined only if $x > 0$, and the second property is true because $\log_b x = 0$, if and only if, $x = 1$. The proof of the third property is too difficult to be included in this text.

Exercises

1. (a) Graph each of the following equations on the same set of axes.

$$y = \log_5 x, \quad y = 5^x$$

Is there a line of folding so that the two graphs would coincide? By what transformation could one equation be obtained from the other?

(b) Graph each of the following equations on the same set of axes.

$$y = \log_2 x, \quad y = \log_3 x, \quad y = \log_5 x, \quad y = \log_{10} x$$

What point does the following family of logarithmic curves have in common?

$$\{y = \log_b x \mid b \text{ a real number, } b > 1\}$$

Using Property 3 of the logarithmic curve with base $b > 1$, give two consecutive integers between which each of the following numbers lies.

2. (a) $\log_2 6.45$
   (b) $\log_{10} 36.125$

3. (a) $\log_{10} .375$
   (b) $\log_2 .3$

4. (a) If $0 < N < 1$, what can be said about $\log_{10} N$?
   (b) If $N > 1$, what can be said about $\log_{10} N$?

---

5. If M is a number greater than the positive number N, how do the numbers $\log_{10} M$ and $\log_{10} N$ compare?

Graph each of the following equations.

6. $y = \log_3 x$ 7. $y = \log_3 2x$ 8. $y = 2 + \log_3 x$

9. $y = \log_3 (x + 2)$ 10. $y = 2 \log_3 x$ 11. $y = \log_3 x^2$

12. $y = \frac{1}{2} \log_3 x$ 13. $y = \log_3 \sqrt{x}$

14. Refer to Exercises 6–13 to answer the following questions.
    (a) Which of the graphs are identical?
    (b) Which of the graphs have the same x-intercept?
    (c) For what set of values of x is each equation defined?

15. (a) Graph $y = \log_2 (-x)$.
    (b) For what set of values of x is $\log_2 (-x)$ defined?

---

16. Graph $y = \log_3(-x)$ and $y = -\log_3 x$ on the same set of axes.

17. For what set of values of x is $\log_2(x + 1)$ defined? Graph the equation $y = \log_2(x + 1)$. Compare the graph with that of $y = \log_2 x$.

18. (a) Sketch the graph of the equation $y = \log_5 1/x$.
    (b) Graph the equation $y = -\log_5 x$.

Preparation for Section 6–3

1. What is the exponential equation equivalent to $\log_b x = r$?

2. What is the exponential equation equivalent to $\log_b y = s$?

3. Simplify $b^r \cdot b^s$.

4. Try to combine your results in the three preceding exercises to write an equation relating $\log_b xy$ to $\log_b x$ and $\log_b y$.

6–3 THE LAWS OF LOGARITHMS

The laws of exponents, which we verified first for use with positive integers and later for use with rational numbers, will now be assumed to be valid for real numbers. Since $\log_b x = y$ if, and only if, $x = b^y$, we might expect that the laws of exponents could be translated into the language of logarithms. This is the case, as we shall show below. In our development, the base b is always assumed to be a real number greater than 1.

According to the first law of exponents, the equation

$$b^{r+s} = b^r \cdot b^s$$

is true for every pair r, s of real numbers. Let us try to convert this equation into one relating logarithms by letting

$$z = b^{r+s}, \quad x = b^r, \quad y = b^s.$$

By the first law of exponents, $z = xy$. Each of the above equations can be translated into the language of logarithms, yielding the three equivalent equations

$$r + s = \log_b z, \quad r = \log_b x, \quad s = \log_b y.$$

Since $r + s$ is the sum of r and s, it follows that

$$\log_b z = \log_b x + \log_b y.$$

If we recall that $z = xy$, then we have proved the following law.

FIRST LAW OF LOGARITHMS

$$\log_b xy = \log_b x + \log_b y$$

This equation is true for every pair x, y of positive real numbers. The first law of logarithms can be stated in words in the following way.

The logarithm of the product of two positive numbers is the sum of the logarithms of the two numbers.

If we start with the fourth law of exponents and reason as we did above, then we can derive the following law.

SECOND LAW OF LOGARITHMS

$$\log_b \frac{x}{y} = \log_b x - \log_b y$$

This equation is also true for every pair x, y of positive real numbers. The second law of logarithms can be stated in words in the following way.

The logarithm of the quotient of two positive numbers is the logarithm of the dividend minus the logarithm of the divisor.

According to the third law of exponents, the equation

$$b^{ar} = (b^a)^r$$

is true for every pair a, r of real numbers. To convert this equation to one relating logarithms, let

$$y = b^{ar} \quad \text{and} \quad x = b^a.$$

By the third law of exponents, $y = x^r$. The two equations above are equivalent to the two logarithmic equations

$$ar = \log_b y, \quad a = \log_b x.$$

Since ar equals r times a, we have

$$\log_b y = r \cdot \log_b x.$$

Replacing y by x^r, we obtain the following law.

THIRD LAW OF LOGARITHMS

$$\boldsymbol{\log_b x^r = r \cdot \log_b x}$$

This equation is true for every real number r and every positive real number x. The third law of logarithms can be stated in words in the following way.

> *The logarithm of the rth power of a positive number is r times the logarithm of the number.*

Problem 1. Find each of the following.

(a) $\log_2 16\sqrt{8}$

(b) $\log_3 \dfrac{\sqrt[4]{27}}{9}$

Solution.

(a)
$$\begin{aligned}
\log_2 16\sqrt{8} &= \log_2 16 + \log_2 \sqrt{8} \\
&= \log_2 16 + \log_2 8^{\frac{1}{2}} \\
&= \log_2 16 + \tfrac{1}{2}\log_2 8 \\
&= \log_2 2^4 + \tfrac{1}{2}\log_2 2^3 \\
&= 4 + (\tfrac{1}{2} \cdot 3), \quad \text{or} \quad \tfrac{11}{2}
\end{aligned}$$

In other words, $\log_2 16\sqrt{8} = \tfrac{11}{2}$.

$\log_{10} = 10^{-\frac{5}{4}}$

$\log_3 = 3^{-5/4}$

(b)
$$\begin{aligned}
\log_3 \frac{\sqrt[4]{27}}{9} &= \log_3 \sqrt[4]{27} - \log_3 9 \\
&= \log_3 27^{\frac{1}{4}} - \log_3 9 \\
&= \tfrac{1}{4}\log_3 27 - \log_3 9 \\
&= \tfrac{1}{4}\log_3 3^3 - \log_3 3^2 \\
&= (\tfrac{1}{4} \cdot 3) - 2, \quad \text{or} \quad -\tfrac{5}{4}
\end{aligned}$$

In other words,
$$\log_3 \frac{\sqrt[4]{27}}{9} = -\frac{5}{4}.$$

Problem 2. Express the following number as the logarithm of a single number.

$$3 \log_5 4 - 2 \log_5 6 + \tfrac{3}{2} \log_5 18$$

Solution. We proceed as follows:

$$
\begin{aligned}
3 \log_5 4 &- 2 \log_5 6 + \tfrac{3}{2} \log_5 18 \\
&= \log_5 4^3 - \log_5 6^2 + \log_5 18^{\frac{3}{2}} \\
&= \log_5 64 - \log_5 36 + \log_5 (\sqrt{18})^3 \\
&= \log_5 \tfrac{64}{36} + \log_5 (3\sqrt{2})^3 \\
&= \log_5 \tfrac{16}{9} + \log_5 54\sqrt{2} \\
&= \log_5 (\tfrac{16}{9} \cdot 54\sqrt{2}) \\
&= \log_5 (96\sqrt{2}).
\end{aligned}
$$

Problem 3. Solve the equation $\log_4 3 + \log_4 (x + 2) = 2$.

Solution. Using the first law of logarithms, we have

$$\log_4 3 + \log_4 (x + 2) = \log_4 3(x + 2).$$

Hence, the given equation is equivalent to the equation

$$\log_4 3(x + 2) = 2. \qquad (\text{\textsl{1}})$$

This logarithmic equation is equivalent to the exponential equation

$$3(x + 2) = 4^2.$$

Hence,

$$3x + 6 = 16 \quad \text{and} \quad x = \tfrac{10}{3}.$$

Exercises

Find the value of each of the following by using the laws of logarithms.

1. (a) $\log_2 \sqrt[3]{32}$ (b) $\log_3 \left(\dfrac{\sqrt[5]{9}}{3} \right)$

2. (a) $\log_5 \left(\dfrac{\sqrt[3]{25}}{\sqrt{5}} \right)$ (b) $\log_{10} (10\sqrt[3]{100})$

3. (a) $\log_5 (25 \cdot 125)$ (b) $\log_6 \sqrt{216}$

4. (a) $\log_3 \sqrt[4]{9^5}$

(b) $\log_7 (49 \div 7^5)$

5. (a) $\log_3 81\sqrt{27}$

(b) $\log_2 \dfrac{\sqrt[4]{8}}{4}$

Express each of the following numbers as the logarithm of a single number.

6. (a) $\log_5 6 - \log_5 2$

(b) $\log_5 80 + \log_5 \frac{1}{4}$

7. (a) $4 \log_3 10 - 2 \log_3 5$

(b) $5 \log_7 9 - 4 \log_7 15 + \frac{3}{2} \log_7 12$

If $\log_{10} 2 = p$ and $\log_{10} 3 = q$, find an expression in terms of p and q for each logarithm in Exercises 8–13.

8. $\log_{10} 4$

9. $\log_{10} \left(\frac{2}{3}\right)$

10. $\log_{10} \sqrt{2}$

11. $\log_{10} .5$

12. $\log_{10} 30$

13. $\log_{10} \frac{1}{3}$

If $\log_{10} 5 = r$ and $\log_{10} 7 = s$, find an expression for each of the following in terms of r and s.

14. $\log_{10} 35$

15. $\log_{10} \frac{7}{5}$

16. $\log_{10} 49$

17. $\log_{10} \frac{343}{25}$

18. $\log_{10} \left(\sqrt{7} \cdot \sqrt[3]{5}\right)$

19. $\log_{10} \frac{7}{10} \cdot \log_{10} 125$

20. $\log_{10} 50 - \log_{10} 700$

21. $\log_{10} \sqrt{\frac{7}{5}}$

Solve each of the following equations.

22. $\log_4 72 - \log_4 9 = N$

23. $\log_5 6 = \log_5 x - \log_5 7$

24. $\log_7 98 + \log_7 3.5 = N$

25. $\log_3 63 - \log_3 7x = \log_3 2$

26. $\log_8 \sqrt{.125} = x$

27. $\log_5 4 + \log_5 (2x - 3) = 20$

28. Prove the second law of logarithms.

In Exercises 29–31, use the laws of logarithms to prove that each of the equations is true.

29. $\log_b 16 - \log_b 8 + \log_b 5 = \log_b 10$

30. $2 \log_x a - 2 \log_x b + 3 \log_x \sqrt{b} - \dfrac{1}{3} \log_x a = \dfrac{1}{6} \log_x \dfrac{a^{10}}{b^3}$

31. $\log_3 \dfrac{x^2 3^x}{3^{x^2}} = x - x^2 + 2 \log_3 x$

32. Solve the following equation for x.

$$\log_2 2 + \log_2 (x + 2) - \log_2 (3x - 5) = 3$$

33. Prove that

$$\log_{10} \frac{3x - \sqrt{9x^2 - 1}}{3x + \sqrt{9x^2 - 1}} = 2 \log_{10} (3x - \sqrt{9x^2 - 1}).$$

34. Solve each of the following equations.

(a) $y = 2 \log_2 8$ (b) $y = 3 \log_3 81$

(c) $y = 10 \log_2 4$ (d) $-y = b \log_b b^5$

Review for Sections 6–1 through 6–3

Write the logarithmic equation that corresponds to each of the following exponential equations.

1. $4^3 = 64$ **2.** $9^0 = 1$

3. $8^{\frac{2}{3}} = 4$ **4.** $49^{\frac{3}{2}} = 343$

5. $10^{-x} = y$ **6.** $a^{-\frac{3}{2}} = c$

Write the exponential equation that corresponds to each of the following logarithmic equations.

7. $\log_6 6 = 1$ **8.** $\log_3 243 = 5$

9. $\log_4 \frac{1}{2} = -\frac{1}{2}$ **10.** $\log_5 \frac{1}{25} = -2$

11. $\log_8 y = 2x$ **12.** $\log_7 3y = x$

Solve each of the following equations for x.

13. $\log_3 27 = x$ **14.** $\log_4 64 = x$

15. $\log_{16} x = \frac{1}{2}$ **16.** $\log_{25} x = \frac{3}{2}$

17. $\log_x \frac{1}{49} = -2$ **18.** $\log_x \frac{1}{81} = -4$

Graph each of the following and name the x-intercept.

19. $y = \log_5 x$ **20.** $y = \log_5 (x + 1)$

21. $y = \frac{1}{2} \log_5 x$ **22.** $y = 2 \log_5 x$

Solve each of the following equations.

23. $y = \frac{1}{2} \log_3 81$ **24.** $y = -\frac{1}{2} \log_2 \frac{1}{64}$

25. $y = \log_2 2\sqrt{2}$ **26.** $y = \log_3 9\sqrt{27}$

Answers to Review for Sections 6–1 through 6–3

1. $\log_4 64 = 3$ **2.** $\log_9 1 = 0$

3. $\log_8 4 = \frac{2}{3}$ **4.** $\log_{49} 343 = \frac{3}{2}$

5. $\log_{10} y = -x$ **6.** $\log_a c = -\frac{3}{2}$

7. $6^1 = 6$ **8.** $3^5 = 243$

9. $4^{-\frac{1}{2}} = \frac{1}{2}$ **10.** $5^{-2} = \frac{1}{25}$

11. $8^{2x} = y$ **12.** $7^x = 3y$

13. $x = 3$ **14.** $x = 3$

15. $x = 4$ **16.** $x = 125$

17. $x = 7$ **18.** $x = 3$

19.

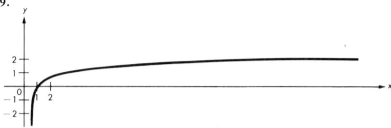

20.

21.

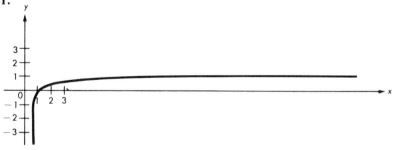

22.

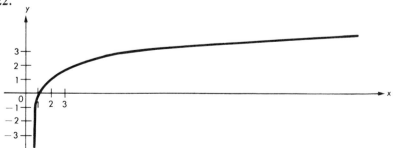

23. $y = 2$ **24.** $y = 3$

25. $y = \frac{3}{2}$ **26.** $y = \frac{7}{2}$

6-4 COMMON LOGARITHMS

There are two bases for logarithms that are extensively used today. One is the base e ($e \doteq 2.71828$) widely used in higher mathematics. Logarithms to the base e are called *natural logarithms*. The other is the base 10, chosen because of our decimal system of notation. Logarithms to the base 10 are called *common logarithms*. We shall discuss only common logarithms in this section. Whenever we write $\log N$ without indicating the base, it is always understood that the base is 10; that is,

$$\log N \quad \text{means} \quad \log_{10} N.$$

By the very definition of logarithms,

$$\log 10^n = n$$

for every real number n. Thus, for example,

$$\log .01 = -2 \quad \text{because} \quad .01 = 10^{-2},$$
$$\log .1 = -1 \quad \text{because} \quad .1 = 10^{-1},$$
$$\log 1 = 0 \quad \text{because} \quad 1 = 10^{0},$$
$$\log 10 = 1 \quad \text{because} \quad 10 = 10^{1},$$
$$\log 100 = 2 \quad \text{because} \quad 100 = 10^{2},$$

and so on.

We do not know, offhand, the logarithm of any positive rational number other than an integral power of 10. For example, we do not know what $\log 7$ is. Since 7 is between 1 and 10, and since $\log 1 = 0$ and $\log 10 = 1$, we have by the third property in Section 6-2 that $\log 7$ is between 0 and 1:

$$0 < \log 7 < 1.$$

Actually, it is shown in more advanced mathematics that $\log 7$ is an irrational number, so that it cannot possibly be represented as a quotient of two integers. However, as is the case with any irrational number, we can *approximate* $\log 7$ by a rational number. It can be shown that

$$\log 7 \doteq .8451$$

to four-decimal-place accuracy.

If we know a four-decimal-place approximation of log 7, we can easily find four-decimal-place approximations of log 70, log 700, log .7, and so on. Thus, since 70 = 10 × 7,

$$
\begin{aligned}
\log 70 &= \log (10 \times 7) \\
&= \log 10 + \log 7 \\
&= 1 + \log 7 \\
&= 1 + .8451 \\
&\doteq 1.8451.
\end{aligned}
$$

Similarly,

$$
\begin{aligned}
\log 700 &= \log (100 \times 7) \\
&= \log 100 + \log 7 \\
&= 2 + \log 7 \\
&\doteq 2 + .8451 \\
&\doteq 2.8451.
\end{aligned}
$$

Also,

$$
\begin{aligned}
\log .7 &= \log (7 \div 10) \\
&= \log 7 - \log 10 \\
&\doteq .8451 - 1 \\
&\doteq -.1549.
\end{aligned}
$$

Furthermore, we can approximate log 49, since $49 = 7^2$, and

$$
\begin{aligned}
\log 49 &= \log 7^2 \\
&= 2 \log 7 \\
&\doteq 2 \times .8451 \\
&\doteq 1.6902.
\end{aligned}
$$

In computing with logarithms, it is usually helpful to think of each positive real number as a number expressed in *scientific notation.* The positive number N is represented in scientific notation if it is expressed as the product of a number between 1 and 10 and an integral power of 10, that is, if

$$N = B \times 10^k, \quad \text{where } 1 \leqq B < 10 \text{ and } k \text{ is an integer.}$$

For example, each of the following positive numbers is expressed in scientific notation.

Number	Scientific notation
123	1.23×10^2
.0123	1.23×10^{-2}
98,752	9.8752×10^4
.1961	1.961×10^{-1}
1,000,000	1×10^6

If the positive integer N is expressed in scientific notation,

$$N = B \times 10^k, \quad \text{where } 1 \leqq B < 10 \text{ and } k \text{ is an integer,}$$

then

$$\log N = \log (B \times 10^k)$$
$$= \log B + \log 10^k.$$

Since $\log 10^k = k$, we have

$$\log N = \log B + k.$$

Note that

$$0 \leqq \log B < 1 \quad \text{since} \quad 1 \leqq B < 10.$$

Thus, $\log N$ is expressed as a sum of an integer and a nonnegative real number less than 1. Clearly,

$$k \leqq \log N < k + 1$$

so that k is the *greatest integer* contained in $\log N$ and $\log B$ is the *fractional part* of $\log N$. The nonnegative number $\log B$ is often called the *mantissa* of $\log N$ and the integer k the *characteristic* of $\log N$.

To summarize, if we express N in scientific notation,

$$N = B \times 10^k, \quad \text{where } 1 \leqq B < 10, k \text{ an integer,}$$

then

$$\log N = \underbrace{\overbrace{k}^{\substack{\text{greatest} \\ \text{integer}}}}_{\text{characteristic}} + \underbrace{\overbrace{\log B,}^{\substack{\text{fractional} \\ \text{part}}}}_{\text{mantissa}} \quad 0 \leqq \log B < 1.$$

The Table of Common Logarithms in the Appendix lists four-decimal-place approximations of the mantissas of the common logarithms of all integers from 100 to 999. The characteristic of $\log N$ if $100 \leqq N < 1000$ is 2, since $10^2 \leqq N < 10^3$ means that

$$2 \leqq \log N < 3.$$

A portion of this table is reproduced below.

N	0	1	2	3	4	5	6	7	8	9
38	.5798	.5809	.5821	.5832	.5843	.5855	.5866	.5877	.5888	.5899
39	.5911	.5922	.5933	.5944	.5955	.5966	.5977	.5988	.5999	.6010

This part of the table lists the mantissa of the logarithm of each integer from 380 through 399. The characteristic of the logarithm of each of these integers is obviously 2. Thus, from the table,

$\log 380 \doteq 2 + .5798, \quad \log 381 \doteq 2 + .5809, \quad \log 387 \doteq 2 + .5877,$
$\log 390 \doteq 2 + .5911, \quad \log 394 \doteq 2 + .5955, \quad \log 399 \doteq 2 + .6010.$

We should keep in mind the definition of the logarithm. Thus, since

$$\log 381 \doteq 2.5809,$$

we have

$$10^{2.5809} \doteq 381,$$

and so on.

In using this table, we can think of it as a table of logarithms of numbers from 1.00 to 9.99. Hence, if we express a given number in scientific notation, the mantissa of the logarithm of the number may be read directly from the table. For example, $39,600 = 3.96 \times 10^4$ in scientific notation. Hence,

$$\log 39,600 = \log 3.96 + \log 10^4,$$
$$\doteq .5977 + 4, \quad \text{or} \quad 4.5977.$$

Also,

$$.0388 = 3.88 \times 10^{-2},$$
$$\log .0388 = \log 3.88 + \log 10^{-2}$$
$$\doteq .5888 - 2.$$

We could express the final answer in the form -1.4112, but to simplify the work of some operations with logarithms we usually want it in the first form, $.5888 - 2$.

Exercises

Express the numbers in each of the following statements in scientific notation.

1. (a) The distance that light travels in one year is called a *light-year*, which is approximately 5,870,000,000,000 miles.

   (b) The diameter of the Einstein universe, according to the theory of relativity, is 2,000,000,000 light-years, or

$$11,740,000,000,000,000,000,000 \text{ miles.}$$

2. (a) The thickness of an oil film is about .0000005 centimeters.

   (b) The diameter of the orbit of an electron of a hydrogen atom is about .000 000 000 53 millimeters.

If $\log 5 \doteq .6990$, find each of the following logarithms.

3. (a) log 500   (b) log .005

4. (a) log 25   (b) log 125

5. Complete each of the following statements.

   (a) $10^2 < 123 < $ _?_ ;   _?_ $< \log 123 < 3$

   (b) _?_ $< 1230 < 10^4$; $3 < \log 1230 <$ _?_

For each number given, first find the successive integral powers of 10 between which the number lies. Then find the successive integers between which the logarithm of the number lies.

6. (a) 15.6   (b) 15,600

7. (a) 1.56   (b) .156

Give the integral part, or characteristic, of the common logarithm of each of the following numbers.

8. (a) 1.23×10^2 (b) 1.23×10^{-1}

9. (a) 1.23×10^{-2} (b) 1.23×10^4

Write each number in scientific notation and give the integral part, or characteristic, of its logarithm to the base 10.

10. (a) 342.1   (b) .4762

11. (a) 20.51   (b) .003021

12. (a) 56,500   (b) .00006789

Use the Table of Common Logarithms to find the common logarithm of each of the following numbers. Then express each number as a power of 10.

13. (a) 1540   (b) .0764

14. (a) 7.08   (b) 650,000

15. (a) .000403   (b) .000008
16. (a) 923   (b) 32,500

Given that N equals each of the numbers in Exercises 17–31, find log N.

17. .256   **18.** 256
19. .0256   **20.** 2560
21. .000256   **22.** 256,000
23. 32.4   **24.** 32,400
25. 3,240,000   **26.** .00852
27. 8.52   **28.** .0000852
29. 2060   **30.** .0206
31. 20,600

32. (a) Consider the set of all numbers with a single digit to the left of the decimal, such as 1, 2.435, and 9.7468. Between which consecutive integral powers of 10 does N lie if $1 \leq N < 10$? What is the characteristic, or integral part, of log N?
　(b) Consider the set of all numbers with two digits to the left of the decimal, such as 10, 21.5, and 99.06. If $10 \leq N < 100$, between which consecutive integral powers of 10 does N lie? What is the characteristic of log N?
　(c) If $100 \leq N < 1000$, what is the integral part of log N?
　(d) If N is a positive number with k digits to the left of the decimal, between which consecutive integral powers of 10 does N lie? What is the characteristic of log N?
　(e) State a rule for finding the characteristic of log N when N is any positive number greater than or equal to 1.

33. (a) Consider the set of all numbers less than 1, but not less than .1, such as .1, .1012, .234, and .9999. If $.1 \leq N < 1$, between which consecutive integral powers of 10 does N lie? What is the characteristic of log N?
　(b) If $.01 \leq N < .1$, between which consecutive integral powers of 10 does N lie? What is the characteristic of log N?
　(c) List six members of the set $\{N \mid .001 \leq N < .01\}$.

For each such N, what is the greatest integer contained in log N?
　(d) If N is a positive number less than 1, having its first nonzero digit in the kth place to the right of the decimal, what is the characteristic of log N?

*6–5 COMPUTING WITH LOGARITHMS

Before computing with logarithms, we must learn how to approximate N if we know log N. In the first place, if

$$0 \leqq \log N < 1,$$

we can approximate N by looking in the body of the Table of Common Logarithms for the closest entry to log N. Then N is approximately the number whose logarithm is this entry.

For example, given that

$$\log N = .8785,$$

we note that .8785 appears in the body of the table in the row marked 75 and in the column marked 6. Hence,

$$\log 7.56 \doteq .8785 \quad \text{and} \quad N \doteq 7.56.$$

If log N is not between 0 and 1, then we express log N as the sum of its fractional part and the greatest integer contained in it, that is,

$$\log N = A + k, \quad \text{where } 0 \leqq A < 1 \text{ and } k \text{ is an integer.}$$

Since A is between 0 and 1, we can find a positive number B whose logarithm is A from the table. Thus, $\log N = \log B + \log 10^k$ and

$$N = B \times 10^k, \quad \text{where } 1 \leqq B < 10 \text{ and } \log B = A.$$

For example, suppose that we are given

$$\log N = 1.8785.$$

Then the fractional part of log N is .8785, and the greatest integer contained in log N is 1. We may write

$$\log N = .8785 + 1.$$

From the preceding example, log 7.56 $\doteq$ .8785. Hence,

$$N \doteq 7.56 \times 10^1, \quad \text{or} \quad 75.6.$$

Let us consider a second example. If

$$\log N = -2.4522,$$

then

$$-3 < \log N < -2.$$

Hence, -3 is the greatest integer contained in log N, and

$$-2.4522 - (-3), \quad \text{or} \; .5478,$$

is the fractional part of log N. Thus,

$$\log N = .5478 - 3.$$

By the Table of Common Logarithms,

$$\log 3.53 \doteq .5478.$$

Therefore,

$$N \doteq 3.53 \times 10^{-3}, \quad \text{or} \; .00353.$$

When we represent log N in the form $A + k$, where $0 \leq A < 1$ and k is an integer, we are expressing log N as the sum of its *mantissa A* and its *characteristic k*. The mantissa determines the digits in N, and the characteristic determines the placement of the decimal point.

If M and N are numbers such that $M = \log N$, then N is often called the *antilogarithm* of M, and we write

$$N = \text{antilog } M.$$

Thus, in the example above, $.00353 \doteq \text{antilog}(-2.4522)$. Of course, if $M = \log N$, then $N = 10^M$ according to the definition of logarithms. Hence, antilog M is just 10^M.

Problem 1. Compute each of the following.
(a) $87,500 \times 314$ (b) $.0147 \div .397$

Solution.
(a) If we let N designate the desired product, then

$$\log N = \log (87,500 \times 314)$$
$$= \log 87,500 + \log 314.$$

Thus,

$$\log 87,500 = \log (8.75 \times 10^4) \doteq .9420 + 4$$
$$+ \quad \log 314 \quad = \log (3.14 \times 10^2) \doteq .4969 + 2$$
$$\log N \doteq 1.4389 + 6 = .4389 + 7.$$

Since log N has characteristic 7 and mantissa .4389,

$$N = B \times 10^7, \quad \text{where} \; \log B = .4389.$$

The mantissa .4389 is not in the body of the Table of Common Logarithms. The closest entry is .4393 $\doteq$ log 2.75. Using this value we have log $B \doteq$ log 2.75 and $B \doteq$ 2.75. Thus,

$$N \doteq 2.75 \times 10^7, \quad \text{or } 27{,}500{,}000.$$

(b) If N designates the desired quotient, then

$$\log N = \log (.0147 \div .397)$$
$$= \log .0147 - \log .397.$$

Thus,

$$\log .0147 = \log (1.47 \times 10^{-2}) \doteq .1673 - 2$$
$$- \quad \log .397 \;\; = \log (3.97 \times 10^{-1}) \doteq .5988 - 1$$

In order to keep a positive mantissa when we subtract, we change .1673 $-$ 2 to 1.1673 $-$ 3, as shown below.

$$\log .0147 \doteq 1.1673 - 3$$
$$- \quad \log .397 \;\; \doteq \quad .5988 - 1$$
$$\overline{\hspace{2cm} .5685 - 2}$$

Hence,

$$\log N = .5685 - 2$$

and

$$N \doteq B \times 10^{-2}, \quad \text{where } \log B = .5685.$$

Again, the mantissa .5685 is not in the Table of Common Logarithms. The closest entry is .5682 $\doteq$ log 3.70. Thus, $B \doteq$ 3.70 and

$$N \doteq 3.70 \times 10^{-2}, \quad \text{or } .0370.$$

If we multiply 87,500 $\times$ 314 in Problem 1(a) we get 27,475,000, which is not the answer that we obtained by using logarithms. However, the answer we obtained by using logarithms is correct to three *significant digits;* that is, if we round off the numeral above, keeping the first three digits (reading from left to right), then we get 27,500,000 as an approximation to three significant digits. We replaced the block of digits 475 by 500 since 475 is closer to 500 than to 400.

Similarly, the answer we obtained for Problem 1(b) is an approximation of the correct answer to three significant digits. If we divide .0147 by .397, we get .03702 ... Note that the three significant digits in this case are 3, 7, and 0, in that order. We wrote the answer in the form

$$.0370 \quad \text{rather than} \quad .037$$

to indicate that the last 0 was a significant digit.

When a physicist declares that the speed of light is 186,000 miles per second, he does not mean to imply that all six digits of this number are necessarily significant. Rather, he probably means that this is the approximate speed of light, accurate to three significant digits. In the early years of this century, the American physicist Michelson determined the speed of light, accurate to six significant digits, to be 186,234 miles per second.

Problem 2. Approximate $\sqrt[3]{.301}$ to three significant digits.

Solution. If we let

$$N = \sqrt[3]{.301},$$

then

$$\log N = \log (.301)^{\frac{1}{3}}$$
$$= \tfrac{1}{3} \log .301.$$

Now

$$\tfrac{1}{3} \log .301 = \tfrac{1}{3} \log (3.01 \times 10^{-1})$$
$$\doteq \tfrac{1}{3}(.4786 - 1)$$
$$\doteq \tfrac{1}{3}(2.4786 - 3)$$
$$\doteq .8262 - 1.$$

Hence, $N \doteq B \times 10^{-1}$, where $\log B = .8262$.
By the Table of Common Logarithms, $B \doteq 6.70$. Hence,

$$N \doteq 6.70 \times 10^{-1}, \quad \text{or} \quad .670,$$

accurate to three significant digits.

Problem 3. Approximate $873 \div \sqrt[5]{.079}$ to three significant digits.

Solution. If

$$N = 873 \div \sqrt[5]{.079},$$

then

$$\log N = \log 873 - \log \sqrt[5]{.079}$$
$$= \log 873 - \tfrac{1}{5} \log .079.$$

First, we find

$$\tfrac{1}{5} \log .079 = \tfrac{1}{5} \log (7.9 \times 10^{-2})$$
$$\doteq \tfrac{1}{5}(.8976 - 2)$$
$$\doteq \tfrac{1}{5}(3.8976 - 5)$$
$$\doteq .7795 - 1$$

and

$$\log 873 \doteq 2.9410.$$

Continuing the solution of Problem 3, we see that

$$\log 873 \;\doteq\; 2.9410$$
$$-\quad \tfrac{1}{5} \log .079 \;\doteq\; \underline{\;.7795 - 1\;}$$
$$2.1615 + 1$$

and

$$\log N \doteq .1615 + 3.$$

Therefore,

$$N = B \times 10^3,$$

where

$$\log B \doteq .1615.$$

From the Table of Common Logarithms, $B \doteq 1.45$. Hence,

$$N = 1.45 \times 10^3, \quad \text{or} \quad 1450,$$

accurate to three significant digits.

Problem 4. Compute $\sqrt[3]{-.136}$.

Solution. We first observe that

$$\sqrt[3]{-.136} = \sqrt[3]{(-1)^3(.136)}$$
$$= -\sqrt[3]{.136}.$$

Since

$$\log \sqrt[3]{.136} = \tfrac{1}{3} \log .136$$
$$\doteq \tfrac{1}{3}(2.1335 - 3)$$
$$\doteq .7112 - 1,$$

we have

$$\sqrt[3]{.136} \doteq .514.$$

Therefore,

$$\sqrt[3]{-.136} \doteq -.514.$$

Exercises

Find an approximate value of N in each of the following exercises.

1. (a) $\log N = 2.5105$ (b) $\log N = .6513 + 1$
2. (a) $\log N = .8149 - 1$ (b) $\log N = .3617 - 2$
3. (a) $\log N = 3.0334$ (b) $\log N = 7.9538 - 10$
4. (a) $\log N = 14.8082 - 10$ (b) $\log N = 0.7042$
5. (a) $\log N = 3.8482 - 4$ (b) $\log N = 18.5752 - 20$
6. (a) $\log N = -.3698$ (b) $\log N = -2.6819$

Use logarithms to approximate each of the following numbers to three significant digits.

7. (a) $(.317)(94.2)$ (b) $\sqrt[5]{1960}$

8. (a) $\dfrac{821}{37,500}$ (b) $\dfrac{2.050}{.00045}$

9. (a) $(.0126)(.115)$ (b) $\sqrt[9]{764}$

Use logarithms to approximate each of the following numbers to three significant digits.

10. $\dfrac{(245)(7.53)}{(6.14)^2}$ 11 $\dfrac{16.8}{(0.871)^{\frac{1}{2}}}$ 12. $\left[\dfrac{\sqrt{647}\,(.0013)}{181}\right]^{\frac{1}{2}}$

13. $\sqrt[3]{\dfrac{3}{4}\left(\dfrac{275}{3.14}\right)}$ 14. $(4.71)^{-\frac{2}{3}}$ 15. $\sqrt[4]{7810}$

16. $\sqrt{(.0417)(.123)}$ 17. $\dfrac{5750}{9.32}$ 18. $(.00752)^{-\frac{3}{5}}$

19. $(186,000)(.445)$ 20. $\sqrt{\dfrac{(6.15)(37.7)}{255}}$ 21. $\sqrt[8]{\dfrac{705}{5.14}}$

---

22. The formula for the volume V of a sphere with radius r units is $V = \frac{4}{3}\pi r^3$. Assuming the earth to be a perfect sphere with a radius of 3960 miles, determine the volume of the earth to three significant digits. (Use $\pi \doteq 3.14$.)

23. The number of seconds required for a complete swing of a pendulum is called the period of the pendulum. The period t (in seconds) of a pendulum L feet long is given by the formula

$$t = 2\pi\sqrt{\frac{L}{g}},$$

where $g \doteq 32.2$. Find, to three significant digits, the period of a pendulum 3 feet long.

24. The weight of a man d miles above the surface of the earth is given by the formula

$$W = \frac{W_0(4000)^2}{(4000 + d)^2},$$

where W_0 is the man's weight at the surface of the earth. Determine the approximate weight of a 160-pound man in a space capsule 500 miles above the earth. Find your own weight if you were in the capsule.

25. When a principal P is invested at an annual interest rate of r per cent compounded k times a year, a formula for the amount A at the end of n years is

$$A = P\left(1 + \frac{r}{k}\right)^{nk}.$$

If the sum of \$1000 is invested at an annual rate of 4%, compute the amount A
(a) after 20 years if interest is compounded semiannually.
(b) after 20 years if interest is compounded quarterly.
(c) after 5 years in a bank which compounds interest daily.

26. Use the formula of the preceding exercise to find how many years it will take a sum of money invested at 4% compounded semiannually to double itself.

27. A certain radioactive substance decays according to the formula

$$A = A_0 \times 2^{-\frac{t}{1500}}.$$

If the initial quantity A_0 is 425 milligrams, how much of the substance remains after 50 years?

28. In 1950 the population of a certain town was 25,000. If the population growth is exponential, the population P after t years have elapsed is given by the formula

$$P = 25,000 \times (\tfrac{6}{5})^{\frac{1}{10}t}.$$

(a) Find the population in 1955.
(b) How long will it take for the population to double?

29. Heron's formula for the area of a triangle in terms of its three sides a, b, c, and semiperimeter s is

$$A = \sqrt{s(s - a)(s - b)(s - c)}.$$

Find, to three significant digits, the area of a triangle having sides of length 57 inches, 62 inches, and 43 inches. (The semiperimeter is one-half the sum of the lengths of the three sides.)

CHAPTER REVIEW

Tell which of the following statements are true and which are false. Correct the ones that you marked false.

1. If $r > s$, then $(-2)^r > (-2)^s$.   **2.** $\dfrac{\log 5}{\log 3} = \log 2$

3. $\log (r + s) = \log r + \log s$ **4.** $\log 3x = 3 \log x$

5. If $f(x) = \log (1 - x)$, the domain of f is $\{x \mid x < 1\}$.

6. If $g(x) = \log (x^2 + 1)$, the domain of g is the set of real numbers.

7. $\log x^n = (\log x)^n$

8. $\log_9 3 = \dfrac{1}{\log_3 9}$

9. $\log \sqrt{\dfrac{a}{b^2}} = \frac{1}{2}(\log a - 2 \log b)$

10. $\log_4 16 = \dfrac{\log_2 16}{\log_2 4}$

Solve each of the following equations for x without referring to logarithm tables.

11. $\log 5 + \log 4 = \log x$ **15.** $2^{3x-2} = 64$

12. $\log_7 x^5 - 3 \log_7 x = 2$ **16.** $\log_x \frac{1}{49} = -2$

13. $\log (4x - 1) - 2 \log x = \log 3$ **17.** $\log_8 x = \frac{4}{3}$

14. $\log_3 42 - \log_3 8 = \log_3 x$ **18.** $\log_{\frac{3}{2}} \frac{8}{27} = x$

Use logarithms to find approximations to three significant digits for each of the following numbers.

19. $45.2 \div 861$

20. $45{,}300 \times .00861$

21. $\sqrt[3]{453}$

22. $(.453)^2$

In Exercises 23–26, graph each of the equations. For what values of x is each equation defined?

23. $y = \log_{12} x$

24. $y = \log_{12} |x|$

25. $y = \log_3 (x + 2)$

26. $y = \log_3 (2 - x)$

27. Solve each of the following equations for x.
  (a) $\log_{10} (x + 1) - \log_{10} x = .3247$
  (b) $3^{1+2x} = 5^{1-2x}$

28. The star Betelgeuse is approximately 1.59×10^{15} miles from the earth. How many years does it take light from Betelgeuse to reach us?

29. The speed of sound in water is 1.46×10^5 centimeters per second. If it takes a sound 2.00×10^{-2} seconds to travel from the surface of a body of water to the bottom and back, how deep is the water?

7 · The Trigonometric Functions

Historically, trigonometry is the study of relationships between the sides and angles of triangles. In its modern meaning, trigonometry is mainly concerned with certain periodic functions, that is, functions whose values repeat themselves in a regular way. In this chapter, we shall look briefly at the historical interpretation of trigonometry before turning to the modern approach.

7–1 TRIGONOMETRIC FUNCTIONS OF ACUTE ANGLES

Every acute angle α may be considered to be an angle of some right triangle ABC, as indicated in Fig. 7–1. If the vertices of a triangle are designated by A, B, and C, then we shall frequently denote the lengths of the opposite sides by a, b, and c, respectively, and the angles at vertices A, B, and C by α, β, and γ, respectively. The small square at vertex C of Fig. 7–1 (b) indicates that the angle at C is a right angle.

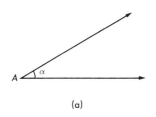

(a)

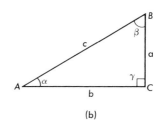

(b)

FIGURE 7–1

173

If α is an acute angle of the right triangle shown in Fig. 7–1, we can define the *sine* of α, the *cosine* of α, and the *tangent* of α in triangle ABC in the following manner.

$$\sin \alpha = \frac{a}{c}, \quad \cos \alpha = \frac{b}{c}, \quad \tan \alpha = \frac{a}{b}$$

In this way, we can associate with each acute angle α three numbers: $\sin \alpha$, $\cos \alpha$, and $\tan \alpha$. Note that we have abbreviated sine to sin, cosine to cos, and tangent to tan.

Although it appears that $\sin \alpha$, $\cos \alpha$, and $\tan \alpha$ could depend on the size of the right triangle containing angle α, this is not the case. If $A'B'C'$ is another right triangle with α as an acute angle (see Fig. 7–2), then it follows that triangles ABC and $A'B'C'$ are similar. Hence

$$\frac{a}{c} = \frac{a'}{c'}, \quad \frac{b}{c} = \frac{b'}{c'}, \quad \frac{a}{b} = \frac{a'}{b'}.$$

This proves that $\sin \alpha$, $\cos \alpha$, and $\tan \alpha$ do not depend on the size of the right triangle containing angle α.

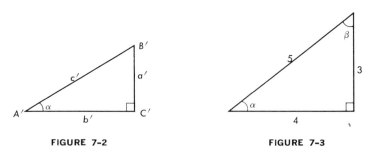

FIGURE 7-2   FIGURE 7-3

One of the simplest right triangles having sides of integral lengths is the right triangle with sides 3, 4, and 5, as shown in Fig. 7–3. If we denote the smaller acute angle by α and the larger acute angle by β, then according to the definitions above,

$$\sin \alpha = \tfrac{3}{5}, \quad \cos \alpha = \tfrac{4}{5}, \quad \tan \alpha = \tfrac{3}{4},$$
$$\sin \beta = \tfrac{4}{5}, \quad \cos \beta = \tfrac{3}{5}, \quad \tan \beta = \tfrac{4}{3}.$$

The correspondence that associates with each acute angle α the number $\sin \alpha$ is a *function*, called the *sine*. This function has the set of all acute angles as its domain and the set of positive real numbers less than 1 as its range. Similarly, *cosine* and *tangent* are *functions* having the same domain. The three functions sine, cosine, and tangent are called *trigonometric functions*.

Problem 1. Find the trigonometric functions of an angle of measure 60°.

Solution. The hypotenuse is twice as long as the shorter leg in a 30°–60° right triangle. If we assume that the hypotenuse has length 2 and the shorter leg length 1, then the length b of the other leg is $\sqrt{3}$ since

$$2^2 = 1^2 + b^2 \quad \text{and} \quad b = \sqrt{3}$$

by the pythagorean theorem. When we look at Fig. 7–4, we see that

$$\sin 60° = \frac{\sqrt{3}}{2}, \quad \cos 60° = \frac{1}{2}, \quad \tan 60° = \frac{\sqrt{3}}{1}.$$

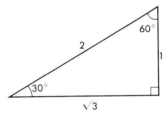

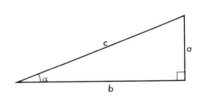

FIGURE 7-4   FIGURE 7-5

Problem 2. Find the values of the $\cos \alpha$ and the $\tan \alpha$, given that α is acute and that $\sin \alpha = .3$.

Solution. Consider α as an angle of a right triangle (Fig. 7–5). The problem tells us that

$$\sin \alpha = \frac{a}{c} = .3.$$

Hence $a = .3c$. Since $a^2 + b^2 = c^2$, we have

$$b^2 = c^2 - a^2$$
$$= c^2 - (.3c)^2, \quad \text{or} \quad .91c^2.$$

Thus

$$b = c\sqrt{.91}.$$

Therefore

$$\cos \alpha = \frac{b}{c} = \frac{c\sqrt{.91}}{c} = \sqrt{.91}, \quad \text{or} \quad \frac{\sqrt{91}}{10},$$

$$\tan \alpha = \frac{a}{b} = \frac{.3c}{c\sqrt{.91}} = \frac{.3}{\sqrt{.91}}, \quad \text{or} \quad \frac{3}{\sqrt{91}}, \quad \text{or} \quad \frac{3\sqrt{91}}{91}.$$

Exercises

1. Complete the following table of values of trigonometric functions.

	30°	45°	60°
sine	?	?	?
cosine	?	?	?
tangent	?	?	?

Find the trigonometric functions of each angle described in Exercises 2–11.

2. The two acute angles of the right triangle whose sides are 5, 12, and 13 units long

3. The acute angle whose tangent is 12

4. The smaller acute angle of a right triangle with one leg of length 6 inches and with hypotenuse of length 9 inches

5. An angle of measure 30°

6. The two acute angles of the right triangle whose sides are 7, 24, and 25 units long

7. The acute angle whose sine is .2

8. The acute angle whose cosine is .7

9. The acute angle whose sine is .99

10. The acute angle whose cosine is .001

11. The larger acute angle of a right triangle with legs of 7 feet and 9 feet

12. For an acute angle α of a right triangle, it is known that $\sin \alpha = \frac{3}{4}$ and that the length of the leg opposite angle α is 12. Find the lengths of the hypotenuse and the other leg.

7–2 THE WRAPPING FUNCTION

Modern trigonometry is not restricted to a discussion of acute angles. The trigonometric functions may be given a more general treatment by relating them to points on a unit circle (that is, a circle of radius 1). In this approach, the domains of the sine and cosine functions are the set of all real numbers, rather than a set of acute angles. When considered in this way, the trigonometric functions are often called *circular functions.* We place the center of a unit circle at the origin of a cartesian coordinate system, and then place a number line (the *s*-axis) parallel to the *y*-axis, as shown in Fig. 7–6. We assume that all three number lines (the *x*-axis, the *y*-axis, and the *s*-axis) have the same unit of length.

Now imagine that the *s*-axis is an infinitely long thread which can be wrapped around the circle. The piece above the *x*-axis can be wrapped in a counterclockwise manner, and the piece below the *x*-axis can be wrapped in a clockwise manner. Then each point on the *s*-axis can be made to coincide with a point on the circle. In other words, this process defines a function *W*, called the *wrapping function*, which associates with each real number *s* (as the coordinate of a point on the *s*-axis) a *point W(s)* on the unit circle. Because the thread is infinitely long and the circle has finite circumference 2π, the thread can be wrapped around the circle infinitely many times.

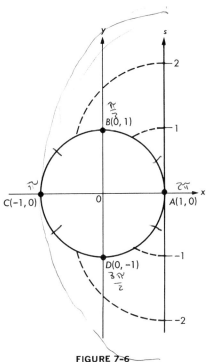

FIGURE 7–6

Each arc $\overset{\frown}{AB}$ of a unit circle has a length. For example, the arc $\overset{\frown}{AB}$ of Fig. 7–6 is a quarter circle, and hence its length is $2\pi/4$, or $\pi/2$. Similarly, arc $\overset{\frown}{AC}$ is a semicircle with length π, and counterclockwise arc $\overset{\frown}{AD}$ is a three-quarter circle with length $3\pi/2$. Thus

$$W(0) = A(1, 0),$$
$$W\left(\frac{\pi}{2}\right) = B(0, 1),$$
$$W(\pi) = C(-1, 0),$$
$$W\left(\frac{3\pi}{2}\right) = D(0, -1),$$
$$W(2\pi) = A(1, 0).$$

If $s > 2\pi$, the piece of thread of length s is wrapped around the circle more than once. For example, $W(3\pi) = C(-1, 0)$. If the negative s-axis is thus wrapped around the circle, as shown in Fig. 7–7, we see that

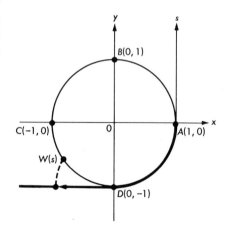

$$W\left(-\frac{\pi}{2}\right) = D(0, -1),$$

$$W(-\pi) = C(-1, 0),$$

$$W\left(-\frac{3\pi}{2}\right) = B(0, 1),$$

$$W(-2\pi) = A(1, 0),$$

$$W(-3\pi) = C(-1, 0),$$

FIGURE 7-7

and so on.

If we increase or decrease the length of a piece of thread by 2π, we end up at the same point on the unit circle. Thus for every real number s,

$$W(s) = W(s + 2\pi), \quad W(s) = W(s - 2\pi).$$

On the other hand, if $0 < c < 2\pi$,

$$W(s) \neq W(s + c), \quad W(s) \neq W(s - c).$$

Thus the function W repeats itself every 2π, and 2π is the least positive number for which this is true. For this reason, we call the function W *periodic* and the number 2π its *period*.

The wrapping function W is periodic with period 2π.

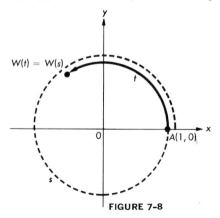

FIGURE 7-8

If $0 \leq s < 2\pi$, then $W(s)$ is the point on the unit circle such that the arc from A to $W(s)$, when traced counterclockwise, has length s. If $s > 2\pi$, then we subtract an integral multiple of 2π from s so that the difference is between 0 and 2π. In this manner, we can express $W(s)$ as $W(t)$ for some number t, where $0 \leq t < 2\pi$, as shown in Fig. 7–8. If $s < 0$, then we add an integral multiple of 2π to s so that the sum t is between 0 and 2π. In either case, $W(s) = W(t)$ by the periodicity of W.

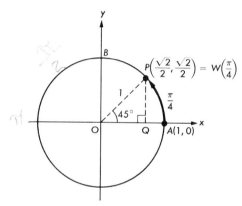

FIGURE 7-9

Problem 1. Find $W\left(\dfrac{\pi}{4}\right)$.

Solution. Since arc $\overset{\frown}{AP}$ is half of arc $\overset{\frown}{AB}$ (Fig. 7–9), the measure of $\angle POA$ must be $45°$, and $\triangle OPQ$ is a $45°$ right triangle. We constructed the circle with a radius of 1; therefore $\overline{OP}$ has length 1. From our previous work with a $45°$ right triangle,

$$OQ = QP$$

and

$$(OP)^2 = (QP)^2 + (OQ)^2.$$

Therefore

$$QP = \frac{\sqrt{2}}{2}$$

and

$$W\left(\frac{\pi}{4}\right) = \left(\frac{\sqrt{2}}{2}, \frac{\sqrt{2}}{2}\right).$$

Problem 2. Find $W\left(\dfrac{-3\pi}{4}\right)$.

Solution. The point

$$W\left(\frac{-3\pi}{4}\right)$$

is halfway between the points $W(\pi)$ and $W(3\pi/2)$. We know from our previous work that the coordinates of all points in the third quadrant are negative. Since the measure of $\angle POQ$ is $45°$, $\triangle OPQ$ is a $45°$ right triangle. (See Fig. 7–10.)

$$W\left(-\frac{3\pi}{4}\right) = \left(-\frac{\sqrt{2}}{2},\ -\frac{\sqrt{2}}{2}\right)$$

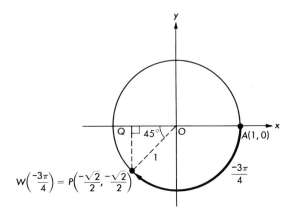

FIGURE 7-10

Problem 3. Find $W\left(\dfrac{\pi}{6}\right)$.

Solution. Since arc $\overset{\frown}{AP}$ is a third of arc $\overset{\frown}{AB}$ (Fig. 7–11), the measure of $\angle POA$ is $30°$ and $\triangle OPQ$ is a $30°$–$60°$ right triangle. Therefore

$$QP = .5, \quad OQ = \frac{\sqrt{3}}{2}$$

and

$$W\left(\frac{\pi}{6}\right) = \left(\frac{\sqrt{3}}{2}, \frac{1}{2}\right).$$

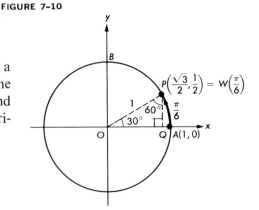

FIGURE 7-11

Problem 4. Find $W\left(\dfrac{21\pi}{4}\right)$ and $W\left(\dfrac{-11\pi}{2}\right)$.

Solution. If we subtract $2(2\pi)$, or 4π, from $21\pi/4$, we get a number t between 0 and 2π:

$$t = \frac{21\pi}{4} - 4\pi, \quad \text{or} \quad \frac{5\pi}{4}.$$

By the periodicity of W,

$$W\left(\frac{21\pi}{4}\right) = W\left(\frac{5\pi}{4}\right).$$

Since $W(5\pi/4)$ is the same point as $W(-3\pi/4)$, as shown in Fig. 7–10,

$$W\left(\frac{21\pi}{4}\right) = \left(-\frac{\sqrt{2}}{2}, -\frac{\sqrt{2}}{2}\right).$$

We must add $3(2\pi)$, or 6π, to $-(11\pi)/2$ in order to obtain a number t between 0 and 2π:

$$t = -\frac{11}{2}\pi + 6\pi = \frac{\pi}{2}.$$

By the periodicity of W,

$$W\left(-\frac{11\pi}{2}\right) = W\left(\frac{\pi}{2}\right), \quad \text{or } (0, 1).$$

Exercises

1. Complete the following table.

s	0	$\dfrac{\pi}{6}$	$\dfrac{\pi}{4}$	$\dfrac{\pi}{3}$	$\dfrac{\pi}{2}$
$W(s)$	$(1, 0)$	$(?, ?)$	$(?, ?)$	$(?, ?)$	$(0, 1)$

s	$\dfrac{2\pi}{3}$	$\dfrac{3\pi}{4}$	$\dfrac{5\pi}{6}$	π
$W(s)$	$(?, ?)$	$(?, ?)$	$(?, ?)$	$(-1, 0)$

s	$\dfrac{7\pi}{6}$	$\dfrac{5\pi}{4}$	$\dfrac{4\pi}{3}$	$\dfrac{3\pi}{2}$
$W(s)$	$(?, ?)$	$(?, ?)$	$(?, ?)$	$(0, -1)$

s	$\dfrac{5\pi}{3}$	$\dfrac{7\pi}{4}$	$\dfrac{11\pi}{6}$	2π
$W(s)$	$(?, ?)$	$(?, ?)$	$(?, ?)$	$(1, 0)$

2. Fill in the bottom row with real numbers t which lie in the interval $0 \leqq t < 2\pi$ and have the property $W(t) = W(s)$.

s	3π	$\dfrac{7\pi}{2}$	4π	$\dfrac{11\pi}{2}$	7π	10π
t	?	?	?	?	?	?

s	-2π	$-\dfrac{5\pi}{2}$	-3π	-5π	-7π	$-\dfrac{15\pi}{2}$
t	?	?	?	?	?	?

3. Complete the following table for the wrapping function W by visualizing a thread wrapped around the unit circle and making sketches.

s	3π	$\dfrac{7\pi}{2}$	4π	$\dfrac{11\pi}{2}$	7π	10π
$W(s)$	$(-1, 0)$	?	?	?	?	?

s	-2π	$-\dfrac{5\pi}{2}$	-3π	-5π	-7π	$-\dfrac{15\pi}{2}$
$W(s)$	$(1, 0)$	?	?	?	?	?

In Exercises 4–9, find a number t such that $0 \leqq t < 2\pi$ and $W(t) = W(s)$.

4. $s = \dfrac{13\pi}{6}$ **5.** $s = \dfrac{19\pi}{6}$ **6.** $s = \dfrac{13\pi}{3}$

7. $s = -\dfrac{22\pi}{3}$ **8.** $s = \dfrac{3\pi}{4}$ **9.** $s = -\dfrac{15\pi}{4}$

10. For each number s in Exercises 4–9, find the coordinates of the point $W(s)$.

Find the coordinates of the point $P = W(s)$ for each value of s in Exercises 11–22.

11. $s = -\dfrac{14\pi}{3}$ **12.** $s = \dfrac{11\pi}{3}$ **13.** $s = \dfrac{27\pi}{4}$

14. $s = -\dfrac{7\pi}{4}$ **15.** $s = \dfrac{41\pi}{6}$ **16.** $s = \dfrac{35\pi}{6}$

17. $s = \dfrac{47\pi}{4}$ **18.** $s = \dfrac{9\pi}{2}$ **19.** $s = -\dfrac{11\pi}{3}$

20. $s = -\dfrac{27\pi}{4}$ **21.** $s = \dfrac{23\pi}{6}$ **22.** $s = \dfrac{22\pi}{3}$

7-3   PROPERTIES OF THE WRAPPING FUNCTION

For every real number s, the points $W(s)$ and $W(-s)$ are mirror images of each other, as shown in Fig. 7–12. This relationship can be stated as follows:

$$\text{If } W(s) = (x, y), \text{ then } W(-s) = (x, -y). \tag{1}$$

For example,

$$W\left(\frac{3\pi}{4}\right) = \left(-\frac{\sqrt{2}}{2}, \frac{\sqrt{2}}{2}\right)$$

and

$$W\left(-\frac{3\pi}{4}\right) = \left(-\frac{\sqrt{2}}{2}, -\frac{\sqrt{2}}{2}\right).$$

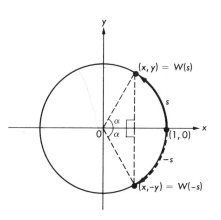

The points $W(s)$ and $W(s + \pi/2)$ are also related. To illustrate this relation, let us consider $s = \pi/6$. Then $s + \pi/2 = 2\pi/3$.   Since

FIGURE 7-12

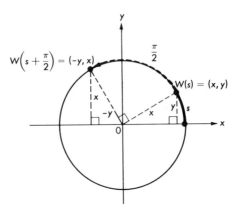

FIGURE 7-13

$s = \pi/6$, we can use the information we know about a 30°–60° right triangle (see Fig. 7–13) to find that

$$W\left(\frac{\pi}{6}\right) = \left(\frac{\sqrt{3}}{2}, \frac{1}{2}\right) \quad \text{and} \quad W\left(\frac{2\pi}{3}\right) = \left(-\frac{1}{2}, \frac{\sqrt{3}}{2}\right).$$

This relationship between $W(s)$ and $W(s + \pi/2)$ will always hold because the triangles involved will always be congruent. We state this relationship in the following way.

$$\text{If } W(s) = (x, y), \text{ then } W\left(s + \frac{\pi}{2}\right) = (-y, x). \qquad (2)$$

In other words, the x-coordinate of $W(s)$ becomes the y-coordinate of $W(s + \pi/2)$, and the opposite of the y-coordinate of $W(s)$ becomes the x-coordinate of $W(s + \pi/2)$.

Since

$$s + \pi = \left(s + \frac{\pi}{2}\right) + \frac{\pi}{2},$$

we can use relationship (2) twice to obtain $W(s + \pi)$: If

$$W(s) = (x, y),$$

then

$$W\left(s + \frac{\pi}{2}\right) = (-y, x)$$

and

$$W\left(\left(s + \frac{\pi}{2}\right) + \frac{\pi}{2}\right) = (-x, -y).$$

Also, $W(s + \pi) = W(s - \pi)$ by the periodicity of W. Thus we have the following result.

$$\text{If } W(s) = (x, y), \text{ then } W(s + \pi) = W(s - \pi) = (-x, -y). \quad (3)$$

We can use relationships (2) and (3) to find functional values of many other combinations of s and $\pi/2$. For example, if

$$W(s + \pi/2) = (-y, x),$$

then $W(s - \pi/2) = W((s + \pi/2) - \pi) = (y, -x)$ by relationship (3). Thus by relationship (2), we have the following.

$$\text{If } W(s) = (x, y), \text{ then } W\left(s - \frac{\pi}{2}\right) = (y, -x). \quad (4)$$

Problem. If $W(s) = (x, y)$, what is $W(\pi/2 - s)$?

Solution. If $W(s) = (x, y)$, then

$$W\left(s - \frac{\pi}{2}\right) = (y, -x)$$

and

$$W\left(\frac{\pi}{2} - s\right) = W\left(-\left(s - \frac{\pi}{2}\right)\right) = (y, x).$$

Exercises

In Exercises 1–5, find the coordinates of each indicated point.

1. $W\left(\frac{3\pi}{4}\right)$, $W\left(-\frac{13\pi}{4}\right)$

2. $W\left(-\frac{2\pi}{3}\right)$, $W\left(\frac{4\pi}{3}\right)$

3. $W\left(\frac{7\pi}{6}\right)$, $W\left(\frac{31\pi}{6}\right)$

4. $W\left(-\frac{3\pi}{4}\right)$, $W(19\pi)$

5. $W(18\pi)$, $W(3\pi)$

6. If the points $W(s)$ and $W(s')$ have the same coordinates, how are s and s' related?

7. Complete the following table.

s	0	$\dfrac{\pi}{6}$	$\dfrac{\pi}{4}$	$\dfrac{\pi}{3}$
$W(s)$	$(1, 0)$	$\left(\dfrac{\sqrt{3}}{2}, \dfrac{1}{2}\right)$	$\left(\dfrac{\sqrt{2}}{2}, \dfrac{\sqrt{2}}{2}\right)$	$\left(\dfrac{1}{2}, \dfrac{\sqrt{3}}{2}\right)$
$W(-s)$	$(?, ?)$	$(?, ?)$	$(?, ?)$	$(?, ?)$
$s + \dfrac{\pi}{2}$	?	?	?	?
$W\left(s + \dfrac{\pi}{2}\right)$	$(?, ?)$	$(?, ?)$	$(?, ?)$	$(?, ?)$

s	$\dfrac{\pi}{2}$	$\dfrac{2\pi}{3}$	$\dfrac{5\pi}{6}$	$\dfrac{3\pi}{4}$
$W(s)$	$(0, 1)$	$(?, ?)$	$(?, ?)$	$(?, ?)$
$W(-s)$	$(?, ?)$	$(?, ?)$	$(?, ?)$	$(?, ?)$
$s + \dfrac{\pi}{2}$	?	?	?	?
$W\left(s + \dfrac{\pi}{2}\right)$	$(?, ?)$	$(?, ?)$	$(?, ?)$	$(?, ?)$

8. Complete the following table.

s	0	$\dfrac{\pi}{6}$	$\dfrac{\pi}{4}$	$\dfrac{\pi}{3}$	$\dfrac{\pi}{2}$	$\dfrac{2\pi}{3}$	$\dfrac{5\pi}{6}$	$\dfrac{3\pi}{4}$
$s - \dfrac{\pi}{2}$								
$W\left(s - \dfrac{\pi}{2}\right)$								
$W\left(\dfrac{\pi}{2} - s\right)$								
$W(s + \pi)$								
$W(s - \pi)$								

7–4　THE SINE AND COSINE

We recall that the wrapping function W associates with each number s a unique point $W(s)$ on the unit circle (Fig. 7–14). The coordinates of $W(s)$ are also functions of s; we make the following definition.

Definition of Sine and Cosine

$$W(s) = (cosine\ s,\ sine\ s) \quad for\ every\ real\ number\ s$$

According to the definition above, the x-coordinate of a point $W(s)$ on the unit circle is the cos s and the y-coordinate is the sin s, that is

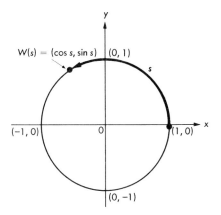

$$\cos s = x \quad and \quad \sin s = y.$$

The function W is periodic with period 2π. Knowing this, we can show the truth of the following statement.

The sine and cosine are periodic functions; each has period 2π.

FIGURE 7-14

Problem 1. Find the sine and cosine of $\pi/4$, $\pi/3$, and $\pi/2$.

Solution. In Fig. 7–9, we saw that $W(\pi/4) = (\sqrt{2}/2, \sqrt{2}/2)$. Hence

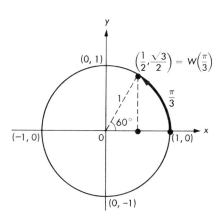

$$\sin \frac{\pi}{4} = \frac{\sqrt{2}}{2}, \quad \cos \frac{\pi}{4} = \frac{\sqrt{2}}{2},$$

and $W(\pi/3) = (1/2, \sqrt{3}/2)$. (See Fig. 7–15.) Therefore

$$\sin \frac{\pi}{3} = \frac{\sqrt{3}}{2}, \quad \cos \frac{\pi}{3} = \frac{1}{2}.$$

Since $W(\pi/2) = (0, 1)$, we have

$$\sin \frac{\pi}{2} = 1, \quad \cos \frac{\pi}{2} = 0.$$

FIGURE 7-15

Problem 2. Find the sine and cosine of $55\pi/4$ and $-10\pi/3$.

Solution. Since $6 \cdot 2\pi$ is the greatest integral multiple of 2π which is less than or equal to $55\pi/4$,

$$W\left(\frac{55\pi}{4}\right) = W\left(\frac{55\pi}{4} - (6 \cdot 2\pi)\right), \quad or\ W\left(\frac{7\pi}{4}\right).$$

According to Fig. 7–16, $W(7\pi/4) = (\sqrt{2}/2, -\sqrt{2}/2)$. Thus

$$\sin \frac{55\pi}{4} = -\frac{\sqrt{2}}{2}, \quad \cos \frac{55\pi}{4} = \frac{\sqrt{2}}{2}.$$

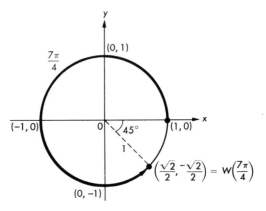

FIGURE 7-16

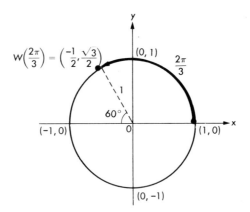

FIGURE 7-17

By the periodicity of W, we have

$$W\left(\frac{-10\pi}{3}\right) = W\left(4\pi - \frac{10\pi}{3}\right), \quad \text{or } W\left(\frac{2\pi}{3}\right).$$

According to Fig. 7–17, $W(2\pi/3) = (-1/2, \sqrt{3}/2)$. Thus

$$\sin\left(-\frac{10\pi}{3}\right) = \frac{\sqrt{3}}{2}, \quad \cos\left(-\frac{10\pi}{3}\right) = -\frac{1}{2}.$$

The unit circle has equation

$$x^2 + y^2 = 1.$$

Therefore for each real number s, the point $W(s)$ on the unit circle has coordinates (cos s, sin s) which are a solution of the above equation. This can be stated in the following way.

First Fundamental Identity

$$sin^2 s + cos^2 s = 1 \quad \textit{for every real number } s$$

Note that we write $\sin^2 s$ for $(\sin s)^2$ and $\cos^2 s$ for $(\cos s)^2$. The first fundamental identity is an example of an equation which is true for all numbers in the domains of the functions. In trigonometry, such an equation is frequently called an *identity*.

It follows from the first fundamental identity that $\sin^2 s \leq 1$ and $\cos^2 s \leq 1$. Hence

$$-1 \leq sin\ s \leq 1 \quad \textit{for every real number } s,$$

$$-1 \leq cos\ s \leq 1 \quad \textit{for every real number } s.$$

In other words, the interval $\{x \mid -1 \leq x \leq 1\}$ is the *range* of the cosine and $\{y \mid -1 \leq y \leq 1\}$ is the range of the sine.

Exercises

1. Complete the following table by telling whether the sin s and cos s are positive or negative numbers in each of the four quadrants in a cartesian coordinate system.

	I	II	III	IV
sin s	+	?	?	?
cos s	+	?	?	?

For each s in Exercises 2–9, find $W(s)$, and give sin s and cos s.

2. $-\dfrac{9\pi}{4}$ 3. $\dfrac{4\pi}{3}$ 4. $-\dfrac{\pi}{6}$ 5. 7π

6. $-\dfrac{5\pi}{2}$ **7.** $\dfrac{23\pi}{6}$ **8.** $\dfrac{11\pi}{4}$ **9.** $-\dfrac{16\pi}{3}$

Evaluate each of the expressions in Exercises 10–19.

10. $\sin \dfrac{9\pi}{4}$ **11.** $\cos\left(-\dfrac{5\pi}{6}\right)$ **12.** $\cos \dfrac{7\pi}{3}$

13. $\sin \dfrac{13\pi}{4}$ **14.** $\cos \dfrac{3\pi}{2}$ **15.** $\cos \dfrac{17\pi}{6}$

16. $\sin \dfrac{5\pi}{6}$ **17.** $\sin(-3\pi)$ **18.** $\sin\left(-\dfrac{5\pi}{6}\right)$

19. $\cos 4\pi$

20. (a) When we say $\sin s = 1$, we mean that the y-coordinate of $W(s)$ is 1. Draw a sketch of the unit circle and locate all such points. How many points have this property?

(b) For what values of s in the interval $0 \le s < 2\pi$ is $\cos s = 1$?

21. (a) For what values of s in the interval $0 \le s \le 2\pi$ is $\sin s = 0$?

(b) For what values of s in the interval $0 \le s < 2\pi$ is $\cos s = 0$?

---

22. Use the first fundamental identity to prove that

$$\cos^2 \theta - \sin^2 \theta = 2\cos^2 \theta - 1.$$

23. (a) If $\sin s = \frac{1}{2}$, use the first fundamental identity to find the two possible values of $\cos s$.

(b) Since $\sin s$ in part (a) is positive, the point $W(s)$ must be in the first or second quadrant. Why?

(c) If $\sin s = \frac{1}{2}$ and $\pi/2 < s < \pi$, what is $\cos s$?

(d) Draw a sketch and find s for part (c).

24. (a) If $-\pi/2 < s < 0$, is $\cos s$ positive or negative?

(b) If $\cos s = \frac{3}{5}$ and $-\pi/2 < s < 0$, find $\sin s$.

25. Given that s is in the interval $-\pi/2 < s < 0$ and $\sin s = -.7$, find $\cos s$.

7–5   PROPERTIES OF SINE AND COSINE

Many identities follow from the properties of the wrapping function given in Section 7-4. The first fundamental identity was stated in Section 7-4. The following are some other fundamental identities.

Second and Third Fundamental Identities

memorize

$$\sin(-s) = -\sin s$$

$$\cos(-s) = \cos s$$

These follow directly from relationship (1) on page 183.

We call f an *odd function* if $f(-x) = -f(x)$ for every x in the domain of f. We call f an *even function* if $f(-x) = f(x)$ for every x in the domain of f. By the second fundamental identity, *sine is an odd function*, and by the third fundamental identity, *cosine is an even function*.

If $W(s) = (\cos s, \sin s)$, then $W(s + \pi/2) = (-\sin s, \cos s)$ by relationship 2 on page 184. This leads us to the fourth and fifth fundamental identities.

$$sin\left(s + \frac{\pi}{2}\right) = \cos s$$

$$cos\left(s + \frac{\pi}{2}\right) = -\sin s$$

Other identities are given below.

$$sin\,(s \pm \pi) = -\sin s$$

$$cos\,(s \pm \pi) = -\cos s$$

$$sin\left(s - \frac{\pi}{2}\right) = -\cos s$$

$$cos\left(s - \frac{\pi}{2}\right) = \sin s$$

Problem. Find $\sin 4\pi/3$ and $\cos 7\pi/4$.

Solution.

$$\sin \frac{4\pi}{3} = \sin\left(\frac{\pi}{3} + \pi\right) \qquad \cos \frac{7\pi}{4} = \cos\left(\frac{3\pi}{4} + \pi\right)$$

$$= -\sin \frac{\pi}{3} \qquad\qquad = -\cos \frac{3\pi}{4}$$

$$= -\frac{\sqrt{3}}{2} \qquad\qquad = -\cos\left(\frac{\pi}{4} + \frac{\pi}{2}\right)$$

$$\qquad\qquad\qquad = \sin \frac{\pi}{4}$$

$$\qquad\qquad\qquad = \frac{\sqrt{2}}{2}$$

The fundamental identities derived in this section will be used in the next chapter. Of those listed, the second, third, sixth, and seventh are the most useful in application and are easiest to recall from the properties of the wrapping function W. For example,

$$\sin\left(-\frac{10\pi}{3}\right) = -\sin\frac{10\pi}{3}$$

$$= -\sin\left(\frac{10\pi}{3} - 2\pi\right)$$

$$= -\sin\frac{4\pi}{3}$$

$$= -\left(-\sin\frac{\pi}{3}\right)$$

$$= \frac{\sqrt{3}}{2}.$$

In the following exercises, you may find it more useful to learn these formulas rather than to refer to them in the text.

Exercises

Evaluate each expression in Exercises 1–15.

1. $\cos\frac{19\pi}{6}$

2. $\sin(-23\pi)$

3. $\cos(-17\pi)$

4. $\sin\left(-\frac{11\pi}{3}\right)$

5. $\cos\left(-\frac{11\pi}{3}\right)$

6. $\sin\left(-\frac{17\pi}{6}\right)$

7. $\sin\frac{5\pi}{3}$

8. $\cos\frac{11\pi}{6}$

9. $\sin\frac{7\pi}{4}$

10. $\cos\frac{2\pi}{3}$

11. $\sin\frac{4\pi}{3}$

12. $\cos\frac{29\pi}{6}$

13. $\cos\left(-\frac{5\pi}{6}\right)$

14. $\sin\left(-\frac{11\pi}{6}\right)$

15. $\cos\left(-\frac{5\pi}{3}\right)$

16. Use relationship (4) to derive the following fundamental identities.

(a) $\sin\left(s - \frac{\pi}{2}\right) = -\cos s$

(b) $\cos\left(s - \frac{\pi}{2}\right) = \sin s$

17. Use relationship (3) to derive the following fundamental identities.

(a) $\sin(s \pm \pi) = -\sin s$

(b) $\cos(s \pm \pi) = -\cos s$

7–6 THE OTHER TRIGONOMETRIC FUNCTIONS

Using the sine and cosine as defined in Section 7–4, we now give names to certain combinations of these functions.

$$\textit{tangent } s = \frac{\textit{sine } s}{\textit{cosine } s}$$

$$\textit{cotangent } s = \frac{\textit{cosine } s}{\textit{sine } s}$$

$$\textit{secant } s = \frac{1}{\textit{cosine } s}$$

$$\textit{cosecant } s = \frac{1}{\textit{sine } s}$$

The domain of each of these four new functions is the set of all real numbers, excluding those numbers for which the function in the denominator is 0. For example,

$$\left\{ s \mid s \neq \frac{\pi}{2} + n\pi,\ n \text{ an integer} \right\}$$

is the domain of both the tangent and the secant.

Problem 1. Find the circular functions of $\pi/4$ and $\pi/3$.

Solution.

$$\sin \frac{\pi}{4} = \frac{\sqrt{2}}{2} \qquad\qquad \sin \frac{\pi}{3} = \frac{\sqrt{3}}{2}$$

$$\cos \frac{\pi}{4} = \frac{\sqrt{2}}{2} \qquad\qquad \cos \frac{\pi}{3} = \frac{1}{2}$$

$$\tan \frac{\pi}{4} = \frac{\dfrac{\sqrt{2}}{2}}{\dfrac{\sqrt{2}}{2}} = 1 \qquad\qquad \tan \frac{\pi}{3} = \frac{\dfrac{\sqrt{3}}{2}}{\dfrac{1}{2}} = \sqrt{3}$$

$$\cot \frac{\pi}{4} = \frac{\dfrac{\sqrt{2}}{2}}{\dfrac{\sqrt{2}}{2}} = 1 \qquad\qquad \cot \frac{\pi}{3} = \frac{\dfrac{1}{2}}{\dfrac{\sqrt{3}}{2}} = \frac{\sqrt{3}}{3}$$

$$\sec \frac{\pi}{4} = \frac{1}{\frac{\sqrt{2}}{2}} = \sqrt{2} \qquad \sec \frac{\pi}{3} = \frac{1}{\frac{1}{2}} = 2$$

$$\csc \frac{\pi}{4} = \frac{1}{\frac{\sqrt{2}}{2}} = \sqrt{2} \qquad \csc \frac{\pi}{3} = \frac{1}{\frac{\sqrt{3}}{2}} = \frac{2}{3}\sqrt{3}$$

Observe that we have abbreviated tangent to tan, cotangent to cot, secant to sec, and cosecant to csc.

We shall leave the proof of the tenth and eleventh identities for the exercises.

$$\sec^2 s = 1 + \tan^2 s$$
$$\csc^2 s = 1 + \cot^2 s$$

Problem 2. If $\pi < s < 3\pi/2$ and $\tan s = \frac{1}{2}$, find the other trigonometric functions of s.

Solution. First, $\cot s = 2$. By the tenth fundamental identity, we have $\sec^2 s = \frac{5}{4}$. Since $\cos s < 0$ if $\pi < s < 3\pi/2$, the sec s must be less than 0 also. Hence

$$\sec s = -\frac{\sqrt{5}}{2}.$$

Therefore

$$\cos s = -\frac{2}{\sqrt{5}},$$

$$\sin s = \cos s \tan s = -\frac{1}{\sqrt{5}}.$$

$$\csc s = -\sqrt{5}.$$

Problem 3. Simplify the expression

$$\frac{1}{1 - \sin s} + \frac{1}{1 + \sin s}.$$

Solution. We proceed as follows:

$$\frac{1}{1 - \sin s} + \frac{1}{1 + \sin s} = \frac{(1 + \sin s) + (1 - \sin s)}{(1 - \sin s)(1 + \sin s)}$$

$$= \frac{2}{1 - \sin^2 s}.$$

Since $1 - \sin^2 s = \cos^2 s$ by the first fundamental identity, and $\sec^2 s = 1/\cos^2 s$, we obtain

$$\frac{2}{\cos^2 s}, \quad \text{or } 2\sec^2 s,$$

as a simplified form of the given expression.

Problem 4. Prove that the following equation is an identity.

$$\csc s - \sin s = \cos s \cot s$$

Solution. What we really wish to show is that the expressions on the two sides of this equation are equivalent, that is, that one may be changed into the other by use of the fundamental identities. One way of doing this is shown below.

$$\csc s - \sin s = \frac{1}{\sin s} - \sin s$$

$$= \frac{1 - \sin^2 s}{\sin s}$$

$$= \frac{\cos^2 s}{\sin s}$$

$$= \cos s \cdot \frac{\cos s}{\sin s}$$

$$= \cos s \cot s$$

Hence $\csc s - \sin s = \cos s \cot s$ for every s in the common domain of the cotangent and the cosecant.

Exercises

In Exercises 1–8, find the other five trigonometric functions of s.

1. $\cos s = \dfrac{1}{\sqrt{2}}$ and $0 < s < \dfrac{\pi}{2}$ 2. $\sin s = \dfrac{1}{2}$ and $\dfrac{\pi}{2} < s < \pi$

3. $\tan s = -2$ and $\dfrac{3\pi}{2} < s < 2\pi$ 4. $\sin s = -1$

5. $\sec s = -\sqrt{2}$ and $\tan s < 0$ 6. $\csc s = 3$ and $\cos s < 0$

7. $\tan s = 1$ and $\sin s < 0$ 8. $\cos s = -1$

9. From the definition of $\sin s$ as the ordinate of the point $W(s)$, we see that the values of the sine function increase from 0 to 1 as s goes from 0 to $\pi/2$. What happens to the values of the cosine function as s goes from 0 to $\pi/2$?

10. Given that s is in the interval

$$\left\{ s \mid 0 \leqq s \leqq \dfrac{\pi}{2} \right\},$$

find the value or values of s for which the following are true.

(a) $\sin s = \cos s$ (b) $\sin s < \cos s$ (c) $\sin s > \cos s$

11. (a) What is the range of $\sin s$?
    (b) What is the range of $\cos s$?

12. (a) What is the range of $\cot s$?
    (b) What is the range of $\sec s$?

13. Complete the table by telling whether the tangent, cotangent, secant, and cosecant are positive or negative numbers in the four quadrants of a cartesian coordinate system.

	I	II	III	IV
tangent	+	?	?	?
cotangent	+	?	?	?
secant	+	?	?	?
cosecant	+	?	?	?

In Exercises 14–16, use a sketch of the unit circle.

14. Describe the behavior of the tangent function in the interval

$$\left\{ s \mid 0 \leqq s < \dfrac{\pi}{2} \right\}.$$

15. Describe the behavior of the tangent function in the interval

$$\left\{ s \,\middle|\, \frac{\pi}{2} < s \leq \pi \right\}.$$

16. What is the range of the tangent function; that is, what is the set of values of $\tan s$?

17. (a) For what values of s is $\sin s = 0$?

(b) Find the domains of the cotangent and the cosecant.

18. Simplify each of the following expressions.

(a) $\cos s \tan s$

(b) $\sec^2 s - \tan^2 s$

(c) $\dfrac{1}{\sec s - \tan s} - \dfrac{1}{\sec s + \tan s}$

(d) $\dfrac{\cot s}{\csc s}$

(e) $\sec s - \sin s \tan s$

(f) $\cot^2 s - \csc^2 s$

19. Prove that each of the following equations is an identity.

(a) $(\sin s + \cos s)^2 = 1 + 2 \sin s \cos s$

(b) $\dfrac{\sin s}{\csc s - \cot s} + \dfrac{\sin s}{\csc s + \cot s} = 2$

(c) $\dfrac{\sin s}{1 - \cos s} = \dfrac{1 + \cos s}{\sin s}$

(d) $\sin s \cos s - \sec s \sin s = -\sin^2 s \tan s$

(e) $\tan s + \cot s = \sec s \csc s$

(f) $\dfrac{\cos s}{1 + \sin s} = \sec s - \tan s$

20. Show that the tangent function is an odd function.

21. Derive $\sec^2 s = 1 + \tan^2 s$ from $\cos^2 s + \sin^2 s = 1$.

22. Show that $\csc^2 s = 1 + \cot^2 s$ for all values of s in the common domain of the cosecant and the cotangent.

7–7   RADIAN MEASURE AND GENERAL ANGLES

In trigonometry, it is convenient for us to think of an angle in a more general way than we did in geometry. We still say that an angle is composed of two rays in a plane having a common endpoint V, called the vertex of the angle. However, let us suppose that we keep V fixed and rotate one of these rays to another position in the given plane. Then the angle is *swept out*. The ray with which we start is called the *initial side* of the angle, and the ray with which we end is called the *terminal side*. The curved arrow in Fig. 7–18 indicates that in the formation of the angle, initial side *I* is rotated in a counterclockwise direction to terminal side *T*. An angle α is said to be in *standard position* relative to a cartesian coordinate system in a plane if the

FIGURE 7–18

vertex of α is at the origin and the initial side of α is along the positive *x*-axis.

We shall assign a measure to each angle in the following way. The measure will be a positive number if the angle is formed by a counterclockwise rotation, and a negative number if the angle is formed by a clockwise rotation. There are two common ways of measuring angles: by degrees and by radians.

Definition of Radian Measure of an Angle

The length of arc swept out by an angle α on the unit circle is called the radian measure of α.

Since the circumference of a unit circle is 2π, an angle formed by one revolution (in a counterclockwise direction) of the terminal side has a radian measure of 2π. If the terminal side is rotated more than one complete revolution, the angle formed will have a radian measure of more than 2π. A straight angle has a radian measure π, and a right angle has radian measure $\pi/2$.

The measure of α is 1 radian if the arc of the unit circle swept out by α is of length 1 and if α is formed by a counterclockwise rotation (Fig. 7–19). If the arc swept out by α had length 2, then α would have radian measure 2 or

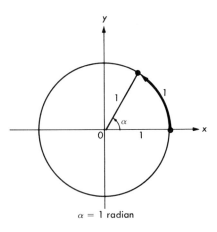

$\alpha = 1$ radian

FIGURE 7–19

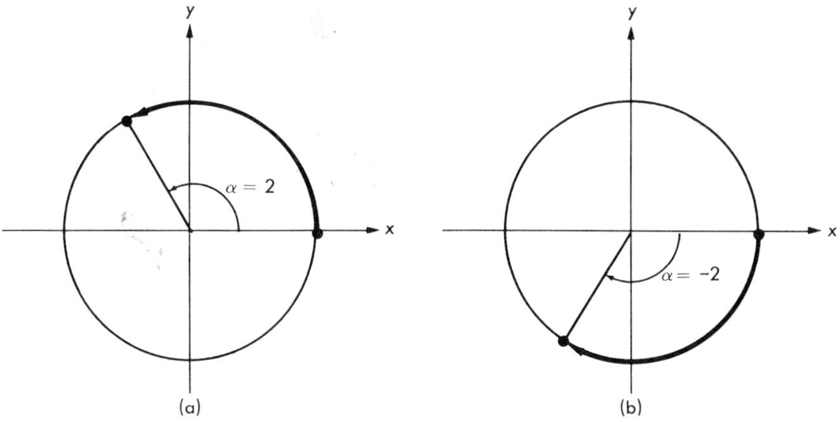

(a)   (b)

FIGURE 7-20

-2, depending on whether α was formed by a counterclockwise or a clockwise rotation. From now on, when we write $\alpha = 2$ without stating units, we mean that α has measure 2 radians. (See Fig. 7–20.)

If we start with the fact that a straight angle has measure 180°, or π radians, the formula

$$r = \frac{\pi}{180} d$$

gives the radian measure r of an angle in terms of its degree measure d.

We can solve the formula above for d in terms of r, obtaining the following:

$$d = \frac{180}{\pi} r.$$

This gives the degree measure d of an angle in terms of its radian measure r. For example,

$$\text{if } r = \frac{\pi}{6}, \text{ then } d = 30°;$$

$$\text{if } r = 1, \text{ then } d = \frac{180}{\pi} \doteq 57.3°.$$

In other words 57.3° $\doteq$ 1 radian.

The first two columns of the Table of Values of Trigonometric Functions in the Appendix give the approximate radian measures of angles of measure 0°, 1°, 2°, . . . , 89°, 90°. Since π is irrational, it follows that if the degree measure of an angle is a rational number, then the radian measure is irrational.

The trigonometric functions of a general angle can now be defined in the following way.

Definition of the Trigonometric Functions of a General Angle

If angle α has radian measure s, then we define

$$\sin \alpha = \sin s \quad and \quad \cos \alpha = \cos s.$$

The other functions of a general angle α are defined in terms of the sine α and cosine α, as before. For example, $\tan \alpha = \sin \alpha / \cos \alpha$.

If angle α is acute, and if α is in standard position as shown in Fig. 7–21, then α is an angle of right triangle ABC. Hence

$$\sin \alpha = \frac{y}{1}, \quad \cos \alpha = \frac{x}{1}$$

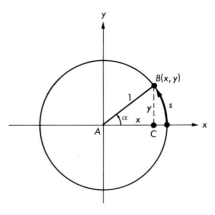

by the definitions of the sine and cosine of an acute angle in Section 7–1. On the other hand, if α has radian measure s, then $W(s)$ is the point B. Since $W(s) = (\cos s, \sin s)$ and $B = (x, y)$, we have $x = \cos s$ and $y = \sin s$. Thus

FIGURE 7-21

$$\sin \alpha = \sin s, \qquad \cos \alpha = \cos s,$$

and the two definitions of sine and cosine agree for acute angles.

From now on, we shall consider the domains of the trigonometric functions as either a set of general angles or as a set of real numbers, whichever is more convenient. Whenever we write $\sin 30°$, we mean the sine of an angle of measure $30°$. If we write $\sin 3$, we mean the sine of the number 3, or, equivalently, the sine of an angle of measure 3 radians.

The Table in the Appendix lists three-decimal-place approximations of $\sin \alpha$, $\cos \alpha$, and $\tan \alpha$ for $\alpha = 0°, 1°, 2°, \ldots, 89°, 90°$. For example, we can find that

$$\sin 24° \doteq .407, \quad \cos 44° \doteq .719, \quad \tan 77° \doteq 4.331.$$

Exercises

Given the radian measure, find the degree measure for each angle below.

1. $\dfrac{8\pi}{9}$　　　2. $\dfrac{7\pi}{4}$　　　3. 2　　　4. $\dfrac{34\pi}{3}$　　　5. $-\dfrac{5\pi}{3}$

6. $-\dfrac{7\pi}{6}$　　　7. $-\dfrac{\pi}{18}$　　　8. 0.7π　　　9. -3　　　10. 0.75

Given the degree measure, find the radian measure for each angle below.

11. $200°$　　　　　　12. $450°$　　　　　　13. $330°$

14. $-150°$　　　　　15. $160°$　　　　　　16. $75°$

17. $900°$　　　　　　18. $48°$　　　　　　19. $-300°$

20. $405°$

In each of the following exercises, sketch the angle in standard position, and find the three trigonometric functions: sine, cosine, and tangent.

21. $45°$　　　　　　22. $120°$　　　　　　23. $-60°$

24. $570°$　　　　　25. $-210°$　　　　　26. $0°$

27. $370°$　　　　　28. $-280°$　　　　　29. $756°$

In Exercises 30–38, find the sine and cosine of each number.

30. $.628$　　　　　　31. $.942$　　　　　　32. $.803$

33. $.401$　　　　　　34. $.262$　　　　　　35. 1.501

36. $.506$　　　　　　37. $.314$　　　　　　38. $.716$

7-8 FUNCTIONS AND COFUNCTIONS

If an acute angle has measure α degrees, then its complement has measure $90 - \alpha$ degrees. Similarly, if an acute angle has radian measure s, then its complement has radian measure $\pi/2 - s$. The trigonometric functions of a number and its complement are related in the following way.

$$\sin\left(\frac{\pi}{2} - s\right) = \sin\left(-\left(s - \frac{\pi}{2}\right)\right)$$

$$= -\sin\left(s - \frac{\pi}{2}\right)$$

$$= \cos s$$

$$\cos\left(\frac{\pi}{2} - s\right) = \cos\left(-\left(s - \frac{\pi}{2}\right)\right)$$

$$= \cos\left(s - \frac{\pi}{2}\right)$$

$$= \sin s$$

Since these equations are true for every number s, they are identities.

$$\sin\left(\frac{\pi}{2} - s\right) = \cos s, \quad \cos\left(\frac{\pi}{2} - s\right) = \sin s$$

Similar identities can be derived for the other trigonometric functions.

$$\tan\left(\frac{\pi}{2} - s\right) = \cot s, \quad \cot\left(\frac{\pi}{2} - s\right) = \tan s$$

$$\sec\left(\frac{\pi}{2} - s\right) = \csc s, \quad \csc\left(\frac{\pi}{2} - s\right) = \sec s$$

The sine and cosine are called *cofunctions* of each other; that is, cosine is the cofunction of sine, and sine is the cofunction of cosine. Similarly, the tangent and cotangent are cofunctions, and the secant and cosecant are cofunctions. In terms of cofunctions, the fundamental identities in this section can be expressed as follows: If f is any one of the six trigonometric functions and cof is its cofunction, then

$$f\left(\frac{\pi}{2} - s\right) = \cos f\, s.$$

For example,

$$\sin\frac{\pi}{6} = \cos\left(\frac{\pi}{2} - \frac{\pi}{6}\right) = \cos\frac{\pi}{3},$$

$$\cot\frac{3\pi}{8} = \tan\left(\frac{\pi}{2} - \frac{3\pi}{8}\right) = \tan\frac{\pi}{8},$$

$$\sec 42° = \csc (90° - 42°) = \csc 48°.$$

If an angle has measure α between $0°$ and $180°$, then its *supplement* has measure $180 - \alpha$ degrees. Similarly, if an acute angle has radian measure s, then its supplement has radian measure $\pi - s$. Using the second, third, sixth, and seventh fundamental identities, we can easily establish the following identity.

$$\sin (\pi - s) = \sin s, \quad \cos (\pi - s) = -\cos s$$

For example,

$$\cos \frac{5\pi}{6} = \cos \left(\pi - \frac{\pi}{6} \right) = - \cos \frac{\pi}{6}, \quad \text{or} \quad - \frac{\sqrt{3}}{2}.$$

Exercises

Using the Table of Values of Trigonometric Functions when necessary, find the value of each of the following functions.

1. $\sin \frac{13\pi}{6}$ **2.** $\cos \frac{9\pi}{4}$ **3.** $\tan 3\pi$

4. $\cos \frac{8\pi}{3}$ **5.** $\sec \frac{11\pi}{4}$ **6.** $\sin 130°$

7. $\cos 95°$ **8.** $\tan 113°$ **9.** $\tan 463°$

10. $\cos 540°$ **11.** $\cos 455°$ **12.** $\sin 450°$

Fill in the blanks in Exercises 13–24.

13. $\sin \frac{\pi}{4} = \cos \underline{\;\;?\;\;}$ **14.** $\cot 63° = \tan \underline{\;\;?\;\;}$

15. $\sec \frac{\pi}{3} = \csc \underline{\;\;?\;\;}$ **16.** $\tan \frac{\pi}{6} = \cot \underline{\;\;?\;\;}$

17. $\csc 46° = \sec \underline{\;\;?\;\;}$ **18.** $\cos 19° = \sin \underline{\;\;?\;\;}$

19. $\cos \frac{\pi}{10} = \sin \underline{\;\;?\;\;}$ **20.** $\csc \frac{2\pi}{3} = \sec \underline{\;\;?\;\;}$

21. $\tan 48° = \cot \underline{\;\;?\;\;}$ **22.** $\sin 74° = \cos \underline{\;\;?\;\;}$

23. $\cot \frac{3\pi}{4} = \tan \underline{\;\;?\;\;}$ **24.** $\sec 54° = \csc \underline{\;\;?\;\;}$

25. Using the Table of Values of Trigonometric Functions when necessary, give the values of the trigonometric functions in Exercises 13–24.

In Exercises 26–31, find the complement of each angle for the given radian measure.

26. .314   **27.** 1.204   **28.** 1.431

29. .646   **30.** 1.047   **31.** 1.309

32. From the fact that $\sin (\pi - s) = \sin s$ and $\cos (\pi - s) = -\cos s$, derive similar identities relating the other four trigonometric functions of s and $\pi - s$.

CHAPTER REVIEW

In Exercises 1–15, find each number.

1. $\sin(-\pi)$

2. $\tan \dfrac{2\pi}{3}$

3. $\cos \dfrac{\pi}{2}$

4. $\sec \dfrac{3\pi}{4}$

5. $\sin(-5\pi)$

6. $\sin\left(-\dfrac{7\pi}{6}\right)$

7. $\tan \dfrac{7\pi}{4}$

8. $\cos 180°$

9. $\sin 270°$

10. $\sec 210°$

11. $\tan 225°$

12. $\csc 240°$

13. $\cot 135°$

14. $\sin\left(-\dfrac{9\pi}{2}\right)$

15. $\cos\left(-\dfrac{11\pi}{6}\right)$

16. Show that

$$W\left(\frac{11\pi}{4}\right) = W\left(-\frac{5\pi}{4}\right).$$

17. Given that

$$W\left(\frac{\pi}{4}\right) = P,$$

determine the coordinates (x, y) of P.

18. Show that if n is an integer, then $W(s + 2\pi n) = W(s)$.

19. Graph $W(s)$ for

$$s = \frac{7\pi}{6}, \quad -\frac{5\pi}{6}, \quad \frac{5\pi}{12}, \quad \frac{21\pi}{4}, \quad 17\pi, \quad -\frac{5\pi}{4}, \quad 2, \quad -3.$$

20. Are there real numbers s such that $\sin s = 2$?

Simplify each of the following expressions.

21. $\sec s \cos s - \cos^2 s$

22. $\dfrac{\cot^2 s}{1 - \sin^2 s}$

23. $\dfrac{\cot^2 s}{1 + \cot^2 s}$

24. $1 - \dfrac{\sin^2 s}{1 + \cos s}$

25. $\dfrac{\tan^2 s + 1}{\cot^2 s + 1}$

Prove the following identities.

26. $\sin s \sec s \cot s = 1$

27. $\cos^4 s - \sin^4 s = \cos^2 s - \sin^2 s$

28. $\cot^2 s - \cos^2 s = \cos^2 s \cot^2 s$

29. $\dfrac{\cos s}{1 + \sin s} + \dfrac{1 + \sin s}{\cos s} = 2 \sec s$

30. $\dfrac{1 - \tan^2 s}{1 - \cot^2 s} = 1 - \sec^2 s$

Find the values of the following trigonometric functions. In each case, convert radian measure to degree measure.

31. $\cos\left(-\dfrac{\pi}{3}\right)$ **32.** $\sin \dfrac{7\pi}{6}$

33. $\tan\left(-\dfrac{3\pi}{4}\right)$ **34.** $\cot\left(-\dfrac{\pi}{2}\right)$

Express each of the following in terms of a trigonometric function of s.

35. $\sin (90° + s)$ **36.** $\cos (180° - s)$

37. $\sin (180° + s)$ **38.** $\cos (360° - s)$

39. $\sin (-s)$ **40.** $\sin \left(\dfrac{\pi}{2} - s\right)$

41. $\tan (\pi + s)$

In Exercises 42–46, which of the functions are odd? Which are even? Which are neither odd nor even?

42. $f(x) = \sec x$ **43.** $f(x) = x \sin x$

44. $f(x) = \sin x$ **45.** $f(x) = x \cos x$

46. $f(x) = x + \cos x$

8 · Topics in Trigonometry

In its traditional role, trigonometry was used to solve problems concerning the sides and angles of a triangle. The solution of such problems is the aim of the first three sections. Some topics not primarily related to triangles are studied in the rest of the chapter.

8–1 RIGHT TRIANGLE TRIGONOMETRY

Using the Table of Trigonometric Functions in the Appendix, how would you find the height x of the telephone pole AT in Fig. 8–1? You were able to measure the angle of elevation of T from a point P 85 ft from A. Clearly

$$\tan 41° = \frac{x}{85}$$
$$x = 85 \tan 41° = 73.9 \text{ ft.}$$

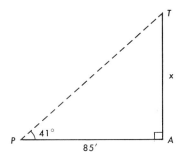
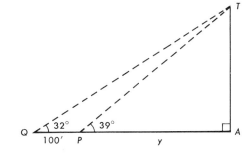

Consider another problem. The tree AT is on the other side of a river from an observer. He measures the angle of elevation of T from two points, P and Q, on a line with A. Distances and angles are as shown in Fig. 8–2. How high is the tree? Evidently

$$\tan 39° = \frac{x}{y}$$

$$\tan 32° = \frac{x}{100 + y}.$$

Thus

$$\begin{cases} x = (\tan 39°)y \\ x = (\tan 32°)(100 + y). \end{cases}$$

This is a system of two linear equations in two unknowns. We easily eliminate x from these equations:

$$(\tan 39°)y = (\tan 32°)(100 + y)$$
$$.810y \doteq .625(100 + y)$$
$$.185y \doteq 62.5$$
$$y \doteq 338$$

Hence,

$$x = .810 \cdot 338 = 274.$$

The tree AT is approximately 274 ft high.

Exercises

Find the distance x to three significant digits.

1.

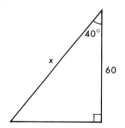

2.

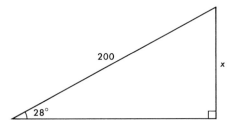

3.

4.

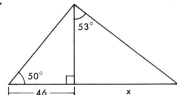

5.

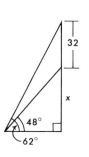

6.

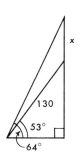

Find the angle α to the closest degree.

7.

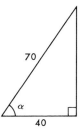

8.

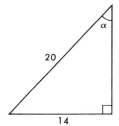

9.

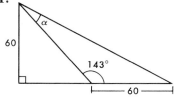

10.

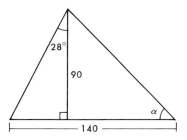

11.

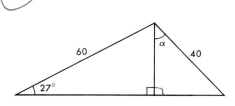

12.

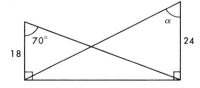

13. An isosceles triangle has two sides of length 16 inches, and two angles of 77°. Find its perimeter.

14. A fence 9 feet high is 7 feet from the side of a building with a flat roof. If the building is 20 feet high, how long must a ladder be to reach over the fence and to the top of the building?

15. A lighthouse is directly east from buoy *A* and directly south from buoy *B*. The buoys are 2,000 meters apart. The angle of elevation of the lighthouse from buoy *A* is 3° and from buoy *B* is 4°. How high is the lighthouse?

8–2 LAW OF COSINES

The sides and angles of every triangle are related in ways that will be discussed in this section. Since the sum of the measures of the angles of a triangle is 180°, each angle of a triangle has a measure between 0° and 180°. Let *ABC* be a given triangle, and let a coordinate system be placed in the plane of the triangle so that the vertex *A* is at the origin and side $\overline{AB}$ is along the positive *x*-axis. Then the vertices of the given triangle will have the coordinates shown in Fig. 8–3.

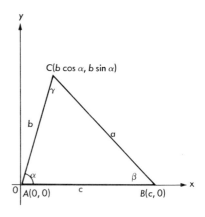

FIGURE 8–3

According to the distance formula, *a*, the distance between points *B* and *C* is given by

$$a = \sqrt{(b \cos \alpha - c)^2 + (b \sin \alpha - 0)^2}.$$

Hence

$$a^2 = b^2 (\cos \alpha)^2 - 2bc \cos \alpha + c^2 + b^2 (\sin \alpha)^2,$$
$$a^2 = b^2 (\cos^2 \alpha + \sin^2 \alpha) + c^2 - 2bc \cos \alpha,$$

and since $\cos^2 \alpha + \sin^2 \alpha = 1$,

$$a^2 = b^2 + c^2 - 2bc \cos \alpha.$$

This is a proof of the following law.

LAW OF COSINES

If α, β, and γ are the angles of a triangle and a, b, and c are the lengths of the respective opposite sides, then

$$a^2 = b^2 + c^2 - 2bc \cos \alpha.$$

We can interchange a and b, and α and β, to obtain the formula

$$b^2 = a^2 + c^2 - 2ac \cos \beta.$$

In a similar way, we can interchange a and c, and α and γ, to obtain the formula

$$c^2 = a^2 + b^2 - 2ab \cos \gamma.$$

The law of cosines is sometimes called the generalized pythagorean theorem. For example, if $\alpha = 90°$, then $\cos \alpha = 0$, and the law of cosines becomes the pythagorean theorem: $a^2 = b^2 + c^2$.

Problem 1. Find a for the triangle in Fig. 8–4.

Solution. By the law of cosines,

$$a^2 = 3^2 + 4^2 - (2 \cdot 3 \cdot 4 \cos 60°).$$

Since $\cos 60° = \frac{1}{2}$,

$$a^2 = 9 + 16 - 12,$$
$$a^2 = 13,$$

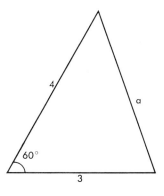

and $a = \sqrt{13}$.

This problem illustrates one of the principal uses of the law of co-sines. The law helps us find the length of one side of a triangle if we are given the lengths of the other two sides and the measure of the angle formed by them.

FIGURE 8-4

Problem 2. If the sides of a triangle have lengths 12, 9, and 5, find approximate measures of the angles.

Solution. If the vertices and angles of this triangle are labeled as shown in Fig. 8–5, then by the law of cosines,

$$12^2 = 9^2 + 5^2 - 2(9 \cdot 5 \cos \alpha),$$

$$144 = 81 + 25 - (90 \cos \alpha),$$

$$\cos \alpha = -\tfrac{38}{90}.$$

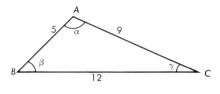

FIGURE 8-5

Thus $\cos \alpha \doteq -.422$. Since $\cos \alpha$ is negative, we know that α is obtuse. Since $\cos (180° - \alpha) = -\cos \alpha \doteq .422$, we see that

$$(180° - \alpha) \doteq 65° \quad \text{and} \quad \alpha \doteq 115°.$$

We can find the other angles of triangle ABC in a similar way. Thus

$$9^2 = 12^2 + 5^2 - (2 \cdot 5 \cdot 12 \cos \beta),$$
$$\cos \beta = \tfrac{88}{120}, \quad \text{or } .733.$$

Thus $\beta \doteq 43°$ and γ has measure $180 - (115 + 43)°$, or $\gamma \doteq 22°$. Thus the angles of the triangle are $\alpha \doteq 115°$, $\beta \doteq 43°$, $\gamma \doteq 22°$.

Exercises

In Exercises 1–10, A, B, and C designate the vertices of a triangle; α, β, and γ designate the measures of the corresponding angles; and a, b, and c designate the lengths of the corresponding opposite sides.

1. Find c, given that $b = 4$, $a = \sqrt{3}$, $\gamma = 150°$.

2. Find α, given that $a = 4$, $b = 6$, $c = 7$.

3. Find c, given that $a = 5$, $b = 5\sqrt{2}$, $\gamma = 45°$.

4. Find c, given that $a = 5$, $b = 5\sqrt{2}$, $\gamma = 135°$.

5. Find the smallest angle, given that $a : b : c = 2 : 3 : 4$.

6. Find c, given that $a = 3$, $b = 7$, $\gamma = 40°$.

7. Find α, given that $a = 3$, $b = 4$, $c = 6$.

8. Find a, given that $b = 3$, $c = 4$, $\alpha = 120°$.

9. Find a, given that $b = 3$, $c = 2$, $\alpha = 60°$.

10. Find β, given that $a = 10$, $c = 8$, $b = 6$.

11. The sides of a parallelogram are 40 feet and 70 feet long, and the smallest angle has measure $36°$. Find the length of the longer diagonal.

---

12. Draw $\triangle ABC$ with an obtuse angle at A in standard position. Follow the method of the proof in the text to prove the law of cosines for this triangle.

13. A triangular lot bounded by three streets has a frontage of 300 feet on one street, 250 feet on the second, and 420 feet on the third street. Find the measure of the smallest angle between two streets bounding the lot.

14. A parallelogram with one angle of measure 120° has sides of length 50 feet and 80 feet. Find the length of the shorter diagonal.

15. Prove that if $\triangle ABC$ has an obtuse angle at C, then $c^2 > a^2 + b^2$.

16. Two planes, one flying at 450 miles per hour and the other at 300 miles per hour, left an airport at the same time. Three hours later, they were 1200 miles apart. What was the measure of the angle between their flight paths?

8-3　LAW OF SINES

Each triangle T has an area $A(T)$, given by

$$A(T) = \tfrac{1}{2}bh,$$

where h is the length of the altitude of the triangle drawn from vertex B. If α is acute, then $\sin \alpha = h/c$ and

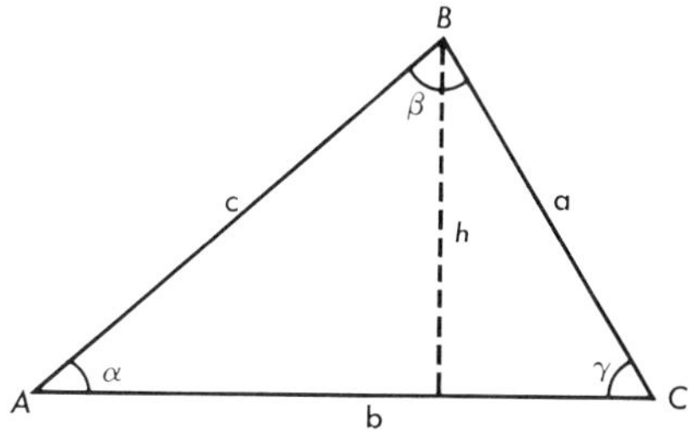

$$h = c \sin \alpha$$

FIGURE 8-6

from Fig. 8-6. This suggests the following formula.

FORMULA FOR THE AREA OF A TRIANGLE T

$$A(T) = \tfrac{1}{2}bc \sin \alpha$$

Although we proved this formula on the assumption that α is acute, the formula is valid even if $\alpha = 90°$ or $\alpha > 90°$. Thus if $\alpha = 90°$, then $\sin \alpha = 1$. The formula $A(T) = \tfrac{1}{2}bc$ is the one most frequently used in finding the area of a right triangle. In the exercises, you will be asked to prove that the formula is true when $\alpha > 90°$.

The formula for $A(T)$ is true for any two sides and the included angle. Thus we also have

$$A(T) = \tfrac{1}{2}ac \sin \beta.$$

From these two formulas for $A(T)$, we obtain the identity

$$\tfrac{1}{2}bc \sin \alpha = \tfrac{1}{2}ac \sin \beta,$$

or, multiplying each side by $2/abc$, we have

$$\frac{\sin \alpha}{a} = \frac{\sin \beta}{b}.$$

This is a proof of the following important law.

LAW OF SINES

If α, β, and γ are the angles of a triangle, and a, b, and c are the lengths of the respective opposite sides, then

$$\frac{\sin \alpha}{a} = \frac{\sin \beta}{b}.$$

We may interchange b and c, and β and γ, to obtain the law of sines in another form:

$$\frac{\sin \alpha}{a} = \frac{\sin \gamma}{c}.$$

Problem 1. Find the length of a for $\triangle ABC$, shown in Fig. 8–7.

Solution. By the law of sines,

$$\frac{\sin 30°}{a} = \frac{\sin 45°}{10}.$$

Since

$$\sin 30° = \tfrac{1}{2}$$

and

$$\sin 45° = 1/\sqrt{2},$$

we obtain

$$a = 5\sqrt{2}.$$

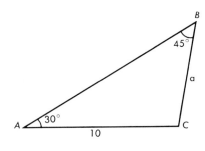

FIGURE 8-7

This problem shows that we can use the law of sines to find the length of one side of a triangle if we are given the length of another side and the measures of two angles of the triangle.

Problem 2. We can also use the
law of sines to find the other parts
of a triangle if we are given the
lengths of two sides and the measure of an angle opposite one of
them. For example, let $\alpha = 30°$,
$a = 8$, and $b = 12$. Find the other
angles and the third side of the
triangle.

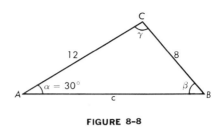

FIGURE 8-8

Solution. If the vertices and angles of the triangle are labeled as shown
in Fig. 8–8, then by the law of sines,

$$\frac{\sin 30°}{8} = \frac{\sin \beta}{12}.$$

Since $\sin 30° = \frac{1}{2}$,

$$\sin \beta = \tfrac{3}{4}, \quad \text{or } .75.$$

From the Table of Values of Trigonometric Functions at the end of
the book, we see that $\beta \doteq 49°$. Now γ has measure $180° - (30 + 49)°$,
or $\gamma \doteq 101°$.
   If c is the third side of the triangle, then

$$\frac{\sin 101°}{c} = \frac{\sin 30°}{8}.$$

We can find $\sin 101°$, using the identity

$$\sin (180 - \gamma)° = \sin \gamma.$$

Therefore

$$\sin 101° = \sin (180 - 101)°, \quad \text{or } \sin 79°.$$

From the Table of Values of Trigonometric Functions, $\sin 79° \doteq 982$.
Hence

$$\frac{.982}{c} = \frac{.5}{8}$$

and

$$c \doteq 15.7.$$

Thus the other angles of the triangle in Fig. 8–8 are $\beta \doteq 49°$ and
$\gamma \doteq 101°$, and the other side is
$c \doteq 15.7$.

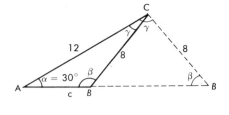

However, since we know that
$\sin (180° - \beta) = \sin \beta$, then we
have $(180 - 49)°$, or $131°$, is also
an angle with sine of .75. Thus
$\beta \doteq 131°$ is another possible solu-

FIGURE 8-9

tion. In other words, the problem has two possible solutions. The
second solution is shown in Fig. 8–9.

In this case, γ has measure $180 - (30 + 131)$ degrees, or $\gamma \doteq 19°$.
To find c, we have

$$\frac{\sin 19°}{c} = \frac{\sin 30°}{8}.$$

From the Table, $\sin 19° \doteq .326$. Hence $c \doteq 5.2$. The other angles
of the triangle in Fig. 8–9 are $\beta \doteq 131°$, $\gamma \doteq 19°$, and the other
side is $c \doteq 5.2$.

The law of sines is ideally suited for logarithmic computation.
Thus from the law of sines, we have

$$\log \left(\frac{\sin \alpha}{a} \right) = \log \left(\frac{\sin \beta}{b} \right),$$

or

$$\log \sin \alpha - \log a = \log \sin \beta - \log b.$$

Given values of three of the four variables in the equation above, we
can quickly compute the value of the other variable. This is illustrated
in the following problem.

Problem 3. Vertices A and B of $\triangle ABC$ are on one bank of a river
and vertex C is on the opposite bank, as shown in Fig. 8–10. The
distance between A and B is 200 feet, and the angles at A and B
have measures $33°$ and $63°$, respectively. Find the distance between
C and A, and the distance between C and B. Also, find the width of
the river.

Solution. The angle at C has measure $180° - (33 + 63)°$, or $84°$. If
b designates the distance from A to C, then

$$\frac{\sin 63°}{b} = \frac{\sin 84°}{200}$$

by the law of sines. From the Table, we find that $\sin 63° \doteq .891$ and that $\sin 84° \doteq .995$. Therefore

$$\log .891 - \log b = \log .995 - \log 200,$$

or

$$\log b = \log 200 + \log .891 - \log .995.$$

From the Table of Common Logarithms, we have $\log 200 \doteq .3010 + 2$ and $\log .891 \doteq .9499 - 1$. Thus

$$\log 200 + \log .891 \doteq 1.2509 + 1.$$

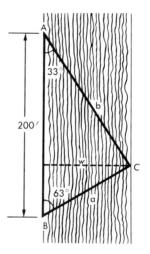

FIGURE 8-10

Also, $\log .995 \doteq .9978 - 1$. Therefore

$$\log 200 + \log .891 - \log .995 = \log b \doteq .2531 + 2.$$

Hence by the Table of Common Logarithms,

$$b \doteq 179 \text{ feet.}$$

If a denotes the distance from B to C in Fig. 8–10 then

$$\frac{\sin 33°}{a} = \frac{\sin 84°}{200}.$$

Since $\sin 33° \doteq .545$, we have

$$\log a = \log 200 + \log .545 - \log .995.$$

From the Table of Common Logarithms,

$$\log 200 + \log .545 - \log .995 = \log a \doteq .0396 + 2.$$

Hence by the Table of Common Logarithms,

$$a \doteq 110 \text{ feet.}$$

If w denotes the width of the river, then

$$\sin 33° = \frac{w}{b}$$

and

$$\log w = \log b + \log \sin 33°.$$

From our previous work,

$$\log b = 2.2531$$

and

$$\log \sin 33° = .7364 - 1.$$

Therefore

$$\log w = \log b + \log \sin 33° = 2.9895 - 1, \quad \text{or} \quad 1.9895.$$

Hence

$$w \doteq 97.6 \text{ feet.}$$

Exercises

In each exercise of Exercises 1–12, A, B, and C designate the vertices of a triangle; α, β, and γ designate the measures of the corresponding angles; and a, b, and c designate the lengths of the corresponding opposite sides.

1. Find a, given that $\alpha = 30°$, $\beta = 135°$, $b = 10\sqrt{2}$.
2. Find c, given that $\alpha = 30°$, $\beta = 105°$, $a = 3\sqrt{2}$.
3. Find β, given that $a = 12$, $b = 8\sqrt{3}$, $\alpha = 60°$.
4. Given that $\beta = 60°$, $a = 10$, $b = 9\sqrt{3}$, find the other side and the angles of the triangle.
5. Given that $\beta = 30°$, $b = 9$, $c = 15$, find the other side and the angles of the triangle.
6. Find the area of the triangle or triangles of Exercise 5.
7. Find c, given that $\alpha = 110°$, $\beta = 55°$, $a = 30$.
8. Find a, given that $\beta = 28°$, $\gamma = 41°$, $c = 100$.
9. Find c, given that $\alpha = 37°$, $\beta = 53°$, $a = 60$.
10. Find γ, given that $a = 9$, $c = 10$, $\alpha = 55°$.
11. Find b and then α, given that $a = 12$, $c = 9$, $\beta = 63°$.
12. Find b, α, and γ, given that $a = \sqrt{2}$, $c = 8$, $\beta = 45°$.
13. Find the area of the triangle in Exercise 11.
14. Find the area of the triangle in Exercise 12.
15. A 10-foot ladder must make an angle of 30° with the ground if it is to reach a certain window. What angle must a 20-foot ladder make with the ground to reach the same window?
16. Prove that the following formula for the area of a triangle T is true if $\alpha > 90°$.

$$A(T) = \tfrac{1}{2}bc \sin \alpha$$

17. A surveyor runs a line due east from A to B, but he cannot continue the line in an easterly direction because of an obstacle. Therefore he runs a line 800 feet long from B to C in a direction 24° east of south, and then runs another line CD in a direction 47° east of north. How long should CD be if D is to be due east of B?

18. The two diagonals of a parallelogram have lengths 10 and 7. The diagonals meet at a 60° angle. Find the lengths of the sides of the parallelogram and the measures of its angles.

19. On a coordinate plane, plot the three points

$$A(-2, 7), \quad B(6, 1), \quad C(-6, -4)$$

and draw $\triangle ABC$. Find the measure of the three angles of this triangle.

20. Find length a in the figure.

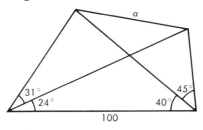

21. (a) Find a formula for the area of a parallelogram with two of its adjacent sides of length b and c, given that the included angle of the sides has a measure of α.

(b) Find the area of the parallelogram, given that $b = 365$, $c = 489$, $\alpha = 132°$.

22. In the figure, $PABC$ is a parallelogram with two adjacent sides of length 300 and 450 forming a 47° angle. The arrows suggest an application to the following physical problem: Two forces, one of 300 pounds and the other of 450 pounds, acting on an object at P with a 47° angle between 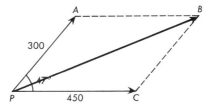 their directions, have the same effect as one force acting on P in the direction of the diagonal PB. The length of the diagonal gives the magnitude of this resultant force. Find the magnitude of the resultant force and the measure of the angle it makes with the 450-pound force.

23. A regular polygon of n sides is inscribed in a circle of radius r. Using trigonometric functions, derive a formula for the perimeter of the polygon.

24. Given that k is the proportionality number $\sin \alpha / a$, encountered in the law of sines, and that $r = 1/(2k)$, prove that r is the radius of the circle circumscribed about $\triangle ABC$.

8-4 THE ADDITION FORMULAS

In this section, we shall develop formulas for finding trigonometric functions of *sums* and *differences* of numbers. For any real numbers u and v, there correspond points $W(u)$ and $W(v)$ on the unit circle, as shown in Fig. 8–11. If $0 < u < v < 2\pi$, then the arc from $W(u)$ to $W(v)$ has length $v - u$. Therefore there is a central angle α of the circle whose radian measure is $v - u$.

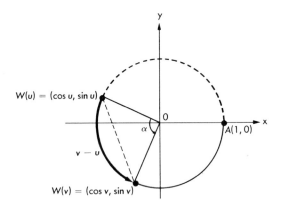

FIGURE 8-11

We can follow the method used in proving the law of cosines to show that the distance d between points $W(u)$ and $W(v)$ can be given by the equation

$$d^2 = 1^2 + 1^2 - (2 \cdot 1 \cdot 1 \cdot \cos \alpha)$$
$$= 2 - 2 \cos \alpha.$$

Since α has radian measure $v - u$, we have proved that

$$d^2 = 2 - 2 \cos (v - u).$$

On the other hand, we can compute the distance between $W(u)$ and $W(v)$ by using the distance formula.

$$
\begin{aligned}
d^2 &= (\cos v - \cos u)^2 + (\sin v - \sin u)^2 \\
&= \cos^2 v - 2 \cos v \cos u + \cos^2 u \\
&\quad + \sin^2 v - 2 \sin v \sin u + \sin^2 u \\
&= (\sin^2 u + \cos^2 u) + (\sin^2 v + \cos^2 v) \\
&\quad - 2(\cos v \cos u + \sin v \sin u) \\
&= 1 + 1 - 2(\cos v \cos u + \sin v \sin u)
\end{aligned}
$$

We now have two different formulas for the distance between points $W(u)$ and $W(v)$ which we combine to obtain the equation

$$ 2 - 2 \cos (v - u) = 2 - 2(\cos v \cos u + \sin v \sin u). $$

By simplifying, we obtain the first *addition formula* of trigonometry.

FIRST ADDITION FORMULA

$$ \cos (v - u) = \cos v \cos u + \sin v \sin u $$

Although the first addition formula was proved on the assumption that $0 < u < v < 2\pi$, it can be shown that it is true for all values of u and v. Although we have used the term *radian measure* in the proof of the first addition formula, the formula continues to be true if we think of u and v as the degree measure of angles.

The following problem indicates how the first addition formula can be used to find the cosine of certain angles and numbers.

Problem 1. Find $\cos 15°$.

Solution. Because $15 = 45 - 30$ and we know the sine and cosine of angles of measure $45°$ and $30°$, we can use the first addition formula to find $\cos 15°$.

$$ \cos 15° = \cos 45° \cos 30° + \sin 45° \sin 30° $$

We substitute the known values of the sine and cosine of $45°$ and $30°$ and obtain

$$ \cos 15° = \left(\frac{\sqrt{2}}{2} \cdot \frac{\sqrt{3}}{2} \right) + \left(\frac{\sqrt{2}}{2} \cdot \frac{1}{2} \right), $$

or

$$\cos 15° = \tfrac{1}{4}(\sqrt{6} + \sqrt{2}).$$

This is the exact value of cos 15°. Using the Table of Square Roots, we obtain

$$\sqrt{6} \doteq 2.449$$

and

$$\sqrt{2} \doteq 1.414.$$

Hence

$$\cos 15° \doteq \tfrac{1}{4}(3.863), \text{ or } .966.$$

Does this result agree with the entry in the Table of Values of Trigonometric Functions?

The addition formulas given below can be derived from the first addition formula. However instead of including the proofs, we shall outline them in the exercises.

SECOND, THIRD, AND FOURTH ADDITION FORMULAS

$$cos \ (v + u) = cos \ v \ cos \ u \ - \ sin \ v \ sin \ u$$
$$sin \ (v - u) = sin \ v \ cos \ u \ - \ cos \ v \ sin \ u$$
$$sin \ (v + u) = sin \ v \ cos \ u \ + \ cos \ v \ sin \ u$$

Problem 2. Find $\sin \dfrac{11\pi}{12}$.

Solution. Since

$$\frac{11\pi}{12} = \frac{2\pi}{3} + \frac{\pi}{4},$$

$$\sin \frac{11\pi}{12} = \sin \left(\frac{2\pi}{3} + \frac{\pi}{4}\right)$$

$$= \sin \frac{2\pi}{3} \cos \frac{\pi}{4} + \cos \frac{2\pi}{3} \sin \frac{\pi}{4}$$

$$= \left(\frac{\sqrt{3}}{2} \cdot \frac{\sqrt{2}}{2}\right) + \left(-\frac{1}{2} \cdot \frac{\sqrt{2}}{2}\right)$$

$$= \frac{1}{4} (\sqrt{6} - \sqrt{2}).$$

Exercises

Find the exact value of each of the following.

1. $\sin 15°$ **2.** $\tan 15°$ **3.** $\sin 75°$ **4.** $\cos 75°$

5. $\tan 75°$ **6.** $\tan 195°$ **7.** $\cos \dfrac{7\pi}{12}$ **8.** $\tan \dfrac{7\pi}{12}$

9. $\tan \dfrac{29\pi}{12}$ **10.** $\tan 105°$

If $\sin u = \frac{3}{5}$ and $\cos v = \frac{5}{13}$, with $\pi/2 < u < \pi$ and $0 < v < \pi/2$, find each of the following.

11. $\cos (u + v)$ **12.** $\sin (u + v)$ **13.** $\tan (u + v)$

If $\sec u = \frac{25}{7}$, $\tan u < 0$, $\tan v = -\frac{4}{3}$, and $\sin v > 0$, find each of the following.

14. $\cos (u - v)$ **15.** $\sin (u - v)$ **16.** $\tan (u - v)$

Given that $\csc u = \frac{7}{3}$, $\cos u < 0$, $\tan v = -\frac{3}{2}$, and $\cos v > 0$, find each of the following.

17. $\sin (u - v)$ **18.** $\cos (u - v)$ **19.** $\tan (u - v)$

Use the addition formulas to simplify each of the following.

20. $\cos \left(\dfrac{3\pi}{2} - u \right)$ **21.** $\sin (2\pi - u)$

22. $\tan (\pi - u)$ **23.** $\cos \left(u + \dfrac{3\pi}{2} \right)$

Prove each of the following identities.

24. $\cos (u + v) \cos (u - v) = \cos^2 u - \sin^2 v$

25. $\sin (u + v) \sin (u - v) = \sin^2 u - \sin^2 v$

8–5   DOUBLE-ANGLE AND HALF-ANGLE FORMULAS

If in the second addition formula we let $u = v$, we then obtain the equation

$$\cos (v + v) = \cos v \cos v - \sin v \sin v,$$

which is equivalent to the equation below.

FIRST DOUBLE-ANGLE FORMULA

$$\cos 2v = \cos^2 v - \sin^2 v$$

If we know $\cos v$ and $\sin v$, we can use the first double-angle formula, to find $\cos 2v$. The second double-angle formula can be derived from the fourth addition formula.

SECOND DOUBLE-ANGLE FORMULA

$$\checkmark \quad \sin 2v = 2 \sin v \cos v$$

Problem 1. Given that $0 < v < \pi/2$ and that $\sin v = \frac{5}{6}$, find $\sin 2v$ and $\cos 2v$.

Solution. Before we can use the first and second double-angle formulas, we must find $\cos v$. By the first fundamental identity,

$$\sin^2 v + \cos^2 v = 1.$$

Then

$$\cos^2 v = 1 - \sin^2 v = 1 - (\tfrac{5}{6})^2, \quad \text{or} \quad \tfrac{11}{36}.$$

Hence

$$\cos v = \frac{\sqrt{11}}{6} \quad \text{or} \quad \cos v = -\frac{\sqrt{11}}{6}.$$

However, since $0 < v < \pi/2$, $\cos v > 0$. Thus $\cos v = \sqrt{11}/6$. Now we can use the double-angle formulas to obtain

$$\sin 2v = 2 \cdot \frac{5}{6} \cdot \frac{\sqrt{11}}{6}, \quad \text{or} \quad \frac{5\sqrt{11}}{18},$$

$$\cos 2v = \left(\frac{\sqrt{11}}{6}\right)^2 - \left(\frac{5}{6}\right)^2,$$

$$\cos 2v = \frac{11}{36} - \frac{25}{36}, \quad \text{or} \quad -\frac{14}{36}, \quad \text{or} \quad -\frac{7}{18}.$$

Two different forms of the first double-angle formula can be obtained by using the first fundamental identity. Thus if we replace $\cos^2 v$ by $1 - \sin^2 v$ in the first double-angle formula, we get

$$\cos 2v = 1 - 2 \sin^2 v. \tag{1}$$

If we replace $\sin^2 v$ by $1 - \cos^2 v$, we get

$$\cos 2v = 2 \cos^2 v - 1. \tag{2}$$

Formulas (1) and (2) can be solved for $\sin^2 v$ and $\cos^2 v$, respectively:

$$\sin^2 v = \tfrac{1}{2}(1 - \cos 2v),$$
$$\cos^2 v = \tfrac{1}{2}(1 + \cos 2v).$$

If we let $u = 2v$ so $v = u/2$ in the identities above, then we obtain the *half-angle formulas* below.

FIRST AND SECOND HALF-ANGLE FORMULAS

$$\cos^2 \frac{u}{2} = \frac{1}{2}(1 + \cos u)$$

$$\sin^2 \frac{u}{2} = \frac{1}{2}(1 - \cos u)$$

If we know $\cos u$ and the quadrant in which $W(u/2)$ lies, we can use the first and second half-angle formulas to find $\sin u/2$ and $\cos u/2$, as illustrated in Problem 2.

Problem 2. Find the sine and cosine of $5\pi/8$.

Solution. If we let $u = 5\pi/4$,

$$\sin^2 \frac{5\pi}{8} = \frac{1}{2}\left(1 - \cos \frac{5\pi}{4}\right)$$
$$= \frac{1}{2}\left(1 - \left(-\frac{\sqrt{2}}{2}\right)\right)$$
$$= \frac{1}{4}(2 + \sqrt{2}).$$

Since $W(5\pi/8)$ is in the second quadrant and the sine is positive in this quadrant,

$$\sin \frac{5\pi}{8} = \frac{1}{2}\sqrt{2 + \sqrt{2}}.$$

Similarly,

$$\cos^2 \frac{5\pi}{8} = \frac{1}{4}(2 - \sqrt{2})$$

and

$$\cos \frac{5\pi}{8} = -\frac{1}{2}\sqrt{2 - \sqrt{2}},$$

since the cosine is negative in the second quadrant.

Exercises

Given that $\sin u = \frac{5}{13}$ and $\pi/2 < u < \pi$, evaluate each trigonometric function in Exercises 1–4.

1. $\cos u$ 2. $\sin 2u$

3. $\tan 2u$ 4. $\sin \frac{u}{2}$

Given that $\cos u = \frac{3}{5}$ and $0 < u < \pi/2$, evaluate each of the following.

5. $\sin u$ 6. $\tan u$

7. $\sin 2u$ 8. $\cos 2u$

9. $\tan 2u$ 10. $\sin \frac{u}{2}$

11. $\cos \frac{u}{2}$ 12. $\tan \frac{u}{2}$

Given that $\tan u = \frac{24}{7}$ and $\sin u < 0$, evaluate each of the following.

13. $\sin u$ 14. $\cos u$ 15. $\cos 2u$ 16. $\tan \frac{u}{2}$

Given that $\sec u = \frac{7}{5}$ and $\tan u < 0$, evaluate each trigonometric function in Exercises 17–19.

17. $\sin u$ 18. $\tan 2u$ 19. $\tan \frac{u}{2}$

20. Use the half-angle formulas to find the values of the six trigonometric functions of the angle with measure $15°$.

8–6 TRIGONOMETRIC EQUATIONS

An equation that involves trigonometric functions, such as

$$2 \sin^2 x - \sin x - 1 = 0,$$

is called a *trigonometric equation*. If this trigonometric equation has any solutions, then it has infinitely many, since the trigonometric functions are all periodic. Therefore in solving such an equation, we shall seek the solutions in one period of the functions involved unless we are instructed otherwise.

Problem 1. Solve the equation $2 \sin^2 x - \sin x - 1 = 0$.

Solution. Let us find every number x, with $0 \leq x < 2\pi$, for which this equation is true. Basically, the given equation is quadratic in $\sin x$:

$$2(\sin x)^2 - (\sin x) - 1 = 0.$$

In other words, it has the same form as the quadratic equation

$$2y^2 - y - 1 = 0.$$

We solve these two equations side by side to illustrate that the method is the same.

$$2y^2 - y - 1 = 0 \qquad 2\sin^2 x - \sin x - 1 = 0$$
$$(2y + 1)(y - 1) = 0 \qquad (2\sin x + 1)(\sin x - 1) = 0$$

The solution set of each of these equations is given below.

$$\{y \mid 2y + 1 = 0\} \cup \{y \mid y - 1 = 0\}$$
$$\{-\tfrac{1}{2}\} \cup \{1\}, \quad \text{or} \quad \{-\tfrac{1}{2}, 1\}$$
$$\{x \mid 2\sin x + 1 = 0\} \cup \{x \mid \sin x - 1 = 0\}$$
$$\{x \mid \sin x = -\tfrac{1}{2}\} \cup \{x \mid \sin x = 1\}$$

For $0 \leq x < 2\pi$, the equation

$$\sin x = -\frac{1}{2} \quad \text{has solution set} \quad \left\{\pi + \frac{\pi}{6}, \; 2\pi - \frac{\pi}{6}\right\},$$

and the equation

$$\sin x = 1 \quad \text{has solution set} \quad \left\{\frac{\pi}{2}\right\}.$$

Hence $\{\pi/2, 7\pi/6, 11\pi/6\}$ is the solution set of the given trigonometric equation in one period of the sine.

Problem 2. Solve the equation $\sin^2 x = 1 + 2\cos x$.

Solution. We can obtain an equivalent equation containing only cosines by replacing $\sin^2 x$ by $1 - \cos^2 x$, according to the first fundamental identity.

$$1 - \cos^2 x = 1 + 2\cos x$$

This equation is equivalent in turn to each of the following.

$$-\cos^2 x = 2\cos x$$
$$0 = \cos^2 x + 2\cos x$$
$$0 = \cos x(\cos x + 2)$$

Hence the solution set of the given equation is

$$\{x \mid \cos x = 0\} \cup \{x \mid \cos x + 2 = 0\}.$$

Since $-1 \leq \cos x \leq 1$ for every x, the equation $\cos x + 2 = 0$ has solution set $\emptyset$. Thus the solution set is

$$\{x \mid \cos x = 0\}.$$

If $0 \leq x < 2\pi$, then the solution set is $\{\pi/2, 3\pi/2\}$.

Exercises

Solve each of the following trigonometric equations for $0 \leq x < 2\pi$.

1. $\sin x = \frac{1}{2}$

2. $2 \sin^2 x - 5 \sin x - 3 = 0$

3. $4 \sin^2 x = 3$

4. $\cos 2x = 1$

5. $4 \sin x \cos x = 1$

6. $3 \cos 4x = 5$

7. $2 \cos \left(x + \frac{\pi}{3}\right) = 1$

8. $2 \tan x = 1 - \tan^2 x$

9. $2 \cos x = -\sqrt{3}$

10. $\tan^2 x = 1$

11. $\tan^2 x - 3 \tan x + 2 = 0$

12. $\cos^2 x - 1 = 2 \sin x$

13. $\cos x - 2 \sin^2 x + 1 = 0$

14. $2 \sin 3x = 1$

8–7 GRAPHS OF THE TRIGONOMETRIC FUNCTIONS

Every reader of this book has probably seen a *sine curve*, either on the screen of an oscilloscope or in some related way. In this section, we shall sketch the sine curve and the other trigonometric curves.

Because of the periodicity of the sine and cosine, we need graph each function only over one period in order to be able to describe its graph completely. Actually, since

$$\sin (\pi + s) = -\sin s,$$

the graph of the sine from π to 2π is the "negative" of its graph from 0 to π. The same is true for the cosine. Thus we can get a rough idea of the graph of the sine function from the short table of values below.

x	0	$\dfrac{\pi}{6}$	$\dfrac{\pi}{3}$	$\dfrac{\pi}{2}$	$\dfrac{2\pi}{3}$	$\dfrac{5\pi}{6}$	π
$\sin x$	0	$\dfrac{1}{2}$	$\dfrac{\sqrt{3}}{2}$	1	$\dfrac{\sqrt{3}}{2}$	$\dfrac{1}{2}$	0

We have sketched the graph of the sine function from -3π to 3π in Fig. 8–12, using this table and our remarks above.

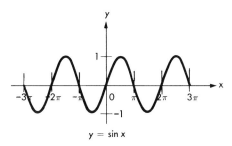

$$y = \sin x$$

FIGURE 8-12

The *cosine curve* is often described as being "90° out of phase" with the sine curve. Thus if we move the sine curve of Fig. 8–12 a distance of $\pi/2$ units (equivalent to 90°) to the left, the resulting curve is the graph of the cosine function. We can see that this is so by using the fourth addition formula, and letting $v = x$ and $u = \pi/2$.

$$\sin\left(x + \frac{\pi}{2}\right) = \sin x \cos \frac{\pi}{2} + \cos x \sin \frac{\pi}{2}$$

$$= \sin x \cdot 0 + \cos x \cdot 1$$

Hence

$$\cos x = \sin\left(x + \frac{\pi}{2}\right).$$

The cosine curve is sketched in Fig. 8–13.

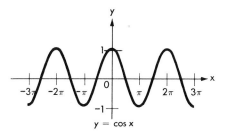

$$y = \cos x$$

FIGURE 8-13

The tangent function has a smaller period than either the sine or the cosine. Because

$$\tan x = \tan (x + \pi)$$

for every real number x, and π is the smallest positive number for which such an equation is true, the period of the tangent function is π. If we recall that the range of the tangent function is the set of all real numbers, then we realize that the graph of the tangent function is unbounded. The graph consists of an infinite number of branches, which are all alike. One of these branches occurs between $x = -\pi/2$ and $x = \pi/2$.

The lines $x = \pi/2$, $x = 3\pi/2$, $x = -\pi/2$, $x = -3\pi/2$, and so on, are called *asymptotes* of the graph. We have sketched the graph in Fig. 8–14, using the Table of Values of Trigonometric Functions. Since

$$\text{secant } x = \frac{1}{\text{cosine } x},$$

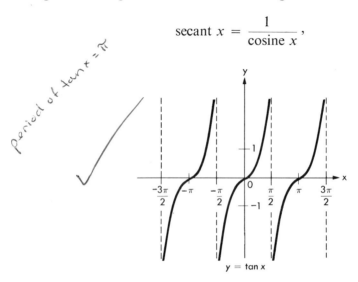

FIGURE 8–14

the domain of the secant is the set

$$\{x \mid \cos x \neq 0\} = \left\{x \mid x \neq \frac{2n + 1}{2}\pi, \, n \text{ an integer}\right\}.$$

Also, since $|\cos x| \leq 1$, we have $|\sec x| \geq 1$ for every number x in its domain. In fact, the range of secant is the set

$$\{y \mid y \geq 1\} \cup \{y \mid y \leq -1\}.$$

We can graph the secant from the cosine by taking reciprocals of ordinates. For every point (a, b) on the graph of the cosine, with $b \neq 0$, the point $(a, 1/b)$ is on the graph of the secant. Thus as $|b|$ gets closer to zero, $|1/b|$ gets larger. In other words, the vertical lines $x = (2n + 1)\pi/2$, $n = 0, \pm1, \pm2, \ldots$, are asymptotes of the graph. A sketch of the graph is shown in Fig. 8–15.

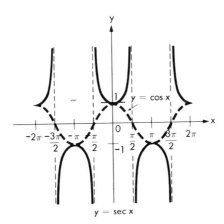

FIGURE 8-15

Exercises

1. On the same set of axes, sketch graphs of each of the following equations.

   (a) $y = \sin x$ (b) $y = -\sin x$ (c) $y = \sin(-x)$

2. On the same set of axes, sketch graphs of each of the following equations.

   (a) $y = \cos x$ (b) $y = 2 \cos x$ (c) $y = 2 + \cos x$

3. Graph the cotangent function.

4. Graph the cosecant function.

Graph each of the following functions by plotting the points obtained by assigning values to x on the interval $-2\pi \leqq x \leqq 2\pi$.

5. $y = \frac{1}{2} \sin x$ 6. $y = \frac{1}{3} \cos x$ 7. $y = -3 \cos x$

8. $y = -\frac{3}{5} \sin x$ 9. $y = \tan(-x)$ 10. $y = \frac{1}{4} \tan x$

8-8 AMPLITUDES AND PERIODS OF TRIGONOMETRIC FUNCTIONS

Equations of the form

$$y = a \sin bx, \quad a \text{ and } b \text{ positive numbers,}$$

are commonplace in the theory of electricity and wave motion. Let us analyze the graph of such an equation by analyzing the function f, defined by

$$f(x) = a \sin bx, \quad a \text{ and } b \text{ positive numbers.}$$

The range of f is the set

$$\{y \mid -a \le y \le a\}.$$

This is so because the range of the sine function is the set

$$\{y \mid -1 \le y \le 1\}.$$

We call a the *amplitude* of the function f. In the same way, we call $|a|$ the amplitude of the functions $a \sin bx$ and $a \cos bx$, whether a is positive or not.

To show that f is periodic, we seek the smallest positive number k such that

$$f(x + k) = f(x) \quad \text{for every number } x.$$

In this case, since $f(x + k) = a \sin [b(x + k)] = a \sin (bx + bk)$, we want to find the smallest positive number k such that

$$\sin (bx + bk) = \sin bx \quad \text{for every number } x.$$

However, the sine function has period 2π. Therefore the smallest positive number bk such that $\sin bx = \sin (bx + bk)$ for every number x is 2π. Hence $bk = 2\pi$ and $k = 2\pi/b$.

In other words, the function f, defined by

$$f(x) = a \sin bx, \ a \text{ and } b \text{ positive numbers,}$$

is periodic with period $2\pi/b$. In the same way, if b is not positive, $a \sin bx$ and $a \cos bx$ are periodic with period $2\pi/|b|$.

Problem 1. Discuss and sketch the graph of the equation

$$y = 2 \sin 3x.$$

Solution. From our remarks above, we know that the function f, defined by

$$f(x) = 2 \sin 3x,$$

has amplitude 2 and period $2\pi/3$. Thus we can sketch its graph from the following table of values. (See Fig. 8–16.)

x	0	$\dfrac{\pi}{18}$	$\dfrac{\pi}{9}$	$\dfrac{\pi}{6}$	$\dfrac{2\pi}{9}$	$\dfrac{5\pi}{18}$	$\dfrac{\pi}{3}$
$2 \sin 3x$	0	1	$\sqrt{3}$	2	$\sqrt{3}$	1	0

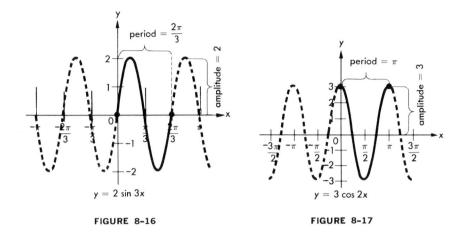

FIGURE 8-16   FIGURE 8-17

Problem 2. Discuss and sketch the graph of the equation

$$y = 3 \cos 2x.$$

Solution. The function g, defined by

$$g(x) = 3 \cos 2x,$$

has amplitude 3 and period $2\pi/2$, or π. Thus we can sketch its graph from the following table of values. (See Fig. 8–17).

x	0	$\dfrac{\pi}{12}$	$\dfrac{\pi}{6}$	$\dfrac{\pi}{4}$	$\dfrac{\pi}{3}$	$\dfrac{5\pi}{12}$	$\dfrac{\pi}{2}$
$3 \cos 2x$	3	$\dfrac{3\sqrt{3}}{2}$	$\dfrac{3}{2}$	0	$-\dfrac{3}{2}$	$\dfrac{-3\sqrt{3}}{2}$	-3

Problem 3. Discuss and sketch the graph of the equation

$$y = 2 \sin 3x + 3 \cos 2x.$$

Solution. The function h, defined by

$$h(x) = 2 \sin 3x + 3 \cos 2x,$$

is simply the sum of the functions f and g, defined in Problems 1 and 2, respectively. Although 2π is not the period of f or g, these functions do repeat their values every 2π. Hence the function h repeats its values every 2π. Therefore the function h is periodic with period less than or equal to 2π. Because the graph of f has three identical pieces in the interval $\{x \mid 0 \leq x \leq 2\pi\}$ and the graph of g has two such pieces in this interval, we can argue that the graph of h

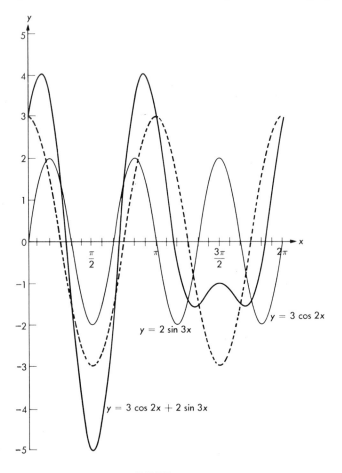

FIGURE 8-18

has the greatest common divisor of two and three pieces, or one identical piece in an interval of 2π. In other words, h has period 2π.

We can construct the graph of h from the graphs of f and g by the method of adding ordinates. This method is illustrated by a few points in the table below. The graph of the function is shown in Fig. 8–18.

x	0	$\dfrac{\pi}{6}$	$\dfrac{\pi}{3}$
$2\sin 3x + 3\cos 2x$	$0 + 3$	$2 + \dfrac{3}{2}$	$0 + \left(-\dfrac{3}{2}\right)$
$h(x)$	3	$\dfrac{7}{2}$	$-\dfrac{3}{2}$

Exercises

Give the period and amplitude of each function, and then graph the function.

1. $y = 4 \sin x$ 2. $y = 3 \sin 2x$

3. $y = -2 \cos 2x$ 4. $y = \sin x/2$

5. $y = |\sin x|$ 6. $y = 2 + \sin x$

7. $y = 2 \sin \pi x$ 8. $y = \frac{1}{2}\cos 2x$

9. $y = \sin(-x)$ 10. $y = -3 \cos x$

11. $y = 4 \cos \dfrac{2x}{3}$ 12. $y = 3 |\cos x|$

13. $y = -2 |\sin x|$ 14. $y = 3 - 3 \cos x$

Give the period of each function and then graph the function.

15. $y = \sin x + \sin 2x$ 16. $y = \sin x + \cos x$

17. $y = \sin 2x + \cos 3x$ 18. $y = \sin x + \cos 2x$

8-9 INVERSE TRIGONOMETRIC FUNCTIONS

For each number x in the interval $I = \{x \mid -1 \leq x \leq 1\}$, there exists an arc $\overset{\frown}{AP}$ of length s, with $0 \leq s \leq \pi$, as shown in Fig. 8–19. Since $x = \cos s$, it is natural to call s the *arc whose cosine is* x and denote s by *arccosine* x.

Definition of Arccosine

arccosine $x = s$, *where* $\cos s = x$ *and* $0 \leq s \leq \pi$

The domain of arccosine is the interval $-1 \leq x \leq 1$.

Similarly, for each number y in $J = \{y \mid -1 \leq y \leq 1\}$, there exists an arc $\overset{\frown}{AP}$ of length s, with $-\pi/2 \leq s \leq \pi/2$, as shown in Fig. 8–20.

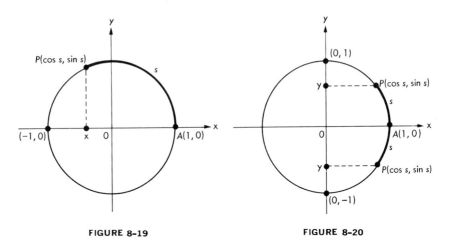

FIGURE 8-19   FIGURE 8-20

The arc $\overset{\frown}{AP}$ is understood to have a positive length if P is above the x-axis and a negative length if P is below the x-axis. Both cases are shown in Fig. 8–20. Since $y = \sin s$ in either case, we call s the *arcsine y*.

Definition of Arcsine

$$arcsine \; y = s, \; where \; \sin s = y \; and \; -\frac{\pi}{2} \leq s \leq \frac{\pi}{2}$$

The domain of arcsine is the interval $-1 \leq y \leq 1.$

In the same way that we abbreviated sine and cosine, we shall abbreviate arccosine to *arccos* and arcsine to *arcsin*.

Problem. Find $\arccos \frac{1}{2}$, $\arcsin 1$, $\arccos\left(-\dfrac{\sqrt{2}}{2}\right)$, and $\arcsin\left(-\dfrac{\sqrt{3}}{2}\right)$.

Solution. Since

$$\cos \frac{\pi}{3} = \frac{1}{2} \; \text{and} \; 0 \leq \frac{\pi}{3} \leq \pi, \; \arccos \frac{1}{2} = \frac{\pi}{3}.$$

Since

$$\sin \frac{\pi}{2} = 1 \; \text{and} \; -\frac{\pi}{2} \leq \frac{\pi}{2} \leq \frac{\pi}{2}, \; \arcsin 1 = \frac{\pi}{2}.$$

Since

$$\cos \frac{3\pi}{4} = -\frac{\sqrt{2}}{2} \text{ and } 0 \leq \frac{3\pi}{4} \leq \pi, \text{ arccos} \left(-\frac{\sqrt{2}}{2}\right) = \frac{3\pi}{4}.$$

Since

$$\sin\left(-\frac{\pi}{3}\right) = -\frac{\sqrt{3}}{2} \text{ and } -\frac{\pi}{2} \leq -\frac{\pi}{3} \leq \frac{\pi}{2}, \text{ arcsin}\left(-\frac{\sqrt{3}}{2}\right) = -\frac{\pi}{3}.$$

The cosine and arccosine functions are related to each other by the following equations.

$$cos \ (arccos \ x) \ = \ x \ for \ every \ number \ x \ in \ \{x \mid -1 \leq x \leq 1\}$$
$$arccos \ (cos \ s) \ = \ s \ for \ every \ number \ s \ in \ \{s \mid 0 \leq s \leq \pi\}$$

If f and g are functions defined by

$$f(s) = \cos s, \text{ domain } f = \{s \mid 0 \leq s \leq \pi\},$$
$$g(x) = \text{arccos } x, \text{ domain } g = \{x \mid -1 \leq x \leq 1\},$$

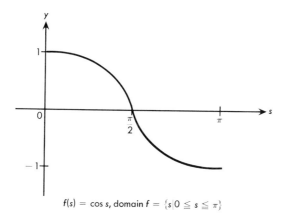

$f(s) = \cos s, \text{ domain } f = \{s \mid 0 \leq s \leq \pi\}$

FIGURE 8-21

then

$$f(g(x)) = x, \quad g(f(s)) = s$$

for all x in domain g and s in domain f, by these equations. Hence f and g are *inverse functions.*
It is important to realize f is *not the cosine function,* since the domain of f is $\{s \mid 0 \leq s \leq \pi\}$ whereas the domain of cosine is the set of all real numbers. However, f and cosine have the same values over the domain of f. The graphs of f and g are shown in Figs. 8–21 and 8–22. The sine and arcsine functions satisfy similar equations:

$\sin(\arcsin y) = y$ for every number y in $\{y \mid -1 \le y \le 1\}$,

$\arcsin(\sin s) = s$ for every number s in $\left\{s \mid -\dfrac{\pi}{2} \le s \le \dfrac{\pi}{2}\right\}$.

Therefore if we define functions f and g by

$$f(s) = \sin s,$$
$$\text{domain } f = \left\{s \mid -\frac{\pi}{2} \le s \le \frac{\pi}{2}\right\},$$

$$g(y) = \arcsin y,$$
$$\text{domain } g = \{y \mid -1 \le y \le 1\},$$

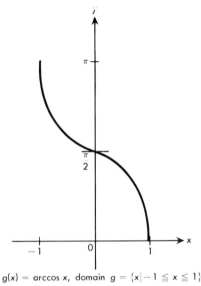

$g(x) = \arccos x$, domain $g = \{x \mid -1 \le x \le 1\}$

FIGURE 8-22

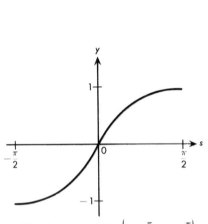

$f(s) = \sin s$, domain $f = \left\{s \mid -\dfrac{\pi}{2} \le s \le \dfrac{\pi}{2}\right\}$

FIGURE 8-23

$g(y) = \arcsin y$, domain $g = \{y \mid -1 \le y \le 1\}$

FIGURE 8-24

the functions f and g are *inverses* of each other. These functions are graphed in Figs. 8–23 and 8–24.

Each trigonometric function has an arc-function defined in a way similar to those above. For example, we have the following definition of arctangent.

Definition of Arctangent

$$\textit{arctan } x = y, \textbf{ where tan } y = x \textbf{ and } -\frac{\pi}{2} < y < \frac{\pi}{2}$$

The domain of arctangent is the set R of all real numbers.

For example,

$$\arctan 1 = \frac{\pi}{4}$$

since

$$\tan \frac{\pi}{4} = 1$$

and

$$-\frac{\pi}{2} < \frac{\pi}{4} < \frac{\pi}{2}.$$

Also,

$$\arctan (-\sqrt{3}) = -\frac{\pi}{3}$$

since

$$\tan \left(-\frac{\pi}{3}\right) = -\sqrt{3}$$

and

$$-\frac{\pi}{2} < -\frac{\pi}{3} < \frac{\pi}{2}.$$

The graph of the arctangent function is the graph of the equation

$$x = \tan y, \quad -\frac{\pi}{2} < y < \frac{\pi}{2},$$

as shown in Fig. 8–25.

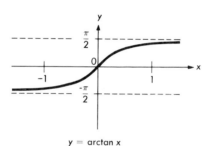

y = arctan x

FIGURE 8-25

Exercises

Find each of the following. Use the Table of Values of Trigonometric Functions, if necessary.

1. $\arcsin \dfrac{\sqrt{3}}{2}$

2. $\arctan (-\sqrt{2})$

3. $\arccos (-1)$

4. $\arctan \sqrt{3}$

5. arcsin 0

6. arcsin $\frac{3}{5}$

7. arccos $\left(-\frac{4}{5}\right)$

8. arctan $\left(-\frac{5}{12}\right)$

Find arctan (tan s) for each given number s.

9. $s = \dfrac{\pi}{4}$

10. $s = \dfrac{5\pi}{4}$

11. $s = -\dfrac{7\pi}{4}$

12. $s = -\dfrac{3\pi}{4}$

13. $s = -\dfrac{\pi}{4}$

Evaluate each of the following.

14. sin (arctan -1)

15. csc (arcsin $\frac{1}{2}$)

16. cot (arccos $-\frac{3}{5}$)

17. tan (arcsin $\frac{7}{25}$)

CHAPTER REVIEW

In Exercises 1–4, $\triangle ABC$ has sides of lengths a, b, and c with opposite angles α, β, and γ.

1. Find c, given that $a = 3$, $b = 2$, $\gamma = 120°$.

2. Find α, given that $a = 5$, $b = 7$, $c = 8$.

3. Find a, given that $\alpha = 30°$, $\beta = 105°$, $c = 10$.

4. Find the area of the triangle in Exercise 1.

If $\sin u = \frac{2}{7}$ and $\cos v = \frac{7}{11}$, with $\pi/2 < u < \pi$ and $0 < v < \pi/2$, find each of the following.

5. cos $(u - v)$

6. sin $(u - v)$

7. tan $(u - v)$

If $\cos u = \frac{3}{10}$, tan $u < 0$, tan $v = -\frac{10}{17}$, and sin $v > 0$, find each of the following.

8. sin $(u + v)$

9. cos $(u + v)$

10. tan $(u + v)$

Use the half-angle formulas to find the sine, cosine, and tangent of each of the following.

11. $\dfrac{\pi}{8}$

12. $\dfrac{3\pi}{8}$

Use the double-angle formulas to find the sine, cosine, and tangent of each of the following.

13. $\dfrac{2\pi}{3}$

14. $\dfrac{5\pi}{3}$

Given $\cos v = -\frac{2}{3}$, with $\pi/2 < v < \pi$, find each of the following.

15. $\sin 2v$ **16.** $\tan \frac{1}{2}v$

Simplify each of the following expressions.

17. $\dfrac{\cos 2x}{\cos x + \sin x}$ **18.** $\sin x \cos 2x + \cos x \sin 2x$

19. $\sin 2x \tan x + \cos 2x$ **20.** $2 \sin^2 \dfrac{x}{2} + \cos x$

For each of the following, find the solution set which lies within the interval $0 \leqq x < 2\pi$.

21. $2 \sin^2 x - 5 \sin x - 3 = 0$

22. $\cos^2 x - 2 \cos x = 0$

23. $\sec^2 x - \tan x = 1$

State the period and amplitude of each of the following functions and draw the graph.

24. $f(x) = 5 \sin 4x$ **25.** $g(x) = 3 \cos 2x$ **26.** $h(x) = 3(1 + \cos 2x)$

Find each of the following.

27. $\arcsin \frac{3}{2}$

28. $\arccos \left(-\frac{1}{2} \right)$

29. $\arctan (-1)$

30. $\arcsin \left(-\frac{1}{2} \right)$

31. $\arccos (-1)$

32. $\tan \left[\arccos \left(-\frac{3}{7} \right) \right]$

33. $\sec \left[\arcsin \left(-\frac{1}{2} \right) \right]$

34. $\cot \left[\text{arccot} (-1) \right]$

In Exercises 35–38, prove each identity.

35. $\csc 2\theta + \cot 2\theta = \cot \theta$

36. $\dfrac{2 \tan \theta}{1 + \tan^2 \theta} = \sin 2\theta$

37. $\cos^4 u - \sin^4 u = \cos 2u$

38. $\dfrac{2 \sin^2 u - 1}{\sin u \cos u} = \tan u - \cot u$

In Exercises 39 and 40, show that each equation is true.

39. $\arctan 2 - \arctan 1 = \arctan \frac{1}{3}$

40. $\arcsin \frac{4}{5} = \pi - 2 \arctan 2$

41. City B is due north of City A. To fly from city A to city B, one must take a plane from city A to city C, which is 50° east of north from A at a distance of 150 miles, and then fly 200 miles to city B. How far due north is City B from City A?

42. A parallelogram has two sides of lengths 50 and 100. One angle of the parallelogram has measure 120°. Find the length of the longer diagonal and the angle made by this diagonal and the longer side.

9 · Complex Numbers

9–1 COMPLEX NUMBERS

In Chapter 1 we defined the nth root of a real number and noted that, while every positive real number has an nth root, whatever the positive integer n, negative numbers do not have nth roots when n is an even integer. Thus -1 has no real square root, since any potential candidate would have to have its square equal to the negative number -1, and we know that the square of a real number is never negative.

In this chapter we shall extend the real number to a larger system of numbers systems by introducing a new number, i, with the property that $i^2 = -1$.*

The fact that $i^2 = -1$ suggests that one writes

$$i = \sqrt{-1}$$

and call i, "a square root of -1."

Using i, we can now write numbers representing the square root of other negative numbers. For example, we write $\sqrt{-4} = 2i$ and, more generally, for r any positive number, we define

$$\sqrt{-r} = \sqrt{r}\, i$$

where $\sqrt{r}$ is the positive real square root of the positive number r.

---

*The symbol i was introduced into mathematics by the famous eighteenth century Swiss mathematician Euler (pronounced "Oiler"). It is possible that he chose i because it is the first letter of the Latin word *imaginarius* (imaginary).

Note that if we agree to allow rearrangement properties of multiplication and consider the number $2i$ as the real number 2 times i, we would have, upon applying the definition of "square root," $(2i)(2i) = 2 \cdot 2 \cdot i \cdot i$, or $4i^2$, that is, $4(-1)$, or -4 as verification of the statement $\sqrt{-4} = 2i$.

We also want to be able to combine these new numbers with the real numbers under addition, for example, to write $3 + 2i$ as the symbol for a number. In general, we wish to define a set of new numbers, $a + bi$, where a and b are real numbers. If we agree that $0i$ is to behave exactly as the real number 0, then a number of the form $a + 0i$ will be merely a new name for the real number a and we will agree that a number of the form $0 + bi$ is simply the number bi.

Definition

Numbers of the form $a + bi$, where a and b are real numbers and $i^2 = -1$, are called complex numbers. It is customary to call a the real part and bi the pure imaginary part of the complex number $a + bi$.

Two complex numbers are said to be equal if, and only if, their real parts are equal and their imaginary parts are equal. That is,

$$a + bi = c + di \qquad \text{if, and only if,} \qquad a = c \quad \text{and} \quad b = d.$$

In particular, $a + bi = 0$ if, and only if, $a = 0$ and $b = 0$ since the real number 0 may be written as $0 + 0i$.

We define the sum of two complex numbers with the familiar basic axioms for real numbers in mind.

Thus,

$$(3 + 4i) + (-7 + 3i) = [3 + (-7)] + (4i + 3i) = -4 + 7i.$$

More generally, we define

$$(a + bi) + (c + di) = (a + c) + (b + d)i.$$

You can easily check that under this definition, addition of complex numbers is commutative and associative. Since the sum of $-a + (-b)i$ and $(a + bi)$ is $0 + 0i$ or 0, we call $-a + (-b)i$ the *negative* of the complex number $a + bi$ and define subtraction by

$$
\begin{aligned}
(a + bi) - (c + di) &= (a + bi) + [-(c + di)] \\
&= (a + bi) + [-c + (-d)i] \\
&= (a - c) + (b - d)i.
\end{aligned}
$$

So far, our definitions are reminiscent of the corresponding definitions made for adding and subtracting polynomials $a + bx$ and $c + dx$.
We proceed next to the problem of finding the product of two complex
numbers. Assuming the distributive axiom and rearrangement properties
to be valid, we compute the product of $3 + 4i$ and $-7 + 3i$ in the following way.

$$
\begin{aligned}
(3 + 4i)(-7 + 3i) &= 3(-7 + 3i) + 4i(-7 + 3i) \\
&= -21 + 9i + (-28)i + 12i^2 \\
&= -21 + 9i - 28i + 12(-1) \\
&= (-21 - 12) + (9i - 28i) \\
&= -33 + (-19)i
\end{aligned}
$$

Similarly,

$$
\begin{aligned}
(a + bi)(c + di) &= a(c + di) + bi(c + di) \\
&= ac + adi + bci + bdi^2 \\
&= ac + adi + bci + bd(-1) \\
&= (ac - bd) + (ad + bc)i.
\end{aligned}
$$

That is, the product of two complex numbers is again a complex
number and the set of complex numbers is closed under multiplication
(as well as addition and subtraction).

In practice, we do not try to keep in mind the form of the product
complex number just defined. Instead we multiply complex numbers
in the same way that we would multiply two linear *polynomials in i* but
then use the fact that i^2 in the resulting form is just the real number -1.

Problem 1. If $r = 3 + 4i$ and $s = -5 + 7i$, find $r + s$, $r - s$, rs.

Solution. $r + s = (3 + 4i) + (-5 + 7i) = -2 + 11i$
$r - s = (3 + 4i) - (-5 + 7i) = 8 - 3i$
$rs = (3 + 4i)(-5 + 7i) = -15 + (21 - 20)i + 28i^2$
$\qquad = -15 + i - 28 = -43 + i$

Exercises

1. Write each of the following using the symbol i.

    (a) $\sqrt{-16}$ (b) $\sqrt{-7}$ (c) $\sqrt{-32}$

2. Find the negative of each of the following complex numbers.

    (a) $-2 + 3i$ (b) $4i$ (c) $\sqrt{5}i$ (d) -5

3. The real number 5 has two real square roots $\sqrt{5}$ and $-\sqrt{5}$. Write the complex numbers $\sqrt{-5}$ and $-\sqrt{-5}$ using the symbol i.

Using complex numbers, we see that if $r \neq 0$ is any real number, then r has two square roots, namely $\sqrt{r}$ and $-\sqrt{r}$, which are complex numbers if $r < 0$. Thus, there are two numbers x for which $x^2 = -4$, namely $x = 2i$ and $x = -2i$. Use this fact to do the following Exercises 4–7.

Find the solution set of each of the following equations allowing complex numbers as solutions.

4. $x^2 = -20$ **5.** $x^2 + 9 = 0$

6. $(x - 1)^2 = -4$ **7.** $(x + 3)^2 + 16 = 0$

Perform the indicated operations in the following exercises. In each exercise, state the real part and the pure imaginary part of the complex number.

8. (a) $(-7 + 2i) + (7 - 6i)$ (b) $(3 + i) - 7$

9. (a) $(2 + 3i) + (5 + i)$ (b) $(2 + 3i) + (2 - 3i)$

10. (a) $(2 + 7i) - (3 + 4i) + (7 - 6i)$
     (b) $(5 + 3i) - (6 + 2i) + (9 - 4i)$

11. (a) $(\sqrt{2} - i)^2$ (b) $(-1 + \sqrt{3}i)^2$

12. (a) $(2 - \sqrt{5}i)^2 - 4(2 - \sqrt{5}i) + 9$

     (b) $\left(\dfrac{\sqrt{3}}{2} + \dfrac{1}{2}i\right)^3$

13. Find the value of the quadratic polynomial $x^2 - 4x + 7$ for each of the given values of x.

    (a) $x = 2 + \sqrt{3}i$ (b) $x = -4 - 3i$

14. Find the value of the quadratic polynomial $x^2 + x + 1$ for each of the given values of x.

    (a) $x = -1 + i$ (b) $x = -\frac{1}{2} + \frac{1}{2}\sqrt{3}i$
    (c) $x = -\frac{1}{2} - \frac{1}{2}\sqrt{3}i$ (d) $x = \frac{1}{2} - \frac{1}{2}\sqrt{3}i$
    (e) $x = \frac{1}{2} + \frac{1}{2}\sqrt{3}i$ (f) $x = \frac{1}{3} + \frac{2}{3}i$

15. (a) Square and simplify $\left(\dfrac{\sqrt{2}}{2} + \dfrac{\sqrt{2}}{2}i\right)^2$.

    (b) Find the complex numbers that are solutions of the equation $x^2 = i$.
    (c) Find two solutions of the equation $x^2 = -i$.

9–2 QUOTIENTS OF COMPLEX NUMBERS

The two complex numbers $3 + 4i$ and $3 - 4i$ are said to be *conjugates* of each other. We note that

$$(3 + 4i) + (3 - 4i) = 6$$
$$(3 + 4i) \cdot (3 - 4i) = (9 + 16) + (-12 + 12)i$$
$$= 25.$$

Every complex number $a + bi$ has a *conjugate:* $a - bi$. You can easily verify that

$$(a + bi) + (a - bi) = 2a,$$
$$(a + bi) \cdot (a - bi) = a^2 + b^2.$$

Thus, the sum of a complex number and its conjugate is a real number, and their product is also a real number.

We saw that 25 is the product of $3 + 4i$ and its conjugate $3 - 4i$. Therefore, it follows that 1 is the product of $3 + 4i$ and $\frac{1}{25}(3 - 4i)$, as shown below.

$$(3 + 4i)[\tfrac{1}{25}(3 - 4i)] = \tfrac{1}{25}[(3 + 4i)(3 - 4i)]$$
$$= \tfrac{1}{25}(25), \quad \text{or } 1$$

Thus,

$$\tfrac{1}{25}(3 - 4i), \quad \text{or } \tfrac{3}{25} - \tfrac{4}{25}i,$$

is the *reciprocal* of $3 + 4i$. We indicate this in the usual way:

$$\frac{1}{3 + 4i} = \frac{3}{25} - \frac{4}{25} i.$$

We can find the reciprocal of every nonzero complex number in the same way. If $a + bi \neq 0$, so that either a or b is nonzero, then $a^2 + b^2 > 0$, and

$$(a + bi)\left[\frac{1}{a^2 + b^2} (a - bi)\right] = 1,$$

according to the formula for the product of a complex number and its conjugate. Hence, the reciprocal of $a + bi$ is

$$\frac{1}{a + bi} = \frac{a}{a^2 + b^2} - \frac{b}{a^2 + b^2} i.$$

For example, we may obtain the reciprocal of $-\sqrt{2} + i$ by letting $a = -\sqrt{2}$, $b = 1$, and $a^2 + b^2 = 3$ in the equation above:

$$\frac{1}{-\sqrt{2} + i} = -\frac{\sqrt{2}}{3} - \frac{1}{3}i.$$

We can now find the quotient of two complex numbers. For example, let us find $(-7 + 3i) \div (5 + 4i)$.

$$(-7 + 3i) \div (5 + 4i) = (-7 + 3i)\left(\frac{1}{5 + 4i}\right)$$
$$= (-7 + 3i)(\tfrac{5}{41} - \tfrac{4}{41}i)$$
$$= (-\tfrac{35}{41} + \tfrac{12}{41}) + (\tfrac{28}{41} + \tfrac{15}{41})i$$
$$= -\tfrac{23}{41} + \tfrac{43}{41}i$$

There is a shorter method for finding the quotient of two complex numbers. For example, to find $(5 - 9i) \div (1 - i)$, we might proceed as follows:

$$\frac{5 - 9i}{1 - i} = \frac{5 - 9i}{1 - i} \cdot \frac{1 + i}{1 + i}$$
$$= \frac{(5 - 9i)(1 + i)}{(1 - i)(1 + i)}$$
$$= \frac{14 - 4i}{2}$$
$$= 7 - 2i.$$

Notice that we simply multiplied the numerator and the denominator of the given quotient by the conjugate of the denominator, to eliminate i from the denominator.

Exercises

Find the conjugate of each of the following complex numbers, and then find the sum and the product of each pair of conjugate complex numbers.

1. (a) $4 + 2i$ (b) $\sqrt{3} - \sqrt{5}i$

2. (a) -7 (b) $-\sqrt{2}i$

3. (a) $\dfrac{1}{2} - \dfrac{\sqrt{3}}{2}i$ (b) $\dfrac{2}{3} - \dfrac{\sqrt{2}}{4}i$

4. (a) What type of complex number is its own conjugate? Give some examples to support your answer.

(b) What type of complex number is the negative of its own conjugate? Give some examples to support your answer.

Express the reciprocal of each of the following complex numbers as a complex number in the form $a + bi$.

5. (a) $1 + i$ (b) $5i$

6. (a) $2 + 3i$ (b) $6 - i$

7. (a) $-2 - 5i$ (b) $\sqrt{3} - 3i$

8. (a) $c - di$ (b) $a - bi$

Perform the indicated operations, and express each answer as a complex number of the form $a + bi$.

9. $\dfrac{1}{2 + i}$ 10. $\dfrac{i}{2 + i}$ 11. $\dfrac{6 + 3i}{2i}$

12. $\dfrac{6 - 3i}{2 + i}$ 13. $\dfrac{1 + i}{1 - i}$ 14. $\dfrac{-3 + 2i}{7 + 4i}$

15. $\dfrac{4 + \sqrt{3}i}{2 - \sqrt{3}i}$ 16. $\left(\dfrac{1 - i}{1 + 3i}\right)\left(\dfrac{2 + 3i}{-1 + 4i}\right)$

17. $\left(\dfrac{2 + i}{3 - i}\right)\left(\dfrac{1 - 4i}{1 + 3i}\right)$ 18. $\dfrac{3}{2 - 5i} - \dfrac{2i}{-2 - 5i}$

19. $\dfrac{1 - i}{1 + 3i} + \dfrac{2 + 3i}{-1 + 4i}$

20. (a) Find the conjugates of $a + bi$ and $c + di$ and add them.
    (b) Add $a + bi$ and $c + di$ and find the conjugate of their sum.
    (c) How is the sum of the conjugates of two complex numbers related to the conjugate of their sum?

21. (a) Find the conjugates of $a + bi$ and $c + di$ and multiply them.
    (b) Multiply $a + bi$ by $c + di$ and find the conjugate of the product.
    (c) How is the product of the conjugates of two complex numbers related to the conjugate of their product?

22. Since two complex numbers are defined as equal if, and only if, their real parts are equal and their pure imaginary parts are equal, the real solutions of the equation $(2x - y) + (x + y)i = 5 + 4i$ are solutions of the system shown below. Solve the system for real values of x and y.

$$\begin{cases} 2x - y = 5, \\ x + y = 4. \end{cases}$$

Find the system defined by each of the following equations, and solve it for real values of x and y.

23. $x + yi = -5 + 4i$ 24. $2x + 3yi - 6 + 9i = 0$

25. $-x + 4yi = (2 + 6i) - (7 - 2i)$ 26. $x + yi = (2 - i)(2 + i)$

9-3 QUADRATIC EQUATIONS AND COMPLETING THE SQUARE

With the introduction of complex numbers we can solve quadratic equations such as $x^2 + 4 = 0$ by considering the equivalent equation $x^2 = -4$, whose solution set is clearly $\{\sqrt{-4}, -\sqrt{-4}\}$ or $\{2i, -2i\}$. As another example, consider the following.

Problem 1. Solve $(7x - 5)^2 = -9$

Solution. x is in the solution set of the given equation if, and only if,

$$7x - 5 = \pm \sqrt{-9}, \quad \text{or} \quad \pm 3i$$

i.e.,

$$7x = 5 \pm 3i$$

$$x = \frac{5}{7} \pm \frac{3}{7} i$$

The solution set is $\{\frac{5}{7} + \frac{3}{7}i, \frac{5}{7} - \frac{3}{7}i\}$.

The reason that the quadratic equation in Problem 1 is as easily solved as the one given in the first paragraph is that the quadratic polynomial on the left side of the equation is the square of a linear form in x.

A quadratic polynomial that can be written as the square of a linear form is called a *perfect square*. Our goal is to express any given quadratic equation in the form of a perfect square quadratic on the left side of the equation and a number on the right side.

If a quadratic polynomial has 1 as its leading coefficient and 0 as the constant term, then it is always possible to add a constant term to make the resulting quadratic polynomial a perfect square. For example, given the quadratic polynomial

$$x^2 + 18x,$$

we can add the square of half of the coefficient of x to make a perfect square:

$$x^2 + 18x + 9^2 = (x + 9)^2.$$

This rule of thumb, of course, is simply a consequence of the fact that the square of a linear form of type $(x + a)^2$ has as its coefficient of x

the number $2a$ and constant term a^2. Since we are given the coefficient $2a$ of x, we know the constant term required in the perfect square is a^2, the square of one-half this coefficient of x.

A second example is

$$y^2 - 11y$$

which can be made into a perfect square by adding $(-\frac{11}{2})^2$ or $\frac{121}{4}$ to it:

$$y^2 - 11y + \tfrac{121}{4} = (y - \tfrac{11}{2})^2$$

[It is always wise to check your end result by computing the special product $(y - \frac{11}{2})^2$.]

The process of adding a constant term to a quadratic polynomial to make it a perfect square is called *completing the square*. We now show how this process enables us to solve quadratic equations which may involve complex roots.

Problem 2. Solve the quadratic equation $3x^2 + 4x + 8 = 0$.

Solution. The following two equations are equivalent to the given one.

$$3x^2 + 4x = -8$$
$$x^2 + \tfrac{4}{3}x = -\tfrac{8}{3}$$

The quadratic polynomial $x^2 + \frac{4}{3}x$ may be made into a perfect square by adding the constant term $(\frac{1}{2} \cdot \frac{4}{3})^2$ or $(\frac{2}{3})^2$. We must, of course, add the number to each side of the last equation above to obtain an equivalent equation:

$$x^2 + \tfrac{4}{3}x + \tfrac{4}{9} = \tfrac{-8}{3} + \tfrac{4}{9}$$

or,

$$(x + \tfrac{2}{3})^2 = \tfrac{-20}{9}.$$

Again

$$(x + \tfrac{2}{3})^2 = \tfrac{-20}{9}$$

if, and only if,

$$x + \tfrac{2}{3} = \sqrt{\tfrac{-20}{9}} \qquad \text{or} \qquad x + \tfrac{2}{3} = -\sqrt{\tfrac{-20}{9}}$$
$$x = -\tfrac{2}{3} + \sqrt{\tfrac{20}{9}}i \qquad \text{or} \qquad x = -\tfrac{2}{3} - \sqrt{\tfrac{20}{9}}i.$$

Thus $\{-\frac{2}{3} + \frac{2}{3}\sqrt{5}i, -\frac{2}{3} - \frac{2}{3}\sqrt{5}i\}$ is the solution set of the given equation.

Problem 3. Solve the quadratic equation

$$x^2 + 6x + 2 = 11x - 4.$$

Solution. The given equation is equivalent to the equation

$$x^2 + 6x + 2 - 11x + 4 = 0,$$

or

$$x^2 - 5x + 6 = 0.$$

We see that the quadratic polynomial on the left side factors easily to give the equivalent equation

$$(x - 3)(x - 2) = 0$$

and hence, by the factor theorem, the zeros of $x^2 - 5x + 6$ are 2 and 3. Since the zeros of $x^2 - 5x + 6$ are just the solutions of the given polynomial equation, the solution set is $\{2, 3\}$.

Thus, for a given quadratic equation, if one rewrites the equation to give an equivalent form in which one has $f(x) = 0$, where f is a quadratic polynomial, one can try to find the solution of the original quadratic equation by factoring the quadratic polynomial $f(x)$ instead of completing the square on this quadratic. If attempted factoring leads to difficulties (if its zeros are complex it has no real factor) the method of completing the square or use of the formula of the next section is called for.

In the next section we shall show, by applying the method of completing squares to the general quadratic equation, that every real quadratic equation has complex solutions (which may be real numbers or of the form $0 + bi$).

Exercises

Solve each real quadratic equation by completing the square, and check each solution.

1. (a) $x^2 - 6x + 10 = 0$ (b) $x^2 + 4x + 13 = 0$
2. (a) $x^2 - 4x - 77 = 0$ (b) $x^2 + x + 1 = 0$
3. (a) $x^2 - 4x + 29 = 0$ (b) $x^2 + 8x + 25 = 0$
4. (a) $x^2 + 2x + 4 = 0$ (b) $x^2 + 2x - 4 = 0$
5. (a) $x^2 - 2\sqrt{3}x + 4 = 0$ (b) $x^2 - x + 1 = 0$

6. (a) If r and s are real numbers, we can find at least one real quadratic equation for which $\{r, s\}$ is the solution set:

$$(x - r)(x - s) = 0, \quad \text{or} \quad x^2 - (r + s)x + rs = 0.$$

According to what property of real numbers is it true that r and s are solutions, and the only solutions, of this quadratic equation?

(b) If r and s are complex numbers, is it still true that

$$x^2 - (r + s)x + rs = 0$$

is a quadratic equation with solution set $\{r, s\}$? For what conditions on r and s is $x^2 - (r + s)x + rs = 0$ a real quadratic equation?

7. (a) Find the sum, $r + s$, and the product, rs, of each pair r, s of your solutions in Exercises 1(a) and 2(a). Then verify that each quadratic has the form given in Exercises 6(a) and (b). (This procedure is a second type of check on your solution.)

(b) Follow the directions of part (a), using your solutions in Exercises 1(b) and 2(b).

Each of the following is a solution set of a quadratic equation. In each case, write a quadratic equation that has the given solution set. (See Exercise 6.)

8. (a) $\{-3, 0\}$ (b) $\{8, -4\}$

9. (a) $\{-\frac{1}{3}, \frac{1}{2}\}$ (b) $\{-2, 4\}$

10. (a) $\{2 + \sqrt{3}, 2 - \sqrt{3}\}$ (b) $\{3 + \sqrt{2}, 3 - \sqrt{2}\}$

11. (a) $\{-3 + 4i, -3 - 4i\}$ (b) $\{0, i\sqrt{5}\}$

12. (a) $\{-1 + i, -1 - i\}$ (b) $\left\{\frac{\sqrt{2}}{2} + \frac{\sqrt{2}}{2}i, \frac{\sqrt{2}}{2} - \frac{\sqrt{2}}{2}i\right\}$

Let each of the following quadratic polynomials equal zero, and solve the resulting equation by completing the square. Then write each polynomial as a product of linear factors.

13. $x^2 + 4x + 20$ **14.** $x^2 + 4x + 1$ **15.** $x^2 - 2x + 4$

16. $6y^2 - 19y + 15$ **17.** $12x - 9x^2 - 5$

Let $a + bi$ and $c + di$ be two complex numbers, with $b \neq 0$ and $d \neq 0$. Verify that each of the following statements is true.

18. If the sum of these two complex numbers is a real number, then $b + d = 0$, or $d = -b$.

19. If the product of these two complex numbers is a real number, then $bc + ad = 0$.

20. If both the sum and product of these two complex numbers are real, then the numbers must be conjugate complex numbers.

21. If a real quadratic equation has one complex solution $a + bi$, with $b \neq 0$, then it must have $a - bi$ as its other solution.

9–4   THE QUADRATIC FORMULA

The method of completing the square can be used to solve any real quadratic equation. Consider the equation

$$ax^2 + bx + c = 0$$

where a, b, c are real numbers and $a \neq 0$.

Each of the following equations is equivalent to the preceding one.

$$ax^2 + bx + c = 0$$

$$x^2 + \frac{b}{a}x + \frac{c}{a} = 0 \qquad \text{(divide each side by } a\text{)}$$

$$x^2 + \frac{b}{a}x = \frac{-c}{a} \qquad (add \ \frac{-c}{a} \text{ to each side)}$$

$$x^2 + \frac{b}{a}x + \left(\frac{b}{2a}\right)^2 = \left(\frac{b}{2a}\right)^2 + \frac{-c}{a} \qquad \left(\text{add } \left(\frac{b}{2a}\right)^2 \text{ to each side}\right)$$

$$\left(x + \frac{b}{2a}\right)^2 = \frac{b^2}{4a^2} + \frac{-c}{a} \qquad \text{(perfect square)}$$

$$\left(x + \frac{b}{2a}\right)^2 = \frac{b^2 - 4ac}{4a^2}$$

Since $4a^2 > 0$, the number on the right side of the equation above is positive if $b^2 - 4ac$ is positive, zero if $b^2 - 4ac$ is zero, and negative if $b^2 - 4ac$ is negative. This number is called the *discriminant* of the given quadratic equation and is designated by D:

$$D = b^2 - 4ac.$$

We have, then,

$$\left(x + \frac{b}{2a}\right)^2 = \frac{D}{4a^2}, \text{ where } D = b^2 - 4ac$$

and hence,

$$x + \frac{b}{2a} = \frac{\pm \sqrt{D}}{2a}$$

or the solution set is

$$\left\{ -\frac{b}{2a} + \frac{\sqrt{D}}{2a}, \ -\frac{b}{2a} - \frac{\sqrt{D}}{2a} \right\}.$$

Since the discriminant, D, may be a positive number, 0, or a negative number, we have three cases.

Case 1. $D > 0$. Then $\sqrt{D}$ is the positive, real square root of the number D and we have a set of two distinct real roots of the quadratic.

Case 2. $D = 0$. The solution set consists of just the number $-(b/2a)$.

Case 3. $D < 0$. Then $\sqrt{D} = (\sqrt{-D})i$ is a pure imaginary number and the two roots are conjugate complex numbers.

The three cases can be summarized in the statement below known as the *quadratic formula.*

QUADRATIC FORMULA

The real quadratic equation

$$ax^2 + bx + c = 0$$

has solution

$$x = \frac{-b \pm \sqrt{b^2 - 4ac}}{2a}.$$

Thus, using the quadratic formula, we see that *every* real quadratic equation has solutions which are real if the discriminant $D = b^2 - 4ac$ is nonnegative and complex if D is negative.

There are comparable formulas for finding all the zeros of a cubic or quartic polynomial although we shall not present them here. This is as far as we can go, however, since it can be proved that there are no algebraic formulas for finding all the zeros of polynomials of degree 5 and higher. Special methods such as the rational zero theorem of Chapter 5 or the graphic approach to approximating zeros of a real polynomial must be used for higher degree polynomials.

Problem 1. Solve $x^2 - 2x + 10 = 0$.

Solution. $a = 1$, $b = -2$, $c = 10$ in the quadratic formula. Thus $b^2 - 4ac = (-2)^2 - 4 \cdot 1 \cdot 10 = -36$ and the solutions are

$$x = \frac{2 \pm \sqrt{-36}}{2} = \frac{2 \pm 6i}{2} \qquad \text{or} \qquad 1 \pm 3i.$$

Thus, $\{1 + 3i, 1 - 3i\}$ is the solution set.

Problem 2. Solve $3x^2 - 4x + 7 = 0$.

Solution. $a = 3$, $b = -4$, $c = 7$ in the quadratic formula. Thus, $b^2 - 4ac = (-4)^2 - 4 \cdot 3 \cdot 7 = -68$ and the solutions are

$$x = \frac{4 \pm \sqrt{-68}}{6} = \frac{4 \pm \sqrt{68}\, i}{6}$$

Since $\sqrt{68} = \sqrt{4 \cdot 17} = 2\sqrt{17}$, the solution set is given by

$$\tfrac{2}{3} + \tfrac{1}{3}\sqrt{17}\, i, \ \tfrac{2}{3} - \tfrac{1}{3}\sqrt{17}\, i$$

Exercises

Use the quadratic formula to solve each of the following:

1. (a) $x^2 - 2x + 7 = 0$ (b) $3y^2 + y + 1 = 0$

2. (a) $t^2 - 8t + 18 = 0$ (b) $2z^2 = 5z - 7$

3. (a) $x^2 + 6 = 3x$ (b) $x^2 + x + 1 = 0$

Each of your solutions in the above examples can be checked, of course, by substituting in the given equation. A less tedious check is furnished by the following example:

4. Using the solutions of the quadratic formula, show that if

$$ax^2 + bx + c = 0$$

has two solutions, real or complex, then
(a) the sum of the solutions is $-(b/a)$.
(b) the product of the solutions is c/a.

Solve each of the following quadratic equations. Check your solutions by comparing the sum and product of the solutions with $-(b/a)$ and c/a, respectively.

5. (a) $x^2 + 9 = 0$ (b) $x^2 + 100 = 0$

6. (a) $2x^2 - 4x + 5 = 0$ (b) $x^2 - 4x + 4 = 0$

7. (a) $x = 1 - 3x^2$ (b) $x^2 + 2 = 4x$

8. (a) $3x^2 + 5x + 4 = 0$ (b) $5z^2 - 13z = 6$

9. (a) $\frac{1}{2}x^2 - \frac{2}{3}x + 1 = 0$ (b) $2 - \frac{1}{2}x - \frac{3}{5}x^2 = 0$

10. (a) $2x^2 + 9x = 0$ (b) $-16t^2 - 32t + 240 = 0$

If the formulas of Exercise 4 are applied to the solution set of a quadratic equation of the form $x^2 + bx + c = 0$, the sum of the solutions is $-b$ and the product of the solutions is c. This provides an alternative method for writing a quadratic equation when its solution set is given. For example, if the solution set is $\{3 + i, 3 - i\}$, then the sum, 6, equals $-b$ and the product, 10, equals c. Hence, $x^2 - 6x + 10 = 0$ is a quadratic equation with the given solution set. Use this method to write quadratic equations having the following solution sets.

11. $\{1 + \sqrt{3}, 1 - \sqrt{3}\}$ **12.** $\{2 + i, 2 - i\}$

13. $\{2, -\frac{3}{2}\}$ **14.** $\{2, -2\}$

15. $\{\frac{1}{2} - \frac{1}{2}\sqrt{5}, \frac{1}{2} + \frac{1}{2}\sqrt{5}\}$ **16.** $\{9, -10\}$

17. $\left\{-\frac{1}{2} + \frac{\sqrt{3}}{2}i, -\frac{1}{2} - \frac{\sqrt{3}}{2}i\right\}$ **18.** $\{i, -i\}$

The equation $x^4 - 17x^2 + 16 = 0$ is not a quadratic equation. However, writing it as $(x^2)^2 - 17(x^2) + 16 = 0$, we see that it is *quadratic in* x^2 and that we may proceed as follows:

$$(x^2 - 16)(x^2 - 1) = 0$$
$$(x - 4)(x + 4)(x - 1)(x + 1) = 0$$

so that the solution set is $\{4, -4, 1, -1\}$.
Solve the following equations which, like the above example, are *quadratic in form.*

19. (a) $x^4 - 13x^2 + 36 = 0$ (b) $x^4 + 5x^2 - 36 = 0$

20. (a) $(x - 1)^2 + 4(x - 1) - 5 = 0$ (b) $2(x + 1)^2 - 5(x + 1) + 2 = 0$

21. (a) $(2x + 1)^2 - 6(2x + 1) + 9 = 0$ (b) $\dfrac{1}{y^2} - \dfrac{3}{y} + 2 = 0$

22. Use the quadratic formula and the factor theorem to show that the following quadratic polynomials cannot be factored into real linear factors.

(a) $x^2 + x + 1$ (b) $3x^2 + 4x + 7$

(c) $4x^2 + 9$ (d) $5x^2 - 7x + 4$

9-5 GRAPHS OF REAL QUADRATIC POLYNOMIAL FUNCTIONS

To graph the real quadratic function c,

$$f(x) = ax^2 + bx + c,$$

we, of course, graph the equation

$$y = ax^2 + bx + c.$$

Hence the points of intersection (if any) of this graph with the x-axis occur at the real zeros of the quadratic polynomial. We have seen in the last section that these zeros (being roots of the polynomial equation $ax^2 + bx + c = 0$) may be real or complex according to the value of the discriminant D of the quadratic. Again we describe the three cases:

Case 1. $D > 0$. The zeros are real and unequal. Hence the graph cuts the x-axis in two points.

Case 2. $D = 0$. There is one real zero, namely $-(b/2a)$. The graph will be *tangent* to the x-axis at this point.

Case 3. $D < 0$. The zeros are complex—i.e., no real zeros and the graph will be completely above or completely below the x-axis (according as the coefficient a is positive or negative, respectively).

Problem 1. For what value or values of m does the graph of $y = x^2 - 5x + m$ cut the x-axis in two points?

Solution. Since $a = 1$, $b = -5$, $c = m$ in the quadratic, the discriminant is

$$D = (-5)^2 - 4 \cdot 1 \cdot m \quad \text{or} \quad 25 - 4m.$$

We must have $D > 0$, or

$$25 - 4m > 0$$
$$25 > 4m, \quad \text{or}$$
$$m < \tfrac{25}{4}.$$

Problem 2. Graph the polynomial function

$$f(x) = x^2 + 6x + 10.$$

Solution. $a = 1, b = 6, c = 10$, so that

$$D = 6^2 - 4 \cdot 1 \cdot 10 = -4$$

and the graph lies entirely on one side of the x-axis.

Before making a table of values, it turns out to be helpful to use our technique of completing the square to rewrite the polynomial itself in an equivalent but more useful form. We proceed as follows:

$$x^2 + 6x + + 10,$$

leaving a space in which to complete the square on the first two terms by adding $(\frac{1}{2} \cdot 6)^2 = 9$. Since we are not working with an *equation* at this point, we must compensate for the insertion of this number 9 in the space we have left by adding, in turn, -9 at the end of the polynomial. Thus, we have

$$x^2 + 6x + 9 + 10 - 9 \qquad \text{or} \qquad (x^2 + 6x + 9) + 1$$

which clearly is equivalent to the original polynomial.

That is, we have

$$f(x) = (x + 3)^2 + 1.$$

We start our table of values of f with $x = -3$ and take numbers for x on either side of -3, working from the middle of the table below outward.

x	-6	-5	-4	-3	-2	-1	0
$f(x)$	10	5	2	1	2	5	10

The graph is sketched in Fig. 1 below.

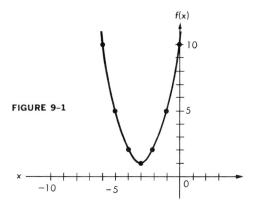

FIGURE 9-1

The reason for completing the square in the quadratic is now apparent. In our example, since $(x + 3)^2$ is never negative for real numbers x and equals 0 when $x = -3$, we see that $f(-3)$ gives the least value of $f(x)$, i.e., gives the height of the lowest point on the graph. We also see that as we take values of x symmetric about $x = -3$ the heights go up equally for such pairs.

Problem 3. Use the technique of completing the square for the polynomial function $f(x) = 5 - 2x - x^2$.

Solution.

$$
\begin{aligned}
5 - 2x - x^2 &= -(x^2 + 2x \qquad\qquad - 5) \\
&= -(x^2 + 2x + 1 - 1 - 5) \\
&= -[(x + 1)^2 - 6], \quad \text{or} \\
&= -(x + 1)^2 + 6, \quad \text{or} \quad 6 - (x + 1)^2
\end{aligned}
$$

We can now see that the *highest* point occurs when $x = -1$, this height being 6.

Exercises

1. For what value or values of m does the graph of $y = x^2 - 3x + m$ cut the x-axis in two points?

2. For what value or values of m is the graph of $y = x^2 - 3x + m$ tangent to the x-axis?

3. For what value or values of m will the graph of $y = x^2 - 3x + m$ fail to cut the x-axis?

4. For what value or values of k is the graph of $y = x^2 - kx + k + 8$ tangent to the x-axis?

5. For what value or values of k is the graph of $y = x^2 + kx + 4$ entirely on one side of the x-axis?

In Exercises 6–11, find the discriminant of the quadratic. If $D \geqslant 0$ find the real zeros of the quadratic function. Find $f(0)$ for each function. Use the complete the square technique to find the highest or lowest point on the graph. Use this information to sketch the graph of each function.

6. $f(x) = x^2 - 6x + 8$ 7. $f(x) = x^2 + 4x + 8$

8. $f(x) = x^2 + 6x + 9$ 9. $f(x) = 3 - 2x - x^2$

10. $f(x) = 9 - x^2$ 11. $f(x) = 4x^2 + 12x + 9$

CHAPTER REVIEW

In Exercises 1–7, perform the indicated operations.

1. $(\sqrt{2}i)^3$

2. $(-7 + \sqrt{2}i) - (6 - 3\sqrt{2}i)$

3. $(3 + 4i)(2 - 7i)$

4. $\left(\dfrac{1}{2} - \dfrac{\sqrt{3}}{2}i\right)\left(\dfrac{1}{2} + \dfrac{\sqrt{3}}{2}i\right)$

5. $\left(\dfrac{1}{2} - \dfrac{\sqrt{2}}{2}i\right)\left(\dfrac{1}{2} + \dfrac{\sqrt{2}}{2}i\right)$

6. $\dfrac{2 + i}{3 - i}$

7. $\dfrac{3 - \sqrt{2}i}{3 + \sqrt{2}i}$

8. (a) Write the conjugate of the complex number $-\sqrt{2} + 7i$, and find the sum and product of the pair of conjugate numbers.
   (b) Find the complex number which is the reciprocal of $-3 + 4i$.

9. Find the real numbers x and y for which

$$(x - y) + (2x + 3y)i = (5 + 4i) - (1 - 7i).$$

Solve each quadratic equation by completing the square, and check each solution.

10. $x^2 - 8x + 8 = 0$

11. $x^2 + 2x + 3 = 0$

12. $x^2 + x - 1 = 0$

13. $x^2 - 6x + 7 = 0$

Solve the following quadratic equations and check your solutions.

14. $6x^2 - 13x + 6 = 0$

15. $x^2 + 4x + 7 = 0$

16. $9 + 4x^2 = 12x$

17. $3x^2 + 4x + 5 = 0$

Write a quadratic equation for each of the following solution sets.

18. $\{2i, -2i\}$

19. $\{3 - \sqrt{5}i, 3 + \sqrt{5}i\}$

20. $\{\frac{1}{2}, -3\}$

21. $\{-2 + 3i, -2 - 3i\}$

22. Show that the cubic polynomial $2x^3 + x^2 + x - 1$ has one real zero which is rational and two complex zeros. Find these three zeros.

23. For what value or values of m does the graph of $y = x^2 + 6x + m$
   (a) cut the x-axis in two points?
   (b) be entirely on one side of the x-axis?

Sketch graphs of the quadratic functions in Exercises 24–26 giving the coordinates of the highest or lowest points of each graph.

24. $f(x) = x^2 - 4x - 5$

25. $f(x) = x^2 - 4x + 5$

26. $f(x) = x^2 - 4x + 4$

10 · Matrices and Determinants

10–1 MATRICES

A rectangular array of numbers, such as

$$\begin{pmatrix} 1 & 4 \\ 2 & -1 \end{pmatrix} \qquad \text{(2 × 2 matrix)}$$

or

$$\begin{pmatrix} 4 & 1 & 3 & 2 \\ -3 & 0 & 1 & 2 \\ 2 & 1 & -3 & 5 \end{pmatrix} \qquad \text{(3 × 4 matrix)}$$

is called a *matrix*. The first matrix has two *rows*,

$$\text{row } 1 = (1 \quad 4),$$
$$\text{row } 2 = (2 \quad -1)$$

and two *columns*,

$$\text{column } 1 = \begin{pmatrix} 1 \\ 2 \end{pmatrix},$$

$$\text{column } 2 = \begin{pmatrix} 4 \\ -1 \end{pmatrix}.$$

The second matrix has three *rows*,

$$(4 \quad 1 \quad 3 \quad 2),$$
$$(-3 \quad 0 \quad 1 \quad 2),$$
$$(2 \quad 1 \quad -3 \quad 5)$$

and four *columns*,

$$\begin{pmatrix} 4 \\ -3 \\ 2 \end{pmatrix}, \quad \begin{pmatrix} 1 \\ 0 \\ 1 \end{pmatrix}, \quad \begin{pmatrix} 3 \\ 1 \\ -3 \end{pmatrix}, \quad \begin{pmatrix} 2 \\ 2 \\ 5 \end{pmatrix}.$$

Our principal interest in matrices is in using them to develop routine methods of solving systems of linear equations.

Associated with a system of two linear equations in two variables x and y such as

$$\begin{cases} x + 2y = 5 \\ -2x + 5y = -1 \end{cases}$$

are two matrices, denoted by A and B below.

$$A = \begin{pmatrix} 1 & 2 \\ -2 & 5 \end{pmatrix} \qquad B = \begin{pmatrix} 1 & 2 & 5 \\ -2 & 5 & -1 \end{pmatrix}$$

We call A the *matrix of coefficients* and B the *augmented matrix* of the system. Clearly A is a 2×2 matrix (it has two rows and two columns) and B is a 2×3 matrix (it has two rows and three columns).

Given any 2×3 matrix such as

$$\begin{pmatrix} 4 & 7 & -2 \\ 3 & 1 & 5 \end{pmatrix},$$

there is a unique system of two linear equations in two variables having this matrix as its augmented matrix, namely

$$\begin{cases} 4x + 7y = -2 \\ 3x + y = 5. \end{cases}$$

A system of three equations in three variables, such as

$$\begin{cases} x + 3y - 2z = 4 \\ 2x + 3z = 7 \\ -4x + 8y - z = -1, \end{cases}$$

has the 3×4 matrix B as its augmented matrix.

$$B = \begin{pmatrix} 1 & 3 & -2 & 4 \\ 2 & 0 & 3 & 7 \\ -4 & 8 & -1 & -1 \end{pmatrix}$$

What is the matrix of coefficients of this system?

Exercises

1. For each of the following matrices, give its dimension (number of rows × number of columns) and list its rows.

(a) $\begin{pmatrix} 1 & 2 \\ 3 & 4 \end{pmatrix}$ 　　(b) $\begin{pmatrix} 0 & 0 \\ 0 & 0 \end{pmatrix}$ 　　(c) $\begin{pmatrix} 1 & 0 \\ 0 & 1 \end{pmatrix}$

(d) $\begin{pmatrix} 1 & 0 \\ -3 & 2 \\ 4 & 2 \end{pmatrix}$ 　(e) $\begin{pmatrix} -2 & 0 & 3 \\ 1 & 5 & -3 \end{pmatrix}$ 　(f) $\begin{pmatrix} 1 & 0 & 2 \\ 0 & 1 & -3 \end{pmatrix}$

2. For each of the following matrices, give its dimension (see Exercise 1) and list its rows.

(a) $\begin{pmatrix} 0 & 0 \\ 0 & 0 \\ 0 & 0 \end{pmatrix}$ 　　　(b) $\begin{pmatrix} 1 & 0 & 0 \\ 0 & 1 & 0 \\ 0 & 0 & 1 \end{pmatrix}$

(c) $\begin{pmatrix} 0 & 1 & 0 \\ 1 & 0 & 1 \\ 0 & 2 & 0 \end{pmatrix}$ 　(d) $\begin{pmatrix} 1 & -1 & 2 & -2 \\ 5 & 4 & -3 & 2 \\ -1 & 0 & 1 & -2 \end{pmatrix}$

3. (a) Write the matrix identified completely by row $1 = (3 \quad 2)$ and row $2 = (7 \quad 4)$.
   (b) Write the matrix identified completely by row $1 = (0 \quad 1 \quad 2)$ and row $2 = (3 \quad 4 \quad 5)$.
   (c) Write the matrix identified completely by

$$\text{column } 1 = \begin{pmatrix} 3 \\ 1 \\ -4 \\ 2 \end{pmatrix} \quad \text{and} \quad \text{column } 2 = \begin{pmatrix} 0 \\ -1 \\ 3 \\ 5 \end{pmatrix}.$$

4. (a) Write the matrix identified completely by row $1 = (1 \quad 0 \quad -5)$, row $2 = (7 \quad -2 \quad 2)$ and row $3 = (0 \quad 0 \quad 1)$.
   (b) Write the matrix identified completely by row $1 = (1 \quad 3 \quad -2 \quad -2)$. row $2 = (0 \quad 1 \quad -3 \quad 4)$, row $3 = (0 \quad 0 \quad 1 \quad -8)$ and row $4 = (0 \quad 0 \quad 0 \quad 1)$.
   (c) Write the matrix identified completely by

$$\text{column } 1 = \begin{pmatrix} 2 \\ -2 \\ -1 \end{pmatrix}, \quad \text{column } 2 = \begin{pmatrix} 0 \\ 3 \\ -3 \end{pmatrix},$$

$$\text{column } 3 = \begin{pmatrix} 2 \\ -4 \\ 1 \end{pmatrix}, \quad \text{column } 4 = \begin{pmatrix} 1 \\ 1 \\ 1 \end{pmatrix}.$$

   (d) Write the matrix identified completely by

$$\text{column } 1 = \begin{pmatrix} -2 \\ 1 \\ 0 \\ 3 \end{pmatrix}, \quad \text{column } 2 = \begin{pmatrix} 1.5 \\ 0 \\ -3 \\ 5 \end{pmatrix},$$

$$\text{column } 3 = \begin{pmatrix} 2 \\ 1 \\ 0 \\ -2 \end{pmatrix}, \quad \text{column } 4 = \begin{pmatrix} 0 \\ 8 \\ 8 \\ 0 \end{pmatrix}.$$

5. Write both the coefficient matrix and the augmented matrix for each of the following systems.

(a) $\begin{cases} 2x - y = 3 \\ x + 3y = 5 \end{cases}$ (b) $\begin{cases} 2x + 3y = -5 \\ -x + 2y = 3 \end{cases}$ (c) $\begin{cases} x - y = 2 \\ y = 7 \end{cases}$

(d) $\begin{cases} x + 2y - 3z = 4 \\ 2x + z = 8 \\ 3x - y = 9 \end{cases}$ (e) $\begin{cases} y + 2z = -1 \\ 3x + 2y - z = 0 \\ 7x + y = 3 \end{cases}$

6. Write both the coefficient matrix and the augmented matrix for each of the following systems.

(a) $\begin{cases} x + y = 2 \\ 3x - 4y = -1 \end{cases}$ (b) $\begin{cases} x + 2y = 9 \\ -x + y = 4 \end{cases}$ (c) $\begin{cases} x = 8 \\ y = 2 \end{cases}$

(d) $\begin{cases} ax + by + cz = d \\ ex + fy + gz = h \\ jx + ky + mz = n \end{cases}$ (e) $\begin{cases} x - y = -2 \\ 2x + 3y + z = 8 \\ y - 4z = 4 \end{cases}$

7. Write a system of equations which has for its augmented matrix the given matrix.

(a) $\begin{pmatrix} 1 & 2 & 3 \\ 4 & 5 & 6 \end{pmatrix}$ (b) $\begin{pmatrix} 1 & 0 & 1 \\ 0 & 1 & 2 \end{pmatrix}$ (c) $\begin{pmatrix} -1 & 2 & 2 \\ 2 & 4 & 6 \end{pmatrix}$

(d) $\begin{pmatrix} 1 & 0 & 1 & 3 \\ 3 & 2 & -3 & 7 \\ 0 & 1 & 2 & 6 \end{pmatrix}$ (e) $\begin{pmatrix} -1 & 1 & 3 & 3 \\ 4 & 2 & 0 & 2 \\ 3 & -2 & -1 & 0 \end{pmatrix}$

8. Write a system of equations which has for its augmented matrix the given matrix.

(a) $\begin{pmatrix} 3 & -1 & 2 \\ -2 & 0 & 7 \end{pmatrix}$ (b) $\begin{pmatrix} 0 & 1 & -1 \\ 1 & 0 & 2 \end{pmatrix}$ (c) $\begin{pmatrix} 2 & 7 & 7 \\ 1 & 8 & -1 \end{pmatrix}$

(d) $\begin{pmatrix} 1 & 0 & 0 & -1 \\ 0 & 1 & 0 & 3 \\ 0 & 0 & 1 & 2 \end{pmatrix}$ (e) $\begin{pmatrix} -3 & 2 & 0 & 8 \\ 0 & 7 & 2 & 5 \\ -2 & 3 & -2 & 3 \end{pmatrix}$

9. Write two different systems of equations, each of which has

$$\begin{pmatrix} 3 & -1 \\ -2 & 4 \end{pmatrix}$$

for its coefficient matrix. How many such systems are there?

10-2 ROW OPERATIONS ON MATRICES

There are three useful operations you can perform on the rows of a matrix A.

Operation 1. Interchange two rows of A.
Operation 2. Multiply a row of A by a nonzero number.
Operation 3. Multiply one row by a number and add the resulting row to another row.

These are called the *elementary row operations* on a matrix. Consider the following matrix.

$$A = \begin{pmatrix} 3 & 1 & 2 \\ 4 & 0 & 3 \\ 1 & -2 & -5 \end{pmatrix} \qquad (3 \times 3 \text{ matrix})$$

Take as Op. 1 "interchange rows 1 and 3 of A." The resulting matrix is

$$B = \begin{pmatrix} 1 & -2 & -5 \\ 4 & 0 & 3 \\ 3 & 1 & 2 \end{pmatrix}.$$

Take as Op. 2 "multiply row 2 of A by 5." This means to multiply each number in row 2 by 5. The resulting matrix is

$$C = \begin{pmatrix} 3 & 1 & 2 \\ 20 & 0 & 15 \\ 1 & -2 & -5 \end{pmatrix}.$$

Take as Op. 3 "multiply row 3 of A by 2 and add the resulting row to row 2 of A." First, multiply $(1 \quad -2 \quad -5)$ by 2, obtaining row $(2 \quad -4 \quad -10)$. Now add $(2 \quad -4 \quad -10)$ to $(4 \quad 0 \quad 3)$: this means to add corresponding numbers in the two rows.

$$(2 \quad -4 \quad -10) + (4 \quad 0 \quad 3) = (6 \quad -4 \quad -7)$$

The resulting row, $(6 \quad -4 \quad -7)$, is the new row 2 of a matrix D having rows 1 and 3 the same as those of A. Thus,

$$D = \begin{pmatrix} 3 & 1 & 2 \\ 6 & -4 & -7 \\ 1 & -2 & -5 \end{pmatrix}.$$

The importance of the elementary row operations is given by the following result.

If the augmented matrix of one system of linear equations is obtained by performing an elementary row operation on the augmented matrix of another system, then the two systems have the same solution set.

We shall not give the proof of this result in this book.

We can thus perform elementary row operations on successive augmented matrices without changing the solution set of the original system. We can use this to solve systems of linear equations, as illustrated below.

Problem 1.   Solve the system

$$\begin{cases} x - 2y = -8 \\ 2x + 3y = 5. \end{cases} \tag{1}$$

Solution.   The augmented matrix of this system is

$$A = \begin{pmatrix} 1 & -2 & -8 \\ 2 & 3 & 5 \end{pmatrix}.$$

Let us multiply the first row by -2 and add to the second row (elementary row Op. 3).

$$-2(1 \quad -2 \quad -8) + (2 \quad 3 \quad 5) = (-2 \quad 4 \quad 16) + (2 \quad 3 \quad 5)$$
$$= (0 \quad 7 \quad 21)$$

The new matrix is

$$B = \begin{pmatrix} 1 & -2 & -8 \\ 0 & 7 & 21 \end{pmatrix}.$$

It is the augmented matrix of system

$$\begin{cases} x - 2y = -8 \\ 7y = 21 \end{cases} \tag{2}$$

having the same solution set as system (1). Clearly $y = 3$ from the second equation and

$$x - 2 \cdot 3 = -8$$
$$x = -2$$

from the first. Thus,

$$x = -2, \quad y = 3$$

is the solution of system (2), and hence also of system (1).

Check.   Always check in the original system.

$$-2 - (2 \cdot 3) \overset{\vee}{=} -8$$
$$2(-2) + 3 \cdot 3 \overset{\vee}{=} 5$$

Problem 2.   Solve the system

$$\begin{cases} 3x + 4y = -3 \\ -2x + 5y = 3. \end{cases} \tag{1}$$

Solution.   The augmented matrix of (1) is

$$A = \begin{pmatrix} 3 & 4 & -3 \\ -2 & 5 & 3 \end{pmatrix}.$$

We multiply row 1 by $\frac{2}{3}$ and add the result to row 2.

$$\tfrac{2}{3}(3 \quad 4 \quad -3) + (-2 \quad 5 \quad 3) = (2 \quad \tfrac{8}{3} \quad -2) + (-2 \quad 5 \quad 3)$$
$$= (0 \quad \tfrac{23}{3} \quad 1)$$

The resulting matrix is

$$B = \begin{pmatrix} 3 & 4 & -3 \\ 0 & \tfrac{23}{3} & 1 \end{pmatrix}.$$

It is the augmented matrix of system

$$\begin{cases} 3x + 4y = -3 \\ \tfrac{23}{3} y = 1. \end{cases} \tag{2}$$

Clearly $y = \tfrac{3}{23}$ from the second equation and

$$3x + 4 \cdot \tfrac{3}{23} = -3$$
$$3x = -\tfrac{81}{23}$$
$$x = -\tfrac{27}{23}.$$

Thus,

$$x = -\tfrac{27}{23}, \quad y = \tfrac{3}{23}$$

is the solution of system (2), and hence also of system (1).

Check.
$$3(-\tfrac{27}{23}) + 4 \cdot \tfrac{3}{23} = -\tfrac{69}{23} = -3$$
$$(-2)\cdot(-\tfrac{27}{23}) + 5 \cdot \tfrac{3}{23} = \tfrac{69}{23} = 3$$

In the two problems above, we multiplied row 1 by some number and added the resulting row to row 2 so as to get zero as the first number in the new second row. This made it easy to solve the new system.

Exercises

1. Consider the matrix $A = \begin{pmatrix} 1 & 2 \\ 3 & 4 \end{pmatrix}$.

(a) Write the matrix obtained from A by interchanging the two rows.
(b) Write the matrix obtained from A by multiplying the first row by 3.
(c) Write the matrix obtained from A by multiplying the first row by -2 and adding the result to the second row.

2. Consider the matrix $B = \begin{pmatrix} 2 & -2 \\ 5 & 3 \end{pmatrix}$.

(a) Write the matrix obtained from B by interchanging the two rows.
(b) Write the matrix obtained from B by multiplying the first row by -1.
(c) Write the matrix obtained from B by multiplying the first row by 2 and adding the result to the second row.

3. Consider the matrix $A = \begin{pmatrix} 2 & -1 & 0 \\ 0 & 2 & -1 \\ 3 & 5 & 2 \end{pmatrix}$.

(a) Write the matrix obtained by interchanging the second and third rows of A.
(b) Write the matrix obtained by multiplying the first row of A by -2.
(c) Write the matrix obtained by multiplying the first row of A by 2 and adding the result to the second row.
(d) Write the matrix obtained by multiplying the second row of A by 2 and adding the result to the third row.

4. Consider the matrix $B = \begin{pmatrix} 3 & 2 & 1 \\ -2 & 0 & 3 \\ 0 & 1 & -3 \end{pmatrix}$.

(a) Write the matrix obtained by interchanging the first and third rows of B.
(b) Write the matrix obtained by multiplying the third row of B by 4.
(c) Write the matrix obtained by multiplying the third row of B by -2 and adding the result to the first row.
(d) Write the matrix obtained by multiplying the third row by 1 and adding the result to the second row (that is, by adding the third row to the second).

5. Write five different matrices, each obtained from $\begin{pmatrix} a & b \\ c & d \end{pmatrix}$ by one elementary row operation.

6. Write five different matrices, each obtained from $\begin{pmatrix} 2 & 3 \\ -1 & 2 \end{pmatrix}$ by one elementary row operation.

7. Consider the system $\begin{cases} x - 2y = 8 \\ 3x + 2y = 0 \end{cases}$ and solve it in the following manner.

   (a) Write A, the augmented matrix of the system.
   (b) Write B, the matrix obtained from A by adding -3 times the first row to the second row.
   (c) Write C, the matrix obtained from B by multiplying the second row by $\frac{1}{8}$.
   (d) Write D, the matrix obtained from C by adding 2 times the second row to the first row.
   (e) Write a system which has D for its augmented matrix.

8. Consider the system $\begin{cases} x + y = 2 \\ 2x + 5y = 16 \end{cases}$ and solve it in the following manner.

   (a) Write A, the augmented matrix of the system.
   (b) Write B, the matrix obtained from A by adding -2 times the first row to the second row.
   (c) Write C, the matrix obtained from B by multiplying the second row by $\frac{1}{3}$.
   (d) Write D, the matrix obtained from C by adding -1 times the second row to the first row.
   (e) Write a system which has D for its augmented matrix.

9. Solve each of the following systems by first writing the augmented matrix and by then simplifying the matrix by elementary row operations.

   (a) $\begin{cases} x + 2y = 4 \\ 2x - 6y = 3 \end{cases}$ (b) $\begin{cases} x + 5y = 8 \\ 3x + 4y = 2 \end{cases}$ (c) $\begin{cases} x + 6y = 2 \\ 2x - 4y = 0 \end{cases}$

10. Solve each of the following systems by first writing the augmented matrix and by then simplifying the matrix by elementary row operations.

   (a) $\begin{cases} x + 2y = 5 \\ 5x - y = 3 \end{cases}$ (b) $\begin{cases} x + 2y = 8 \\ -2x + y = 9 \end{cases}$ (c) $\begin{cases} x - 4y = -5 \\ 3x + 6y = 9 \end{cases}$

11. Solve each of the following systems by first writing the augmented matrix and by then simplifying the matrix by elementary row operations.

   (a) $\begin{cases} 3x + 2y = 0 \\ 2x + 3y = 5 \end{cases}$ (b) $\begin{cases} 3x - y = 2 \\ 2x + 6y = 4 \end{cases}$ (c) $\begin{cases} 2x + y = 2 \\ -3x + 2y = 11 \end{cases}$

12. Solve each of the following systems by first writing the augmented matrix and by then simplifying the matrix by elementary row operations.

(a) $\begin{cases} 4x - 3y = 7 \\ 3x + 2y = 1 \end{cases}$ (b) $\begin{cases} 5x + 3y = -1 \\ 4x + 5y = 7 \end{cases}$ (c) $\begin{cases} 5x + y = 4 \\ 3x - 6y = -2 \end{cases}$

10-3   ECHELON FORM OF A MATRIX

Look at the matrix

$$A = \begin{pmatrix} 2 & 1 & 3 & -4 \\ 0 & 2 & 1 & 2 \\ 0 & 0 & 1 & -2 \end{pmatrix}.$$

Row 1 starts with the nonzero number 2; row 2 starts with one zero; row 3 starts with two zeros. This is an example of a matrix in echelon form.

A matrix is said to be in *echelon form* if the second row starts with more zeros than the first, the third row starts with more zeros than the second, and so on for every row of the matrix.

If the augmented matrix of a system of linear equations is in echelon form, then the system is easily solved. For example, matrix A above is the augmented matrix of the system

$$\begin{cases} 2x + y + 3z = -4 \\ 2y + z = 2 \\ z = -2. \end{cases}$$

From the third equation, $z = -2$. Then, from the second,

$$2y - 2 = 2, \quad y = 2.$$

Finally, from the first,

$$2x + 2 + 3(-2) = -4$$
$$2x = 0$$
$$x = 0.$$

Thus, the solution of the system is

$$x = 0, \quad y = 2, \quad z = -2.$$

Every matrix can be put into echelon form by performing a succession of elementary row operations. This process is illustrated below.

Problem 1. Put the matrix A into echelon form.

$$A = \begin{pmatrix} 1 & 4 \\ 3 & -2 \end{pmatrix}$$

Solution. Add -3 times row 1 to row 2.

$$-3(1 \quad 4) + (3 \quad -2) = (-3 \quad -12) + (3 \quad -2)$$
$$= (0 \quad -14)$$

This elementary row operation changes A into echelon form

$$B = \begin{pmatrix} 1 & 4 \\ 0 & -14 \end{pmatrix}.$$

Problem 2. Put the matrix A into echelon form.

$$A = \begin{pmatrix} 5 & 10 & 0 & 3 \\ -2 & -4 & 2 & -1 \end{pmatrix}$$

Solution. Since $5 \cdot \frac{2}{5} = 2$, if we add $\frac{2}{5}$ times row 1 to row 2, the new row 2 will start with a zero.

$$\frac{2}{5}(5 \quad 10 \quad 0 \quad 3) + (-2 \quad -4 \quad 2 \quad -1)$$
$$= (2 \quad 4 \quad 0 \quad \frac{6}{5}) + (-2 \quad -4 \quad 2 \quad -1)$$
$$= (0 \quad 0 \quad 2 \quad \frac{1}{5})$$

This elementary row operation changes A into echelon form

$$B = \begin{pmatrix} 5 & 10 & 0 & 3 \\ 0 & 0 & 2 & \frac{1}{5} \end{pmatrix}.$$

Note that row 2 of B starts with two more zeros than row 1.

Problem 3. Put the matrix A into echelon form.

$$A = \begin{pmatrix} 1 & 2 & -1 \\ -2 & -5 & 0 \\ 4 & 1 & -3 \end{pmatrix}$$

Solution. Our first task is to make row 2 start with zero. This can be done by multiplying row 1 by 2 and adding the result to row 2.

$$2(1 \quad 2 \quad -1) + (-2 \quad -5 \quad 0) = (2 \quad 4 \quad -2) + (-2 \quad -5 \quad 0)$$
$$= (0 \quad -1 \quad -2).$$

This gives

$$B = \begin{pmatrix} 1 & 2 & -1 \\ 0 & -1 & -2 \\ 4 & 1 & -3 \end{pmatrix}$$

obtained from A by an elementary row operation. Clearly B is not in echelon form. We must get some zeros in row 3.

Starting with matrix B, multiply row 1 by -4, and add the resulting row to row 3.

$$-4(1 \quad 2 \quad -1) + (4 \quad 1 \quad -3) = (-4 \quad -8 \quad 4) + (4 \quad 1 \quad -3)$$
$$= (0 \quad -7 \quad 1)$$

This gives

$$C = \begin{pmatrix} 1 & 2 & -1 \\ 0 & -1 & -2 \\ 0 & -7 & 1 \end{pmatrix}$$

obtained from B by an elementary row operation. Now C is not in echelon form; rows 2 and 3 start with the same number of zeros. However, if we multiply row 2 of C by -7 and add to row 3,

$$-7(0 \quad -1 \quad -2) + (0 \quad -7 \quad 1) = (0 \quad 7 \quad 14) + (0 \quad -7 \quad 1)$$
$$= (0 \quad 0 \quad 15),$$

we get a new row 3 starting with more zeros than row 2. This gives

$$D = \begin{pmatrix} 1 & 2 & -1 \\ 0 & -1 & -2 \\ 0 & 0 & 15 \end{pmatrix}$$

obtained from C by an elementary row operation.

Finally, we have found a matrix D which is equivalent to matrix A and which is in echelon form. It was obtained from matrix A by a succession of three elementary row operations.

Problem 4. Put the matrix A into echelon form.

$$A = \begin{pmatrix} 2 & 1 & 3 & 1 \\ -4 & 1 & -1 & 2 \\ 6 & 6 & 5 & 3 \end{pmatrix}$$

Solution.   Matrix B is obtained from A as indicated below.

$$B = \begin{pmatrix} 2 & 1 & 3 & 1 \\ 0 & 3 & 5 & 4 \\ 6 & 6 & 5 & 3 \end{pmatrix} \qquad \begin{array}{l} \text{row 1 of } A \\ 2(\text{row 1}) + (\text{row 2}) \text{ of } A \\ \text{row 3 of } A \end{array}$$

Matrix C is obtained from B as indicated below.

$$C = \begin{pmatrix} 2 & 1 & 3 & 1 \\ 0 & 3 & 5 & 4 \\ 0 & 3 & -4 & 0 \end{pmatrix} \qquad \begin{array}{l} \text{row 1 of } B \\ \text{row 2 of } B \\ -3(\text{row 1}) + (\text{row 3}) \text{ of } B \end{array}$$

Matrix D is obtained from C as indicated below.

$$D = \begin{pmatrix} 2 & 1 & 3 & 1 \\ 0 & 3 & 5 & 4 \\ 0 & 0 & -9 & -4 \end{pmatrix} \qquad \begin{array}{l} \text{row 1 of } C \\ \text{row 2 of } C \\ -1(\text{row 2}) + (\text{row 3}) \text{ of } C \end{array}$$

Maxtrix D, obtained from A by a succession of elementary row operations, is in echelon form.

Exercises

1. Put each of the following matrices into echelon form.

(a) $\begin{pmatrix} 1 & 2 \\ 3 & 4 \end{pmatrix}$ (b) $\begin{pmatrix} 1 & 0 \\ -2 & 3 \end{pmatrix}$ (c) $\begin{pmatrix} 1 & -1 \\ 4 & 5 \end{pmatrix}$

2. Put each of the following matrices into echelon form.

(a) $\begin{pmatrix} 1 & 3 \\ 1 & 4 \end{pmatrix}$ (b) $\begin{pmatrix} 1 & 2 \\ -1 & -2 \end{pmatrix}$ (c) $\begin{pmatrix} 1 & 1 \\ 2 & -2 \end{pmatrix}$

3. Put each of the following matrices into echelon form.

(a) $\begin{pmatrix} 1 & 2 & 3 \\ 4 & 5 & 6 \end{pmatrix}$ (b) $\begin{pmatrix} 1 & 0 & 2 \\ -2 & 1 & 0 \end{pmatrix}$

(c) $\begin{pmatrix} 1 & 0 & 3 & 4 \\ 2 & 0 & 2 & 2 \end{pmatrix}$

4. Put each of the following matrices into echelon form.

(a) $\begin{pmatrix} 1 & 2 & -1 \\ 2 & 4 & 2 \end{pmatrix}$ (b) $\begin{pmatrix} 1 & 0 & 1 \\ -3 & 2 & 2 \end{pmatrix}$

(c) $\begin{pmatrix} 1 & 2 & 0 & 5 \\ 2 & 4 & 0 & 1 \end{pmatrix}$

5. Put each of the following matrices into echelon form.

(a) $\begin{pmatrix} 2 & 1 \\ 3 & 1 \end{pmatrix}$ (b) $\begin{pmatrix} 3 & 0 \\ 2 & 2 \end{pmatrix}$ (c) $\begin{pmatrix} 2 & 2 \\ -1 & 0 \end{pmatrix}$

6. Put each of the following matrices into echelon form.

(a) $\begin{pmatrix} -2 & 2 \\ 3 & 4 \end{pmatrix}$ (b) $\begin{pmatrix} 5 & 2 \\ 2 & 5 \end{pmatrix}$ (c) $\begin{pmatrix} 4 & 3 \\ 3 & 2 \end{pmatrix}$

7. Put each of the following matrices into echelon form.

(a) $\begin{pmatrix} 2 & 3 & 4 \\ 4 & 0 & 2 \end{pmatrix}$ (b) $\begin{pmatrix} 2 & -2 & 3 \\ 3 & -3 & \frac{1}{2} \end{pmatrix}$

(c) $\begin{pmatrix} 4 & 2 & 5 & 0 & 2 \\ 3 & 0 & 3 & 0 & 3 \end{pmatrix}$

·8. Put each of the following matrices into echelon form.

(a) $\begin{pmatrix} 2 & -2 & -1 \\ 5 & 3 & 1 \end{pmatrix}$ (b) $\begin{pmatrix} 3 & -4 & 1 \\ -6 & 8 & 3 \end{pmatrix}$

(c) $\begin{pmatrix} -2 & 2 & 2 & 1 & 3 \\ 3 & 2 & 3 & 2 & 3 \end{pmatrix}$

9. Put each of the following matrices into echelon form.

(a) $\begin{pmatrix} 1 & 0 & 2 \\ -2 & 2 & 3 \\ 3 & 4 & 5 \end{pmatrix}$ (b) $\begin{pmatrix} 1 & 2 & 3 \\ -1 & -3 & 1 \\ 2 & 2 & 2 \end{pmatrix}$ (c) $\begin{pmatrix} 1 & -2 & 2 \\ 2 & -4 & 3 \\ -2 & 4 & 4 \end{pmatrix}$

10. Put each of the following matrices into echelon form.

(a) $\begin{pmatrix} 1 & 0 & 1 \\ 4 & 4 & 2 \\ -3 & 2 & 0 \end{pmatrix}$ (b) $\begin{pmatrix} 1 & 2 & 2 \\ 2 & 2 & 1 \\ -1 & 4 & 4 \end{pmatrix}$ (c) $\begin{pmatrix} 1 & 3 & 3 \\ -3 & 1 & 0 \\ 2 & -4 & 1 \end{pmatrix}$

11. Put each of the following matrices into echelon form.

(a) $\begin{pmatrix} 2 & 2 & 4 \\ 3 & -1 & 0 \\ -1 & 1 & 3 \end{pmatrix}$ (b) $\begin{pmatrix} -2 & 4 & 1 \\ 4 & 0 & 3 \\ -6 & 4 & 1 \end{pmatrix}$ (c) $\begin{pmatrix} 3 & -6 & 6 \\ 2 & -1 & 1 \\ -1 & 7 & 2 \end{pmatrix}$

12. Put each of the following matrices into echelon form.

(a) $\begin{pmatrix} 2 & -2 & 6 \\ -1 & 3 & 2 \\ 3 & 3 & 4 \end{pmatrix}$ (b) $\begin{pmatrix} -3 & 2 & 6 \\ 1 & \frac{1}{3} & -2 \\ -2 & \frac{1}{3} & 4 \end{pmatrix}$ (c) $\begin{pmatrix} -2 & 2 & 2 \\ 3 & 5 & -3 \\ 2 & 4 & 1 \end{pmatrix}$

13. Put each of the following matrices into echelon form.

(a) $\begin{pmatrix} 1 & 2 & 2 & 4 \\ 2 & 2 & 1 & 2 \\ -2 & 2 & 7 & 3 \\ 0 & 4 & 4 & 0 \end{pmatrix}$ (b) $\begin{pmatrix} 1 & 0 & 4 & 2 & -3 \\ -2 & 1 & -3 & -3 & 5 \\ 3 & 2 & 10 & 5 & 15 \\ 2 & 0 & 8 & 4 & 5 \end{pmatrix}$

10–4 ECHELON METHOD OF SOLVING SYSTEMS OF LINEAR EQUATIONS

We use the method of the preceding section to solve systems of linear equations.

Problem 1. Solve the system

$$\begin{cases} x + 5y = 7 \\ 3x + 2y = -5. \end{cases} \tag{1}$$

Solution. We write the augmented matrix A of this system

$$A = \begin{pmatrix} 1 & 5 & 7 \\ 3 & 2 & -5 \end{pmatrix}$$

and put it into echelon form.

$$B = \begin{pmatrix} 1 & 5 & 7 \\ 0 & -13 & -26 \end{pmatrix} \qquad \begin{array}{l} \text{row 1 of } A \\ -3 \,(\text{row 1}) + \text{row 2 of } A \end{array}$$

Now B is the augmented matrix of the system

$$\begin{cases} x + 5y = 7 \\ -13y = -26. \end{cases} \tag{2}$$

From the second equation, $y = 2$; and from the first equation,

$$x + 5 \cdot 2 = 7, \quad x = -3.$$

Thus,

$$x = -3, \quad y = 2$$

is the solution of system (2) and hence of system (1) also.

Check.
$$-3 + 5 \cdot 2 \stackrel{\checkmark}{=} 7$$
$$3(-3) + 2 \cdot 2 \stackrel{\checkmark}{=} -5$$

Problem 2. Solve the system

$$\begin{cases} x - 2y - z = 2 \\ -3x + 7y + z = 0 \\ 2x + y + 3z = 4. \end{cases} \tag{1}$$

Solution. We put the augmented matrix A of this system

$$A = \begin{pmatrix} 1 & -2 & -1 & 2 \\ -3 & 7 & 1 & 0 \\ 2 & 1 & 3 & 4 \end{pmatrix}$$

into echelon form by using elementary row operations as indicated below.

$$B = \begin{pmatrix} 1 & -2 & -1 & 2 \\ 0 & 1 & -2 & 6 \\ 2 & 1 & 3 & 4 \end{pmatrix} \qquad \begin{matrix} \text{row 1 of } A \\ 3(\text{row 1}) + (\text{row 2}) \text{ of } A \\ \text{row 3 of } A \end{matrix}$$

$$C = \begin{pmatrix} 1 & -2 & -1 & 2 \\ 0 & 1 & -2 & 6 \\ 0 & 5 & 5 & 0 \end{pmatrix} \qquad \begin{matrix} \text{row 1 of } B \\ \text{row 2 of } B \\ -2(\text{row 1}) + (\text{row 3}) \text{ of } B \end{matrix}$$

$$D = \begin{pmatrix} 1 & -2 & -1 & 2 \\ 0 & 1 & -2 & 6 \\ 0 & 0 & 15 & -30 \end{pmatrix} \qquad \begin{matrix} \text{row 1 of } C \\ \text{row 2 of } C \\ -5(\text{row 2}) + (\text{row 3}) \text{ of } C \end{matrix}$$

While D is in echelon form, we can simplify the matrix further using elementary row operations, as shown below.

$$E = \begin{pmatrix} 1 & 0 & -5 & 14 \\ 0 & 1 & -2 & 6 \\ 0 & 0 & 15 & -30 \end{pmatrix} \qquad \begin{matrix} 2(\text{row 2}) + (\text{row 1}) \text{ of } D \\ \text{row 2 of } D \\ \text{row 3 of } D \end{matrix}$$

$$F = \begin{pmatrix} 1 & 0 & -5 & 14 \\ 0 & 1 & -2 & 6 \\ 0 & 0 & 1 & -2 \end{pmatrix} \qquad \begin{matrix} \text{row 1 of } E \\ \text{row 2 of } E \\ \tfrac{1}{15}(\text{row 3}) \text{ of } E \end{matrix}$$

$$G = \begin{pmatrix} 1 & 0 & 0 & 4 \\ 0 & 1 & -2 & 6 \\ 0 & 0 & 1 & -2 \end{pmatrix} \qquad \begin{matrix} 5(\text{row 3}) + (\text{row 1}) \text{ of } F \\ \text{row 2 of } F \\ \text{row 3 of } F \end{matrix}$$

$$H = \begin{pmatrix} 1 & 0 & 0 & 4 \\ 0 & 1 & 0 & 2 \\ 0 & 0 & 1 & -2 \end{pmatrix} \qquad \begin{matrix} \text{row 1 of } G \\ 2(\text{row 3}) + (\text{row 2}) \text{ of } G \\ \text{row 3 of } G \end{matrix}$$

Matrix H is the augmented matrix of the system

$$\begin{cases} x = 4 \\ y = 2 \\ z = -2 \end{cases}$$

with the obvious solution

$$x = 4, \quad y = 2, \quad z = -2.$$

This is also the solution of the given system (1).

Check.
$$4 - (2 \cdot 2) - (-2) \overset{\vee}{=} 2$$
$$-3 \cdot 4 + 7 \cdot 2 + (-2) \overset{\vee}{=} 0$$
$$2 \cdot 4 + 2 + 3(-2) \overset{\vee}{=} 4$$

Problem 3.   Solve the system

$$\begin{cases} 2x + y - z = 2 \\ 4x - 3y + z = 5 \\ 2x + 11y - 7z = 1. \end{cases} \tag{1}$$

Solution.   The system has augmented matrix

$$A = \begin{pmatrix} 2 & 1 & -1 & 2 \\ 4 & -3 & 1 & 5 \\ 2 & 11 & -7 & 1 \end{pmatrix}$$

which can be put into echelon form by the following series of elementary row operations.

$$B = \begin{pmatrix} 2 & 1 & -1 & 2 \\ 0 & -5 & 3 & 1 \\ 2 & 11 & -7 & 1 \end{pmatrix} \qquad \begin{array}{l} \text{row 1 of } A \\ -2(\text{row 1}) + (\text{row 2}) \text{ of } A \\ \text{row 3 of } A \end{array}$$

$$C = \begin{pmatrix} 2 & 1 & -1 & 2 \\ 0 & -5 & 3 & 1 \\ 0 & 10 & -6 & -1 \end{pmatrix} \qquad \begin{array}{l} \text{row 1 of } B \\ \text{row 2 of } B \\ -1(\text{row 1}) + (\text{row 3}) \text{ of } B \end{array}$$

$$D = \begin{pmatrix} 2 & 1 & -1 & 2 \\ 0 & -5 & 3 & 1 \\ 0 & 0 & 0 & 1 \end{pmatrix} \qquad \begin{array}{l} \text{row 1 of } C \\ \text{row 2 of } C \\ 2(\text{row 2}) + (\text{row 3}) \text{ of } C \end{array}$$

D is the augmented matrix of the system

$$\begin{cases} 2x + y - z = 2 \\ -5y + 3z = 1 \\ 0 = 1. \end{cases} \tag{2}$$

The third equation of system (2) is false. Therefore, the system has no solution. This means that the given system (1) also has no solution, or, if you wish, that the solution set is the empty set $\varnothing$. We call such a system inconsistent.

Problem 4. Solve the system

$$\begin{cases} 7x + 3y = -2 \\ 2x + y + z = 0 \\ 3x + y - 2z = -2. \end{cases} \quad (1)$$

Solution. The system has augmented matrix

$$A = \begin{pmatrix} 7 & 3 & 0 & -2 \\ 2 & 1 & 1 & 0 \\ 3 & 1 & -2 & -2 \end{pmatrix}.$$

It can be put into echelon form by a series of elementary row operations, as follows.

$$B = \begin{pmatrix} 1 & \frac{3}{7} & 0 & -\frac{2}{7} \\ 2 & 1 & 1 & 0 \\ 3 & 1 & -2 & -2 \end{pmatrix} \qquad \begin{array}{l} \frac{1}{7}(\text{row } 1) \text{ of } A \\ \text{row } 2 \text{ of } A \\ \text{row } 3 \text{ of } A \end{array}$$

In going from matrix B to C, we do *two* elementary row operations at once to save steps.

$$C = \begin{pmatrix} 1 & \frac{3}{7} & 0 & -\frac{2}{7} \\ 0 & \frac{1}{7} & 1 & \frac{4}{7} \\ 0 & -\frac{2}{7} & -2 & -\frac{8}{7} \end{pmatrix} \qquad \begin{array}{l} \text{row } 1 \text{ of } B \\ -2(\text{row } 1) + \text{row } 2 \text{ of } B \\ -3(\text{row } 1) + \text{row } 3 \text{ of } B \end{array}$$

$$D = \begin{pmatrix} 1 & \frac{3}{7} & 0 & -\frac{2}{7} \\ 0 & 1 & 7 & 4 \\ 0 & -\frac{2}{7} & -2 & -\frac{8}{7} \end{pmatrix} \qquad \begin{array}{l} \text{row } 1 \text{ of } C \\ 7(\text{row } 2) \text{ of } C \\ \text{row } 3 \text{ of } C \end{array}$$

Again, we do two elementary row operations in going from D to E.

$$E = \begin{pmatrix} 1 & 0 & -3 & -2 \\ 0 & 1 & 7 & 4 \\ 0 & 0 & 0 & 0 \end{pmatrix} \qquad \begin{array}{l} -\frac{3}{7}(\text{row } 2) + \text{row } 1 \text{ of } D \\ \text{row } 2 \text{ of } D \\ \frac{2}{7}(\text{row } 2) + \text{row } 3 \text{ of } D \end{array}$$

Matrix E is the augmented matrix of the system

$$\begin{cases} x - 3z = -2 \\ y + 7z = 4 \\ 0 = 0 \end{cases} \quad (2)$$

which is equivalent to system (1).

The last equation of system (2) is always true. The first two equations can be solved for x and y for any given value of z:

if $z = 0$, $x = -2$ and $y = 4$,
if $z = 5$, $x = 13$ and $y = -31$,
if $z = k$, $x = 3k - 2$ and $y = -7k + 4$.

In other words

$$x = 3k - 2, \quad y = -7k + 4, \quad z = k$$

is a solution of (2) and hence of the given system (1), for every number k. Hence, there are infinitely many different solutions of the system.

Check. $7(3k - 2) + 3(-7k + 4) \overset{?}{=} -2$
$2(3k - 2) + (-7k + 4) + k \overset{?}{=} 0$
$3(3k - 2) + (-7k + 4) - 2k \overset{?}{=} -2$

As shown in Problems 2 and 4 above, the augmented matrix of a system of linear equations can be put in a *reduced echelon form* by elementary row operations. The reduced echelon form has two characteristics in addition to being in echelon form:

1. Each row which has nonzero elements has 1 as its first non-zero element.
2. Each column containing one of the beginning 1's of a row has zeros as its other elements.

For example, the matrix below is in reduced echelon form.

$$\begin{pmatrix} 1 & 0 & 5 & 0 \\ 0 & 1 & 2 & 0 \\ 0 & 0 & 0 & 1 \end{pmatrix}$$

Note that each row has 1 as its first nonzero element. The columns containing these three beginning 1's are the first, second, and fourth, and each consists of two zeros and one 1.

Exercises

1. Solve each of the following systems.

(a) $\begin{cases} x - y = -1 \\ 3x + y = 5 \end{cases}$

(b) $\begin{cases} x - 2y = -5 \\ 2x + y = 0 \end{cases}$

2. Solve each of the following systems.

(a) $\begin{cases} x + 2y = 5 \\ 2x - 3y = 3 \end{cases}$

(b) $\begin{cases} x - y = 2 \\ 2x + 3y = 4 \end{cases}$

3. Solve each of the following systems.

(a) $\begin{cases} 4x + y = 0 \\ 3x + 2y = 5 \end{cases}$

(b) $\begin{cases} 3x + 2y = 2 \\ 2x - 5y = 14 \end{cases}$

4. Solve each of the following systems by putting its augmented matrix in reduced echelon form.

(a) $\begin{cases} 2x + 3y = 9 \\ 3x - y = -3 \end{cases}$

(b) $\begin{cases} 5x - 2y = 0 \\ 3x - y = 1 \end{cases}$

5. Solve each of the following systems by putting its augmented matrix in reduced echelon form.

(a) $\begin{cases} 4x - 3y = 4 \\ 2x + 9y = 9 \end{cases}$

(b) $\begin{cases} 3x - 5y = 5 \\ x + 10y = 4 \end{cases}$

6. Solve each of the following systems.

(a) $\begin{cases} 4x + 5y = 0 \\ 8x + 15y = -3 \end{cases}$

(b) $\begin{cases} 2x - 3y = 1 \\ 4x - 6y = 3 \end{cases}$

7. Solve each of the following systems.

(a) $\begin{cases} 2x + 5y = 3 \\ 6x + 15y = 9 \end{cases}$

(b) $\begin{cases} 3x - 6y = 5 \\ 9x - 18y = 7 \end{cases}$

8. Solve each of the following systems.

(a) $\begin{cases} x + 4y = -2 \\ 2x + 8y = -2 \end{cases}$

(b) $\begin{cases} 2x - 7y = -5 \\ 4x - 14y = -10 \end{cases}$

9. Solve each of the following systems.

(a) $\begin{cases} x - 2y + z = -5 \\ 2x + y + 2z = 0 \\ 3x + 2y - 2z = 11 \end{cases}$

(b) $\begin{cases} x + 2y - 2z = -4 \\ -2x + 4y + z = -1 \\ 2x - 3y + 2z = 10 \end{cases}$

10. Solve each of the following systems.

(a) $\begin{cases} x + 2y - 5z = -1 \\ -3x - y + 2z = 5 \\ -4x + y - 6z = 5 \end{cases}$

(b) $\begin{cases} a - 2b = 4 \\ 2a - b + c = 8 \\ 3a + b = 5 \end{cases}$

11. Solve each of the following systems.

(a) $\begin{cases} 3p - q + 2r = -1 \\ p + 2q + 3r = 9 \\ -3p + 5q - 4r = -7 \end{cases}$

(b) $\begin{cases} 3x + 4y - z = 2 \\ 2x - 3y - 4z = 5 \\ x + 2y + z = 0 \end{cases}$

12. Solve each of the following systems.

(a) $\begin{cases} 2x - 3y + 8z = 2 \\ 3x - 3y + 2z = 1 \\ 5x + 6y - 6z = 3 \end{cases}$

(b) $\begin{cases} 2r - 3s + 4t = 6 \\ 5r + s + 3t = 14 \\ 3r + 2s - t = 0 \end{cases}$

13. Solve each of the following systems.

(a) $\begin{cases} 2x + 3y - z = 5 \\ 7x - 2y - 3z = -5 \\ 5x + 4y - 2z = 8 \end{cases}$
(b) $\begin{cases} 3x - 5y + z = 1 \\ 2x - z = 0 \\ 5x + y - 3z = 4 \end{cases}$

14. Solve each of the following systems.

(a) $\begin{cases} 5p + 3q - r = 4 \\ 2p + q + 2r = 5 \\ 3p + 2q - 3r = 2 \end{cases}$
(b) $\begin{cases} 3a - 2c + b = -1 \\ 2a - b + 3c = 9 \\ b + 3a - c = 2 \end{cases}$

15. Solve each of the following systems.

(a) $\begin{cases} 2x + y - 4z = 9 \\ 3x + 2y - 5z = 14 \\ 2x + 5y + 4z = 13 \end{cases}$
(b) $\begin{cases} 2x + 2y - 2z = 6 \\ 3x - 9z = 12 \\ 4y + 8z = 4 \end{cases}$

16. Solve each of the following systems.

(a) $\begin{cases} 3x + 4y - 7z = 10 \\ 2x + 5y - 14z = 9 \\ 4x - 3y + 24z = 4 \end{cases}$
(b) $\begin{cases} 2x + 3y - 6z = 7 \\ 5x - 2y + 23z = 8 \\ 3x + 2y + z = 8 \end{cases}$

17. Consider the system $\begin{cases} ax + by = c \\ dx + ey = f \end{cases}$. If the system has no solution, what relation, if any, is there between the ratios a/d, b/e, and c/f?

18. Consider the system $\begin{cases} ax + by = c \\ dx + ey = f \end{cases}$. If the system has infinitely many solutions, what relation, if any, is there between the ratios a/d, b/e, and c/f?

10–5 MULTIPLICATION OF MATRICES

Among matrices, one special type consists of only one row. It is called a *row vector* and is described by the number of elements it contains. For example,

$$(3 \quad 2 \quad -1)$$

is a 1×3 matrix and is also a *three-dimensional row vector*, and

$$(-4 \quad 0 \quad 2 \quad 7 \quad 5)$$

is a 1×5 matrix and is also a *five-dimensional row vector*.

Another type of special interest consists of only one column and is called a *column vector*. It is also described by the number of elements it contains. For example,

$$\begin{pmatrix} 2 \\ 1 \end{pmatrix}$$

is a 2×1 matrix and also a *two-dimensional column vector*, and

$$\begin{pmatrix} 7 \\ 2 \\ 0 \\ 4 \\ 1 \end{pmatrix}$$

is a 5×1 matrix and also a *five-dimensional column vector*.

If A is an n-dimensional row vector and B is an n-dimensional column vector, we define the product of A and B, denoted by AB, to be the sum of the products obtained by multiplying the first element of A by the first element of B, the second element of A by the second element of B, the third element of A by the third element of B, etc., and adding all of the products. Thus the product of two vectors can only be taken if they have the same dimension, and the product is a number.

If $A = (1 \quad 7)$ and $B = \begin{pmatrix} 2 \\ -2 \end{pmatrix}$, then

$$AB = (1)(2) + (7)(-2) = -12.$$

If $C = (4 \quad 2 \quad -1)$ and $D = \begin{pmatrix} 3 \\ 0 \\ 5 \end{pmatrix}$, then

$$CD = (4)(3) + (2)(0) + (-1)(5) = 7.$$

Generally, if

$$E = (a_1 \quad a_2 \quad \ldots \quad a_n) \quad \text{and} \quad F = \begin{pmatrix} b_1 \\ b_2 \\ \vdots \\ b_n \end{pmatrix}$$

we can find EF and it is equal to $a_1b_1 + a_2b_2 + \cdots + a_nb_n$. But if $G = (c_1c_2 \cdots c_k)$ and $k \neq n$, we say that the product GF is *not* defined.

Problem 1. If $A = \begin{pmatrix} 1 \\ 0 \\ 4 \end{pmatrix}$, $B = \begin{pmatrix} 7 \\ 3 \\ 2 \end{pmatrix}$, $C = (2 \quad 3 \quad 0)$, find

(a) CA, (b) CB, (c) AB.

Solution. (a) $CA = (2)(1) + (3)(0) + (0)(4) = 2$
         (b) $CB = (2)(7) + (3)(3) + (0)(2) = 23$
         (c) AB is not defined—multiplication of vectors is defined only for a row vector on the left and a column vector on the right.

From the definition of the multiplication of vectors, we shall define the multiplication of matrices. First we impose a restriction analogous to the dimension restriction on vectors. We can, so far, only multiply a $1 \times n$ matrix, on the left, by an $n \times 1$ matrix, on the right. We shall extend the definition so that we can multiply any matrix of n columns, on the left, by any matrix of n rows, on the right. We shall thus be able to multiply any $m \times n$ matrix by any $n \times p$ matrix and, as we shall see, the product is an $m \times p$ matrix.

Let us first multiply a three-dimensional row vector on the right by a 3×2 matrix.

$$(a_1 \quad a_2 \quad a_3) \begin{pmatrix} b_{11} & b_{12} \\ b_{21} & b_{22} \\ b_{31} & b_{32} \end{pmatrix}$$

We can multiply the row vector which is the first matrix by the column vector which is the first column of the second matrix to get $a_1 b_{11} + a_2 b_{21} + a_3 b_{31}$. This number, which is the product of the first (and only) row of the left matrix and the first column of the right matrix, is the element in the first row and first column of the product matrix. Similarly, we can take the product of the first row of the left matrix and the second column of the right matrix to get $a_1 b_{12} + a_2 b_{22} + a_3 b_{32}$ and this is the element in the first row and second column of the product. The product of the 1×3 matrix and the 3×2 is a 1×2 matrix:

$$(a_1 \quad a_1 \quad a_3) \begin{pmatrix} b_{11} & b_{12} \\ b_{21} & b_{22} \\ b_{31} & b_{32} \end{pmatrix} = (a_1 b_{11} + a_2 b_{21} + a_3 b_{31} \quad a_1 b_{12} + a_2 b_{22} + a_3 b_{32}).$$

Problem 2. If $A = (3 \quad 0 \quad -1 \quad 4)$ and $B = \begin{pmatrix} 2 & 3 & 3 \\ 1 & 2 & 2 \\ -2 & 4 & 4 \\ 0 & 1 & -4 \end{pmatrix}$, find AB.

Solution. We are multiplying a 1×4 matrix by a 4×3 matrix and, from what we have been told, the product will be a 1×3 matrix. We find the element in the first row and first column of the product by multiplying A by the first column of B to get $(3)(2) + (0)(1) + (-1)(-2) + (4)(0) = 8$. Similarly the element in the first row and second column of AB is $(3)(3) + (0)(2) + (-1)(4) + (4)(1) = 9$. We find the element in the first row and third column of AB by multiplying the first row of A by the third column of B, obtaining $(3)(3) + (0)(2) + (-1)(4) + (4)(-4) = -11$. Hence

$$AB = (8 \quad 9 \quad -11).$$

The technique just illustrated may be extended to any pair of matrices, if the left matrix has as many columns as the right matrix has rows. For then each row of the left matrix is a row vector and each column of the right matrix is a column vector and these row vectors and column vectors are all of the same dimension. Thus, we can multiply the third row of the left matrix by the second column of the right matrix to find the number which is the entry in the third row and second column of the product. More generally, the element in the ith row and jth column of the product is the product of the row vector which is the ith row of the left matrix and the column vector which is the jth column of the right matrix. These can be multiplied only if they are of the same dimension and hence the requirement that the left matrix have exactly as many columns as the right matrix has rows.

In symbols, if A is an $m \times n$ matrix and B is an $n \times p$ matrix, we can find the product $C = AB$ and $c_{ij} = a_{i1}b_{1j} + a_{i2}b_{2j} + \cdots + a_{in}b_{nj}$. If A is an $m \times n$ matrix and B is an $r \times p$ matrix and $n \neq r$, the product AB is undefined.

Problem 3. If

$$A = \begin{pmatrix} 4 & -2 & 1 \\ 3 & 2 & 4 \end{pmatrix}, \quad B = \begin{pmatrix} 2 & 3 & -1 \\ 0 & 3 & 1 \\ -1 & 2 & 5 \end{pmatrix} \quad \text{and} \quad C = \begin{pmatrix} 2 \\ 3 \\ -4 \end{pmatrix},$$

find (a) AB, (b) AC, (c) BC.

Solution.

(a) AB is the product of a 2×3 matrix and a 3×3 matrix; hence it can be found and is a 2×3 matrix:

$$AB = \begin{pmatrix} 7 & 8 & -1 \\ 2 & 23 & 19 \end{pmatrix}.$$

To see where a particular entry comes from, the element in the second row and second column of the product is

$$(3 \quad 2 \quad 4)\begin{pmatrix} 3 \\ 3 \\ 2 \end{pmatrix} = (3)(3) + (2)(3) + (4)(2) = 23.$$

(b) AC is the product of a 2×3 matrix and a 3×1 matrix. Hence it can be found and is a 2×1 matrix. The entries are

$$(4 \quad -2 \quad 1)\begin{pmatrix} 2 \\ 3 \\ -4 \end{pmatrix} = (4)(2) + (-2)(3) + (1)(-4) = -2 \text{ and}$$

$$(3 \quad 2 \quad 4)\begin{pmatrix} 2 \\ 3 \\ -4 \end{pmatrix} = (3)(2) + (2)(3) + (4)(-4) = -4.$$

$$AC = \begin{pmatrix} -2 \\ -4 \end{pmatrix}$$

(c) BC is the product of a 3×3 matrix and a 3×1 matrix. It is a 3×1 matrix:

$$BC = \begin{pmatrix} 17 \\ 5 \\ -16 \end{pmatrix}.$$

You check the various entries.

Let $A = \begin{pmatrix} a_{11} & a_{12} \\ a_{21} & a_{22} \end{pmatrix}$ and $B = \begin{pmatrix} 1 & 0 \\ 0 & 1 \end{pmatrix}$. Since each is a 2×2 matrix

we can find both products AB and BA and each will be a 2×2 matrix. The elements of the first row of AB are $(a_{11})(1) + (a_{12})(0) = a_{11}$ and $(a_{11})(0) + (a_{12})(1) = a_{12}$. The elements of the second row of AB are $(a_{21})(1) + (a_{22})(0) = a_{21}$ and $(a_{21})(0) + (a_{22})(1) = a_{22}$. Hence

$$AB = \begin{pmatrix} a_{11} & a_{12} \\ a_{21} & a_{22} \end{pmatrix} = A.$$

Similarly, the elements of the first row of BA are $(1)(a_{11}) + (0)(a_{21}) = a_{11}$ and $(1)(a_{12}) + (0)(a_{22}) = a_{12}$. Those of the second row of BA are $(0)(a_{11}) + (1)(a_{21}) = a_{21}$ and $(0)(a_{12}) + (1)(a_{22}) = a_{22}$. And so, we see that

$$BA = \begin{pmatrix} a_{11} & a_{12} \\ a_{21} & a_{22} \end{pmatrix} = A.$$

B is thus the special matrix, among all 2×2 matrices, which has the property that

$$AB = BA = A \qquad \text{for every } 2 \times 2 \text{ matrix } A.$$

It is called the *identity matrix* and usually designated by I, with last result written

$$I = \begin{pmatrix} 1 & 0 \\ 0 & 1 \end{pmatrix}$$

$$AI = IA = A \qquad \text{for every } 2 \times 2 \text{ matrix } A.$$

In one of your exercises, you will verify that

$$\begin{pmatrix} 1 & 0 & 0 \\ 0 & 1 & 0 \\ 0 & 0 & 1 \end{pmatrix}$$

is the multiplicative identity matrix among all 3×3 matrices.

If P is a 2×3 matrix and Q is a 3×2 matrix, we can find PQ and it will be a 2×2 matrix. We can also find QP and it will be a 3×3 matrix. Since we can only talk about equality of matrices if they have the same dimension, we cannot even suggest that PQ and QP are equal. Since $PQ \neq QP$, we see that matrix multiplication is *noncommutative*, probably your first exposure to algebraic multiplication without commutativity.

Exercises

1. If $A = (2 \quad -1)$, $B = (0 \quad 3)$, $C = \begin{pmatrix} -3 \\ 1 \end{pmatrix}$, $D = \begin{pmatrix} 2 \\ -2 \end{pmatrix}$, find

   (a) AC (b) AD (c) BC (d) BD.

2. If $E = (0 \quad 1)$, $F = (2 \quad 2)$, $G = \begin{pmatrix} -1 \\ 4 \end{pmatrix}$, $H = \begin{pmatrix} 3 \\ 0 \end{pmatrix}$, find

   (a) EG (b) EH (c) FG (d) FH

3. If $R = (2 \quad 3)$ and $S = \begin{pmatrix} -3 \\ 2 \end{pmatrix}$, find

   (a) RS (b) SR

4. If $P = (a \quad b)$ and $Q = \begin{pmatrix} c \\ d \end{pmatrix}$, find

   (a) PQ (b) QP

5. If $A = (2 \quad 0 \quad -2)$, $B = (-1 \quad 3 \quad 4)$, $C = \begin{pmatrix} 4 \\ 2 \\ 1 \end{pmatrix}$, $D = \begin{pmatrix} 0 \\ 1 \\ -1 \end{pmatrix}$, find

    (a) AC (b) AD (c) BC (d) BD

6. If $E = (0 \quad -1 \quad 3)$, $F = (2 \quad 3 \quad 1)$, $G = \begin{pmatrix} 1 \\ 0 \\ -4 \end{pmatrix}$, $H = \begin{pmatrix} 2 \\ -2 \\ 1 \end{pmatrix}$, find

    (a) EG (b) EH (c) FG (d) FH

7. If $J = (2 \quad 0 \quad 1)$ and $K = \begin{pmatrix} -1 \\ 2 \\ 2 \end{pmatrix}$, find

    (a) JK (b) KJ

8. If $M = (a \quad b \quad c)$ and $N = \begin{pmatrix} d \\ e \\ f \end{pmatrix}$, find

    (a) MN (b) NM

9. If $A = (2 \quad 3)$, $B = (0 \quad 1)$, $C = \begin{pmatrix} 2 & -1 \\ 1 & 2 \end{pmatrix}$, $D = \begin{pmatrix} 3 & 0 \\ -1 & 2 \end{pmatrix}$, find

    (a) AC (b) AD (c) BC (d) BD

10. If $E = (-1 \quad 1)$, $F = (2 \quad 4)$, $G = \begin{pmatrix} 0 & 1 \\ 1 & 0 \end{pmatrix}$, $H = \begin{pmatrix} -1 & 2 \\ 2 & 3 \end{pmatrix}$, find

    (a) EG (b) EH (c) FG (d) FH

11. If $J = (1 \quad 0 \quad -1)$, $K = (-2 \quad 1 \quad 3)$, $L = \begin{pmatrix} 2 & 4 \\ 0 & -1 \\ 3 & 2 \end{pmatrix}$,

    $M = \begin{pmatrix} 2 & 0 & 3 \\ -1 & 1 & 2 \\ 2 & -3 & 0 \end{pmatrix}$, find

    (a) JL (b) JM (c) KL (d) KM

12. If $P = (2 \quad 1 \quad -1)$, $Q = (0 \quad 1 \quad 3)$, $R = \begin{pmatrix} 1 & -3 \\ 2 & -2 \\ 3 & -1 \end{pmatrix}$,

    $S = \begin{pmatrix} 0 & 1 & 4 \\ 2 & -1 & 1 \\ 3 & 0 & 1 \end{pmatrix}$, find

    (a) PR (b) PS (c) QR (d) RS

13. If $T = (a \quad b)$, $U = \begin{pmatrix} c \\ d \end{pmatrix}$, $V = \begin{pmatrix} 1 & 0 \\ 0 & 1 \end{pmatrix}$, find

    (a) TU (b) TV (c) VU

14. If $W = (a \quad b \quad c)$, $X = \begin{pmatrix} d \\ e \\ f \end{pmatrix}$, $Y = \begin{pmatrix} 1 & 0 & 0 \\ 0 & 1 & 0 \\ 0 & 0 & 1 \end{pmatrix}$, find

    (a) WX (b) WY (c) YX

15. If $A = \begin{pmatrix} 2 & 3 \\ 1 & 2 \end{pmatrix}$, $B = \begin{pmatrix} 2 & 0 & -1 \\ 1 & -3 & 2 \end{pmatrix}$, $C = \begin{pmatrix} 1 & 2 & 3 \\ 0 & 1 & -1 \\ 2 & 0 & 2 \end{pmatrix}$,

    $D = \begin{pmatrix} 1 & 0 & 0 \\ 0 & 1 & 0 \\ 0 & 0 & 1 \end{pmatrix}$, find

    (a) AB (b) BC (c) BD (d) CD (e) DC

16. If $E = \begin{pmatrix} 1 & 3 \\ 0 & -1 \end{pmatrix}$, $F = \begin{pmatrix} 0 & -1 & 2 \\ 3 & -4 & 5 \end{pmatrix}$, $G = \begin{pmatrix} 0 & -1 & 2 \\ 1 & 2 & -2 \\ -2 & 0 & 5 \end{pmatrix}$ and

    $H = \begin{pmatrix} 1 & 0 & 0 \\ 0 & 1 & 0 \\ 0 & 0 & 1 \end{pmatrix}$, find

    (a) EF (b) FG (c) FH (d) GH (e) HG

17. If $A = \begin{pmatrix} 1 & 0 \\ 0 & 1 \end{pmatrix}$ and $B = \begin{pmatrix} 0 & 1 \\ -1 & 0 \end{pmatrix}$, find

    (a) $AA(=A^2)$ (b) AB (c) BA (d) $BB \ (=B^2)$
    (e) $B^4 \ (=B^2B^2)$

18. If $P = \begin{pmatrix} 1 & 0 \\ 0 & 2 \end{pmatrix}$ and $Q = \begin{pmatrix} 2 & 0 \\ 0 & 1 \end{pmatrix}$, find

    (a) $PP(=P^2)$ (b) PQ (c) QP (d) $QQ(=Q^2)$

19. If $A = \begin{pmatrix} a_{11} & a_{12} & a_{13} \\ a_{21} & a_{22} & a_{23} \\ a_{31} & a_{32} & a_{33} \end{pmatrix}$ and $B = \begin{pmatrix} 1 & 0 & 0 \\ 0 & 1 & 0 \\ 0 & 0 & 1 \end{pmatrix}$, find

    (a) AB (b) BA (c) $BB(=B^2)$

20. What can you say about matrix B of exercise 19?

21. If $P = \begin{pmatrix} 2 & 1 \\ 5 & 3 \end{pmatrix}$ and $Q = \begin{pmatrix} 3 & -1 \\ -5 & 2 \end{pmatrix}$, find

    (a) PQ (b) QP

22. If $R = \begin{pmatrix} 4 & 3 \\ 5 & 4 \end{pmatrix}$ and $S = \begin{pmatrix} 4 & -3 \\ -5 & 4 \end{pmatrix}$, find

    (a) RS (b) SR

23. If $T = \begin{pmatrix} 2 & 3 \\ 4 & 6 \end{pmatrix}$ and $U = \begin{pmatrix} 3 & -9 \\ -2 & 6 \end{pmatrix}$, find

    (a) TU (b) UT

24. If $V = \begin{pmatrix} 1 & 4 \\ 4 & 16 \end{pmatrix}$ and $W = \begin{pmatrix} -8 & 4 \\ 2 & -1 \end{pmatrix}$, find

(a) VW (b) WV

25. If $A = \begin{pmatrix} 4 & 0 & 5 \\ 0 & 1 & -6 \\ 3 & 0 & 4 \end{pmatrix}$ and $B = \begin{pmatrix} 4 & 0 & -5 \\ -18 & 1 & 24 \\ -3 & 0 & 4 \end{pmatrix}$, find

(a) AB (b) BA

26. Verify that the multiplication of 2×2 matrices is an associative. That is, if A, B, C are 2×2 matrices then $A(BC) = (AB)C$.

Preparation for Section 10–6

1. If $A = \begin{pmatrix} a & b \\ c & d \end{pmatrix}$ and $B = \begin{pmatrix} d & -b \\ -c & a \end{pmatrix}$, find (a) AB (b) BA

2. If $C = \begin{pmatrix} a & b \\ c & d \end{pmatrix}$ and $D = \begin{pmatrix} \dfrac{d}{ad-bc} & \dfrac{-b}{ad-bc} \\ \dfrac{-c}{ad-bc} & \dfrac{a}{ad-bc} \end{pmatrix}$, find (a) CD (b) DC

10–6 INVERTING A MATRIX

If

$$A = \begin{pmatrix} 2 & 7 \\ 1 & 4 \end{pmatrix}, \quad B = \begin{pmatrix} 4 & -7 \\ -1 & 2 \end{pmatrix}$$

then we have

$$AB = \begin{pmatrix} 1 & 0 \\ 0 & 1 \end{pmatrix}, \quad BA = \begin{pmatrix} 1 & 0 \\ 0 & 1 \end{pmatrix}.$$

Thus,

$$AB - BA = I,$$

where I is the 2×2 identity matrix. This means that A and B are *multiplicative inverses* of each other. We often indicate the inverse of a matrix A by

$$A^{-1}.$$

The system of linear equations

$$\begin{cases} 2x + 7y = 2 \\ x + 4y = -3 \end{cases} \tag{1}$$

can be expressed in matrix form

$$\begin{pmatrix} 2x + 7y \\ x + 4y \end{pmatrix} = \begin{pmatrix} 2 \\ -3 \end{pmatrix}.$$

In turn, the 2×1 matrix on the left is a product of two matrices:

$$\begin{pmatrix} 2 & 7 \\ 1 & 4 \end{pmatrix} \begin{pmatrix} x \\ y \end{pmatrix} = \begin{pmatrix} 2 \\ -3 \end{pmatrix}$$

This matrix equation has the form

$$AX = K, \qquad (2)$$

where

$$A = \begin{pmatrix} 2 & 7 \\ 1 & 4 \end{pmatrix}, \quad X = \begin{pmatrix} x \\ y \end{pmatrix}, \quad K = \begin{pmatrix} 2 \\ -3 \end{pmatrix}.$$

We saw above that matrix A has an inverse (labeled B above),

$$A^{-1} = \begin{pmatrix} 4 & -7 \\ -1 & 2 \end{pmatrix}.$$

Now multiply each side of equation (2) on the left by A^{-1}:

$$A^{-1}(AX) = A^{-1}K.$$

Since matrix multiplication is associative, $A^{-1}(AX) = (A^{-1}A)X$ and

$$(A^{-1}A)X = A^{-1}K$$
$$IX = A^{-1}K, \quad (I \text{ is the identity matrix})$$
$$X = A^{-1}K \qquad (3)$$

Thus,

$$\begin{pmatrix} x \\ y \end{pmatrix} = \begin{pmatrix} 4 & -7 \\ -1 & 2 \end{pmatrix} \begin{pmatrix} 2 \\ -3 \end{pmatrix},$$

or

$$\begin{pmatrix} x \\ y \end{pmatrix} = \begin{pmatrix} 29 \\ -8 \end{pmatrix}. \qquad (4)$$

From (4), we see that the solution of system (1) is

$$x = 29, \ y = -8.$$

Any system of n linear equations in n unknowns can be written in matrix form

$$AX = K$$

in the way it was done above for a system of two linear equations in two unknowns. If the $n \times n$ matrix A has an inverse A^{-1}, then the system has solution

$$X = A^{-1}K$$

as shown above.

Not every matrix has an inverse so the method above cannot always be used. Even if matrix A can be proved to have an inverse, it is often very time-consuming to find it.

Does the matrix

$$A = \begin{pmatrix} 4 & 3 \\ 5 & 4 \end{pmatrix}$$

have an inverse? Yes, if there exists a matrix

$$B = \begin{pmatrix} b_{11} & b_{12} \\ b_{21} & b_{22} \end{pmatrix}$$

such that

$$AB = I \qquad \left(I = \begin{pmatrix} 1 & 0 \\ 0 & 1 \end{pmatrix} \right).$$

On multiplying A by B, we get the matrix equation

$$\begin{pmatrix} 4b_{11} + 3b_{21} & 4b_{12} + 3b_{22} \\ 5b_{11} + 4b_{21} & 5b_{12} + 4b_{22} \end{pmatrix} = \begin{pmatrix} 1 & 0 \\ 0 & 1 \end{pmatrix}.$$

Since two matrices are equal if, and only if, their corresponding elements are equal, the matrix equation above is equivalent to the two systems

$$\begin{cases} 4b_{11} + 3b_{21} = 1 \\ 5b_{11} + 4b_{21} = 0 \end{cases} \text{ and } \begin{cases} 4b_{12} + 3b_{22} - 0 \\ 5b_{12} + 4b_{22} = 1 \end{cases}.$$

Both of these systems have the same coefficient matrix and can be solved at the same time, using the echelon method. Combining the two augmented matrices into one and inserting a vertical line to separate the coefficient matrix we have,

$$C = \begin{pmatrix} 4 & 3 & | & 1 & 0 \\ 5 & 4 & | & 0 & 1 \end{pmatrix}.$$

In the problems of Section 10–4, we saw that we could simplify a matrix beyond echelon form to the stage that (a) each row had its first nonzero element a one, (b) each row had its first nonzero element in a later column than the one above it, and (c) each column which contained a one which was the first nonzero element of some row had zero for each of its other elements. This simplification, called the *row reduced echelon form*, exhibited the solution of a system most readily. Matrix C above can be put in row reduced echelon form by a series of elementary row operations, as follows:

$$D = \begin{pmatrix} 1 & \frac{3}{4} & \frac{1}{4} & 0 \\ 5 & 4 & 0 & 1 \end{pmatrix} \qquad \begin{array}{l} \frac{1}{4}(\text{row 1}) \text{ of } C \\ \text{row 2 of } C \end{array}$$

$$E = \begin{pmatrix} 1 & \frac{3}{4} & \frac{1}{4} & 0 \\ 0 & \frac{1}{4} & -\frac{5}{4} & 1 \end{pmatrix} \qquad \begin{array}{l} \text{row 1 of } D \\ -5(\text{row 1}) + \text{row 2 of } D \end{array}$$

$$F = \begin{pmatrix} 1 & \frac{3}{4} & \frac{1}{4} & 0 \\ 0 & 1 & -5 & 4 \end{pmatrix} \qquad \begin{array}{l} \text{row 1 of } E \\ 4(\text{row 2}) \text{ of } E \end{array}$$

$$G = \begin{pmatrix} 1 & 0 & 4 & -3 \\ 0 & 1 & -5 & 4 \end{pmatrix} \qquad \begin{array}{l} -\frac{3}{4}(\text{row 2}) + \text{row 1 of } F \\ \text{row 2 of } F \end{array}$$

The first column to the right of the vertical bar in G is the solution of the first system of equations above, the second column is the solution of the second system. Hence,

$$b_{11} = 4, \ b_{12} = -3$$
$$b_{21} = -5, \ b_{22} = 4.$$

Thus, the inverse of matrix A is

$$A^{-1} = \begin{pmatrix} 4 & -3 \\ -5 & 4 \end{pmatrix}$$

Check

$$\begin{pmatrix} 4 & -3 \\ -5 & 4 \end{pmatrix} \begin{pmatrix} 4 & 3 \\ 5 & 4 \end{pmatrix} = \begin{pmatrix} 1 & 0 \\ 0 & 1 \end{pmatrix}, \quad (A^{-1} A = I)$$

If we stand back to look at the work we have just performed, we see that we have formed a 2×4 matrix with the matrix A comprising the first two columns and the matrix I the last two. We have separated A and I by a vertical bar. In transforming this 2×4 matrix by elementary row operations into row reduced echelon form, we have transformed A into I and I into A^{-1}.

Problem. 1. Find the inverse of

$$A = \begin{pmatrix} 1 & 1 \\ -1 & 1 \end{pmatrix},$$

if, indeed, A has an inverse.

Solution. Form the 2×4 matrix

$$C = \begin{pmatrix} 1 & 1 & 1 & 0 \\ -1 & 1 & 0 & 1 \end{pmatrix}$$

and proceed as above.

$$E = \begin{pmatrix} 1 & 1 & 1 & 0 \\ 0 & 2 & 1 & 1 \end{pmatrix} \qquad \qquad \begin{matrix} \text{row 1 of } C \\ \text{row 1 + row 2 of } C \end{matrix}$$

$$F = \begin{pmatrix} 1 & 1 & 1 & 0 \\ 0 & 1 & \frac{1}{2} & \frac{1}{2} \end{pmatrix} \qquad \qquad \begin{matrix} \text{row 1 of } E \\ \frac{1}{2}(\text{row 2}) \text{ of } E \end{matrix}$$

$$G = \begin{pmatrix} 1 & 0 & \frac{1}{2} & -\frac{1}{2} \\ 0 & 1 & \frac{1}{2} & \frac{1}{2} \end{pmatrix} \qquad \qquad \begin{matrix} -(\text{row 2}) + \text{row 1 of } F \\ \text{row 2 of } F \end{matrix}$$

Hence,

$$A^{-1} = \begin{pmatrix} \frac{1}{2} & -\frac{1}{2} \\ \frac{1}{2} & \frac{1}{2} \end{pmatrix}$$

Check

$$\begin{pmatrix} \frac{1}{2} & -\frac{1}{2} \\ \frac{1}{2} & \frac{1}{2} \end{pmatrix} \begin{pmatrix} 1 & 1 \\ -1 & 1 \end{pmatrix} = \begin{pmatrix} 1 & 0 \\ 0 & 1 \end{pmatrix} \qquad (A^{-1} A = I)$$

Problem 2. Find the inverse of

$$A = \begin{pmatrix} 1 & 4 \\ 4 & 16 \end{pmatrix}$$

if, indeed, A has an inverse.

Solution. Form the 2×4 matrix

$$C = \begin{pmatrix} 1 & 4 & 1 & 0 \\ 4 & 16 & 0 & 1 \end{pmatrix}$$

and proceed as above.

$$E = \begin{pmatrix} 1 & 4 & 1 & 0 \\ 0 & 0 & -4 & 1 \end{pmatrix} \qquad \qquad \begin{matrix} \text{row 1 of } C \\ -4(\text{row 1}) + \text{row 2 of } C \end{matrix}$$

However, we cannot continue as above because of the two zeros in the bottom row. This says, in effect, that

$$0b_{11} + 0b_{21} = -4, \; 0b_{12} + 0b_{22} = 1$$

or $$0 = -4, \qquad\qquad 0 = 1$$

Since the two equations above are false, the matrix A has no inverse.

The problem of finding the inverse of a 3×3 matrix is similar to that of finding the inverse of a 2×2 matrix.

If $A = \begin{pmatrix} a_{11} & a_{12} & a_{13} \\ a_{21} & a_{22} & a_{23} \\ a_{31} & a_{32} & a_{33} \end{pmatrix}$, we want to find a 3×3 matrix B which has the

property that $AB = BA = \begin{pmatrix} 1 & 0 & 0 \\ 0 & 1 & 0 \\ 0 & 0 & 1 \end{pmatrix}$.

This last matrix is, of course, the multiplicative identity among 3×3 matrices. The first column of B can be found by putting the matrix

$$\begin{pmatrix} a_{11} & a_{12} & a_{13} & 1 \\ a_{21} & a_{22} & a_{23} & 0 \\ a_{31} & a_{32} & a_{33} & 0 \end{pmatrix}$$

into row reduced form. In the process A will be transformed into I and the last column into the first column of B. Similarly the second column of B can be found by putting the matrix

$$\begin{pmatrix} a_{11} & a_{12} & a_{13} & 0 \\ a_{21} & a_{22} & a_{23} & 1 \\ a_{31} & a_{32} & a_{33} & 0 \end{pmatrix}$$

into row reduced form. In this process A will be transformed into I and the last column into the second column of B. And the last column of B can be found by putting the matrix

$$\begin{pmatrix} a_{11} & a_{12} & a_{13} & 0 \\ a_{21} & a_{22} & a_{23} & 0 \\ a_{31} & a_{32} & a_{33} & 1 \end{pmatrix}$$

into row reduced form, transforming A into I and the last column into the last column of B. Since each of the three problems involves the same operations—putting an augmented matrix into row reduced form and thereby transforming A into I—the three can be performed at one time by writing the 3×6 matrix

$$\begin{pmatrix} a_{11} & a_{12} & a_{13} & 1 & 0 & 0 \\ a_{21} & a_{22} & a_{23} & 0 & 1 & 0 \\ a_{31} & a_{32} & a_{33} & 0 & 0 & 1 \end{pmatrix}$$

and transforming it into row reduced form. In the process, we can transform the 3×3 matrix A on the left of the vertical line into I and the 3×3 matrix I on the right of the vertical line into A^{-1}.

Problem 3. If $A = \begin{pmatrix} 4 & 0 & -5 \\ -18 & 1 & 24 \\ -3 & 0 & 4 \end{pmatrix}$, find A^{-1}.

Solution. We form the 3×6 matrix

$$C = \begin{pmatrix} 4 & 0 & -5 & 1 & 0 & 0 \\ -18 & 1 & 24 & 0 & 1 & 0 \\ -3 & 0 & 4 & 0 & 0 & 1 \end{pmatrix}$$

and put it into row reduced form by elementary row operations, as follows:

$$D = \begin{pmatrix} 1 & 0 & -\frac{5}{4} & \frac{1}{4} & 0 & 0 \\ -18 & 1 & 24 & 0 & 1 & 0 \\ -3 & 0 & 4 & 0 & 0 & 1 \end{pmatrix} \qquad \begin{matrix} \frac{1}{4}(\text{row } 1) \text{ of } C \\ \text{row } 2 \text{ of } C \\ \text{row } 3 \text{ of } C \end{matrix}$$

$$E = \begin{pmatrix} 1 & 0 & -\frac{5}{4} & \frac{1}{4} & 0 & 0 \\ 0 & 1 & \frac{3}{2} & \frac{9}{2} & 1 & 0 \\ 0 & 0 & \frac{1}{4} & \frac{3}{4} & 0 & 1 \end{pmatrix} \qquad \begin{matrix} \text{row } 1 \text{ of } D \\ 18(\text{row } 1) + \text{row } 2 \text{ of } D \\ 3(\text{row } 1) + \text{row } 3 \text{ of } D \end{matrix}$$

$$F = \begin{pmatrix} 1 & 0 & -\frac{5}{4} & \frac{1}{4} & 0 & 0 \\ 0 & 1 & \frac{3}{2} & \frac{9}{2} & 1 & 0 \\ 0 & 0 & 1 & 3 & 0 & 4 \end{pmatrix} \qquad \begin{matrix} \text{row } 1 \text{ of } E \\ \text{row } 2 \text{ of } E \\ 4 \,(\text{row } 3) \text{ of } E \end{matrix}$$

$$G = \begin{pmatrix} 1 & 0 & 0 & 4 & 0 & 5 \\ 0 & 1 & 0 & 0 & 1 & -6 \\ 0 & 0 & 1 & 3 & 0 & 4 \end{pmatrix} \qquad \begin{matrix} \frac{5}{4}(\text{row } 3) + \text{row } 1 \text{ of } F \\ -\frac{3}{2}(\text{row } 3) + \text{row } 2 \text{ of } F \\ \text{row } 3 \text{ of } F \end{matrix}$$

Hence $A^{-1} = \begin{pmatrix} 4 & 0 & 5 \\ 0 & 1 & -6 \\ 3 & 0 & 4 \end{pmatrix}$.

You can check this result by multiplication.

This technique is useful in that it will find the inverse of a matrix if it has one and will demonstrate the nonexistence of an inverse if there is none. In the latter case, the given matrix cannot be transformed into I as a row of zeros will appear on the left of the vertical line.

The inverse of a matrix has use in solving systems of equations. It also has interest for the student of abstract algebra and is used in problems in linear algebra and in probability. In the field of probability, probabilities are frequently displayed in a matrix and the inverse of a matrix is fundamental to analysis of certain problems. These are, unfortunately, beyond the scope of this book.

Exercises

1. If $A = \begin{pmatrix} a \\ b \end{pmatrix}$, $B = (c \quad d)$ and $I = \begin{pmatrix} 1 & 0 \\ 0 & 1 \end{pmatrix}$, find

   (a) IA (b) BI

2. If $C = \begin{pmatrix} c_{11} & c_{12} & c_{13} \\ c_{21} & c_{22} & c_{23} \end{pmatrix}$, $D = \begin{pmatrix} d_{11} & d_{12} \\ d_{21} & d_{22} \\ d_{31} & d_{32} \end{pmatrix}$ and $I = \begin{pmatrix} 1 & 0 \\ 0 & 1 \end{pmatrix}$,

   find (a) IC (b) DI

3. (a) Find the inverse of the matrix $\begin{pmatrix} 3 & -2 \\ -4 & 3 \end{pmatrix}$.

   (b) Use the inverse found in (a) to solve the system
   $$\begin{cases} 3x - 2y = 2 \\ -4x + 3y = 3. \end{cases}$$

   (c) Use the inverse found in (a) to solve the system
   $$\begin{cases} 3x - 2y = 4 \\ -4x + 3y = 1. \end{cases}$$

4. (a) Find the inverse of the matrix $\begin{pmatrix} 7 & 2 \\ -4 & -1 \end{pmatrix}$.

   (b) Use the inverse found in (a) to solve the system
   $$\begin{cases} 7x + 2y = 5 \\ -4x - y = 2. \end{cases}$$

   (c) Use the inverse found in (a) to solve the system
   $$\begin{cases} 7x + 2y = 0 \\ -4x - y = 3. \end{cases}$$

5. (a) Find the inverse of the matrix $\begin{pmatrix} a & b \\ c & d \end{pmatrix}$.

   (b) What condition must a, b, c, and d satisfy if the matrix in (a) is to have an inverse?

(c) If a, b, c, and d are all integers, what conditions must they satisfy if the matrix in (a) is to have an inverse all of whose entries are integers?

6. (a) If A, B, and C are 2×2 matrices and B and C are both inverses of A, i.e., $AB = BA = I$ and $AC = CA = I$, supply the reason for each step in the continued equation $C = CI = C(AB) = (CA)B = IB = B$.

(b) How many different multiplicative inverses can a matrix have?

7. (a) Find the inverse of the matrix $\begin{pmatrix} 3 & 2 \\ -4 & 1 \end{pmatrix}$.

(b) Use the inverse found in (a) to solve the system
$$\begin{cases} 3x + 2y = 8 \\ -4x + y = 3. \end{cases}$$

(c) Use the inverse found in (a) to solve the system
$$\begin{cases} 3x + 2y = 7 \\ -4x + y = 0. \end{cases}$$

8. (a) Find the inverse of the matrix $\begin{pmatrix} 4 & 1 \\ 2 & 3 \end{pmatrix}$.

(b) Use the inverse found in (a) to solve the system
$$\begin{cases} 4x + y = 5 \\ 2x + 3y = -1. \end{cases}$$

(c) Use the inverse found in (a) to solve the system
$$\begin{cases} 4x + y = 2 \\ 2x + 3y = -2. \end{cases}$$

9. (a) Find the inverse of the matrix $\begin{pmatrix} -1 & -2 & -\frac{1}{2} \\ 2 & 3 & 1 \\ 0 & 1 & \frac{1}{2} \end{pmatrix}$.

(b) Use the inverse found in (a) to solve the system
$$\begin{cases} -x - 2y - \frac{1}{2}z = 3 \\ 2x + 3y + z = -1 \\ y + \frac{1}{2}z = 2. \end{cases}$$

(c) Use the inverse found in (a) to solve the system
$$\begin{cases} -x - 2y - \frac{1}{2}z = 1 \\ 2x + 3y + z = 0 \\ y + \frac{1}{2}z = -3. \end{cases}$$

10. Show that the matrix $\begin{pmatrix} 1 & 1 & 1 \\ 1 & 0 & 1 \\ 1 & 3 & 1 \end{pmatrix}$ does not have an inverse.

11. (a) Find the inverse of the matrix $\begin{pmatrix} 0 & 1 & 2 \\ -1 & 3 & 0 \\ 1 & -2 & 1 \end{pmatrix}$.

(b) Use the inverse found in (a) to solve the system
$$\begin{cases} y + 2z = 3 \\ -x + 3y = 8 \\ x - 2y + z = -1. \end{cases}$$

(c) Use the inverse found in (a) to solve the system
$$\begin{cases} y + 2z = 4 \\ -x + 3y = 0 \\ x - 2y + z = 1. \end{cases}$$

12. (a) Find the inverse of the matrix $\begin{pmatrix} 2 & 0 & 3 \\ 0 & -1 & 7 \\ 9 & 2 & 0 \end{pmatrix}$.

(b) Use the inverse found in (a) to solve the system
$$\begin{cases} 2x + 3z = 4 \\ -y + 7z = 0 \\ 9x + 2y = -1. \end{cases}$$

(c) Use the inverse found in (a) to solve the system
$$\begin{cases} 2x + 3z = 2 \\ -y + 7z = 5 \\ 9x + 2y = 0. \end{cases}$$

10–7 DETERMINANTS

A matrix is called *square* if it has the same number of rows and columns. Thus,

$$\begin{pmatrix} 4 & 1 \\ -1 & 3 \end{pmatrix} \qquad \text{(2 × 2 matrix)}$$

and

$$\begin{pmatrix} -1 & 0 & 5 \\ 7 & 3 & 2 \\ 0 & 5 & 9 \end{pmatrix} \qquad \text{(3 × 3 matrix)}$$

are square matrices.

Associated with each square matrix A is a number called the *determinant* of A and denoted by

$$|A|.$$

The 2×2 matrix

$$A = \begin{pmatrix} a & b \\ c & d \end{pmatrix}$$

has determinant

$$|A| = \begin{vmatrix} a & b \\ c & d \end{vmatrix} = ad - bc.$$

For example,

$$A = \begin{vmatrix} 8 & 5 \\ 2 & 3 \end{vmatrix} = 8 \cdot 3 - 5 \cdot 2 = 14,$$

$$A = \begin{vmatrix} 4 & 1 \\ -1 & 3 \end{vmatrix} = 4 \cdot 3 - 1 \cdot (-1) = 13.$$

For 3×3 and larger square matrices, the determinant of a matrix is given in terms of determinants of matrices of smaller size, as described below.

If we cross out a row and a column of a square matrix, we have left a smaller square matrix. For example, if we cross out row 2 and column 3 of the 3×3 matrix

$$A = \begin{pmatrix} -1 & 0 & 5 \\ 7 & 3 & 2 \\ 0 & 5 & 9 \end{pmatrix} \begin{matrix} \text{column 3} \\ \\ \leftarrow \text{row 2} \end{matrix}$$

we have left the 2×2 matrix

$$A_{23} = \begin{pmatrix} -1 & 0 \\ 0 & 5 \end{pmatrix}.$$

Notice that the subscripts indicate which row and column are crossed out. We call A_{23} a *minor matrix* of A, or simply a *minor* of A. Other minor matrices of A are

$$\begin{matrix} \text{column 1} \\ \text{row 1} \rightarrow \end{matrix} \begin{pmatrix} -1 & 0 & 5 \\ 7 & 3 & 2 \\ 0 & 5 & 9 \end{pmatrix}, \quad A_{11} = \begin{pmatrix} 3 & 2 \\ 5 & 9 \end{pmatrix},$$

similarly,

$$A_{12} = \begin{pmatrix} 7 & 2 \\ 0 & 9 \end{pmatrix}, \qquad A_{13} = \begin{pmatrix} 7 & 3 \\ 0 & 5 \end{pmatrix}.$$

We evaluate the determinant of a 3×3 matrix by an expansion by minors of a row in the following manner.

If A is a 3×3 matrix with row 1 $= (a \quad b \quad c)$, then

$$|A| = (-1)^{1+1}a|A_{11}| + (-1)^{1+2}b|A_{12}| + (-1)^{1+3}c|A_{13}|.$$

If row 2 $= (d \quad e \quad f)$, then we could also evaluate the determinants by using minors of the second row:

$$|A| = (-1)^{2+1}d|A_{21}| + (-1)^{2+2}e|A_{22}| + (-1)^{2+3}f|A_{23}|$$

And similarly, if row 3 $= (g \quad h \quad i)$.
For example, if

$$A = \begin{pmatrix} -1 & 0 & 5 \\ 7 & 3 & 2 \\ 0 & 5 & 9 \end{pmatrix}$$

then the expansion of $|A|$ by minors of row 1 is given by

$$|A| = (-1)^{1+1} \cdot (-1) \cdot |A_{11}| + (-1)^{1+2} \cdot 0 \cdot |A_{12}| + (-1)^{1+3} \cdot 5 \cdot |A_{13}|.$$

$$= - \begin{vmatrix} 3 & 2 \\ 5 & 9 \end{vmatrix} - 0 \begin{vmatrix} 7 & 2 \\ 0 & 9 \end{vmatrix} + 5 \begin{vmatrix} 7 & 3 \\ 0 & 5 \end{vmatrix}$$

$$= -(3 \cdot 9 - 2 \cdot 5) + 5(7 \cdot 5 - 3 \cdot 0)$$

$$= -17 + 175 = 158.$$

The determinant of any square matrix may be evaluated by minors of any one of its rows. For example, if A is a 4×4 matrix and row 2 $= (a \quad b \quad c \quad d)$, then

$$|A| = (-1)^{2+1}a|A_{21}| + (-1)^{2+2}b|A_{22}|$$
$$+ (-1)^{2+3}c|A_{23}| + (-1)^{2+4}d|A_{24}|.$$

The matrices A_{21}, A_{22}, A_{23}, A_{24} are 3×3 matrices, whose determinants can be found as above. The pattern should be clear!

Problem 1. Find $|A|$, where

$$A = \begin{pmatrix} 2 & 1 & -2 \\ 1 & 3 & 1 \\ 4 & 2 & -3 \end{pmatrix}.$$

Solution. Let us expand $|A|$ by minors of row 3.

$$|A| = (-1)^{3+1} \cdot 4 \cdot |A_{31}| + (-1)^{3+2} \cdot 2 \cdot |A_{32}| + (-1)^{3+3} \cdot (-3) \cdot |A_{33}|$$

$$= 4 \begin{vmatrix} 1 & -2 \\ 3 & 1 \end{vmatrix} - 2 \begin{vmatrix} 2 & -2 \\ 1 & 1 \end{vmatrix} - 3 \begin{vmatrix} 2 & 1 \\ 1 & 3 \end{vmatrix}$$

$$= 4[1 \cdot 1 - (-2) \cdot 3] - 2[2 \cdot 1 - (-2) \cdot 1] - 3[2 \cdot 3 - 1 \cdot 1]$$

$$= 4 \cdot 7 - 2 \cdot 4 - 3 \cdot 5 = 5$$

Problem 2. Find $|A|$, where

$$A = \begin{pmatrix} 3 & 1 & -1 \\ 2 & 0 & 0 \\ -1 & 2 & 0 \end{pmatrix}.$$

Solution. Because of the zeros appearing in row 2 of A, it will be less work to expand $|A|$ by minors of row 2 than by minors of another row.

$$|A| = (-1)^{2+1} \cdot 2 \cdot |A_{21}| + (-1)^{2+2} \cdot 0 \cdot |A_{22}| + (-1)^{2+3} \cdot 0 \cdot |A_{23}|$$

$$= -2 \begin{vmatrix} 1 & -1 \\ 2 & 0 \end{vmatrix} + 0 + 0$$

$$= -2[1 \cdot 0 - (-1) \cdot 2] = -4$$

The determinant of a matrix A can also be evaluated in an expansion by minors of a *column* of A. If, for example,

$$A = \begin{pmatrix} 2 & 3 & -1 \\ 4 & 2 & 5 \\ 3 & -4 & 2 \end{pmatrix},$$

then the expansion of $|A|$ by minors of column 3 is

$$|A| = (-1)^{1+3} \cdot (-1) \cdot |A_{13}| + (-1)^{2+3} \cdot 5 \cdot |A_{23}| + (-1)^{3+3} \cdot 2 \cdot |A_{33}|$$

$$= - \begin{vmatrix} 4 & 2 \\ 3 & -4 \end{vmatrix} - 5 \begin{vmatrix} 2 & 3 \\ 3 & -4 \end{vmatrix} + 2 \begin{vmatrix} 2 & 3 \\ 4 & 2 \end{vmatrix}$$

$$= -(-16 - 6) - 5(-8 - 9) + 2(4 - 12) = 91.$$

Problem 3. Find $|A|$, where

$$A = \begin{pmatrix} 3 & 2 & 4 \\ -2 & 0 & 1 \\ 3 & 0 & 5 \end{pmatrix}.$$

Solution. We could expand by minors of any row or column, but it is easiest to expand $|A|$ by minors of column 2, since it contains two zeros.

$$|A| = (-1)^{1+2} \cdot 2 \cdot |A_{12}| + (-1)^{2+2} \cdot 0 \cdot |A_{22}| + (-1)^{3+2} \cdot 0 \cdot |A_{32}|$$

$$= -2 \begin{vmatrix} -2 & 1 \\ 3 & 5 \end{vmatrix} + 0 + 0$$

$$= -2(-10 - 3) = 26$$

Exercises

1. Find $|A|$ in Problem 1 by expanding it by minors of row 2; by minors of column 1.

2. Expand $|A|$ in Problem 3 by expanding it by minors of column 1, by minors of row 3.

3. Evaluate the following determinants.

(a) $\begin{vmatrix} 1 & 0 \\ 0 & 1 \end{vmatrix}$ (b) $\begin{vmatrix} 0 & 1 \\ 1 & 0 \end{vmatrix}$

4. Evaluate the following determinants.

(a) $\begin{vmatrix} 1 & 1 \\ 0 & 0 \end{vmatrix}$ (b) $\begin{vmatrix} 0 & 1 \\ -1 & 0 \end{vmatrix}$

5. Evaluate the following determinants.

(a) $\begin{vmatrix} 3 & 4 \\ 4 & 5 \end{vmatrix}$ (b) $\begin{vmatrix} 2 & 1 \\ 7 & 3 \end{vmatrix}$

6. Evaluate the following determinants.

(a) $\begin{vmatrix} -1 & 2 \\ 3 & 4 \end{vmatrix}$ (b) $\begin{vmatrix} 3 & -2 \\ 3 & 2 \end{vmatrix}$

7. Evaluate the following determinants.

(a) $\begin{vmatrix} p & q \\ r & s \end{vmatrix}$ (b) $\begin{vmatrix} 3 & -2 \\ 9 & -6 \end{vmatrix}$

8. Evaluate the following determinants.

(a) $\begin{vmatrix} w & x \\ y & z \end{vmatrix}$ (b) $\begin{vmatrix} 4 & 5 \\ 8 & 10 \end{vmatrix}$

9. Evaluate the following determinants.

(a) $\begin{vmatrix} 1-x & 2 \\ -1 & 1+x \end{vmatrix}$ (b) $\begin{vmatrix} -2 & -3 \\ -4 & -5 \end{vmatrix}$

10. Evaluate the following determinants.

(a) $\begin{vmatrix} a+b & -b \\ b & a-b \end{vmatrix}$ (b) $\begin{vmatrix} 3 & 2 \\ 9 & 4 \end{vmatrix}$

11. Evaluate the following determinants.

(a) $\begin{vmatrix} 1 & 0 & 0 \\ 0 & 1 & 0 \\ 0 & 0 & 1 \end{vmatrix}$
(b) $\begin{vmatrix} 1 & 0 & 0 \\ 0 & 2 & 0 \\ 0 & 0 & 3 \end{vmatrix}$

12. Evaluate the following determinants.

(a) $\begin{vmatrix} 1 & 0 & 0 \\ 0 & -1 & 0 \\ 0 & 0 & -1 \end{vmatrix}$
(b) $\begin{vmatrix} 2 & 0 & 0 \\ 0 & -3 & 0 \\ 0 & 0 & -4 \end{vmatrix}$

13. Evaluate the following determinants.

(a) $\begin{vmatrix} 2 & 0 & 0 \\ 3 & 5 & 2 \\ 4 & 1 & -2 \end{vmatrix}$
(b) $\begin{vmatrix} 0 & -3 & 0 \\ 5 & -8 & 3 \\ 3 & 13 & 2 \end{vmatrix}$

14. Evaluate the following determinants.

(a) $\begin{vmatrix} 0 & 2 & 11 \\ -2 & 6 & 8 \\ 0 & 1 & 5 \end{vmatrix}$
(b) $\begin{vmatrix} 7 & 9 & 2 \\ 0 & 4 & 0 \\ 3 & 13 & 1 \end{vmatrix}$

15. Evaluate the following determinants.

(a) $\begin{vmatrix} b & c & 0 \\ f & g & a \\ d & e & 0 \end{vmatrix}$
(b) $\begin{vmatrix} 2 & 4 & 6 \\ 5 & 3 & 7 \\ 0 & 0 & -1 \end{vmatrix}$

16. Evaluate the following determinants.

(a) $\begin{vmatrix} u & q & r \\ v & s & t \\ p & 0 & 0 \end{vmatrix}$
(b) $\begin{vmatrix} 4 & 0 & 6 \\ 7 & 0 & 5 \\ 8 & 3 & 9 \end{vmatrix}$

17. Evaluate the following determinants.

(a) $\begin{vmatrix} 1 & 0 & -3 \\ 2 & 4 & 5 \\ 3 & 6 & 7 \end{vmatrix}$
(b) $\begin{vmatrix} 2 & 4 & 1 \\ -3 & 2 & 0 \\ -1 & 2 & 3 \end{vmatrix}$

18. Evaluate the following determinants.

(a) $\begin{vmatrix} 1 & 6 & -3 \\ 2 & 0 & -3 \\ -2 & 4 & 1 \end{vmatrix}$
(b) $\begin{vmatrix} 3 & -1 & 2 \\ 2 & -2 & -1 \\ 0 & 2 & 3 \end{vmatrix}$

19. Evaluate the following determinants.

(a) $\begin{vmatrix} a & b \\ c & d \end{vmatrix}$
(b) $\begin{vmatrix} a & b \\ a+c & b+d \end{vmatrix}$

20. Evaluate the following determinants.

(a) $\begin{vmatrix} a & b \\ -c & -d \end{vmatrix}$
(b) $\begin{vmatrix} a & b \\ 2a-c & 2b-d \end{vmatrix}$

10–8 ELEMENTARY ROW OPERATIONS AND DETERMINANTS

The expansion of a determinant by minors of a row can be made easier by judicious use of the elementary row operations. This is true because of the following properties of determinants, stated without proof:

PROPERTIES OF DETERMINANTS

1. *If two rows of a matrix are interchanged, the determinant changes signs.*
2. *If a row of a matrix is multiplied by a number, the determinant is multiplied by the same number.*
3. *If one row is multiplied by a number and the resulting row is added to another row, the determinant is unchanged.*

Thus,

$$\begin{vmatrix} 4 & 1 \\ 2 & -1 \end{vmatrix} = -\begin{vmatrix} 2 & -1 \\ 4 & 1 \end{vmatrix} \qquad \text{(two rows interchanged)}$$

$$\begin{vmatrix} 2 & 1 & 4 \\ 3 & -6 & 9 \\ 1 & -1 & 2 \end{vmatrix} = 3\begin{vmatrix} 2 & 1 & 4 \\ 1 & -2 & 3 \\ 1 & -1 & 2 \end{vmatrix} \qquad \text{(multiply row 2 by 3)}$$

$$\begin{vmatrix} 2 & 1 & 4 \\ 1 & -2 & 3 \\ 1 & -1 & 2 \end{vmatrix} = \begin{vmatrix} 2 & 1 & 4 \\ 5 & 0 & 11 \\ 1 & -1 & 2 \end{vmatrix} \begin{array}{l} \text{(multiply row 1 by 2 and} \\ \text{add to row 2: } 2(2 \quad 1 \quad 4) \\ + (1 \quad -2 \quad 3) = (5 \quad 0 \quad 11)) \end{array}$$

Problem 1. Find $|A|$, where

$$A = \begin{pmatrix} 2 & 1 & 4 \\ 1 & -2 & 3 \\ 1 & -1 & 2 \end{pmatrix}.$$

Solution. From our work above,

$$\begin{vmatrix} 2 & 1 & 4 \\ 1 & -2 & 3 \\ 1 & -1 & 2 \end{vmatrix} = \begin{vmatrix} 2 & 1 & 4 \\ 5 & 0 & 11 \\ 1 & -1 & 2 \end{vmatrix}$$

In turn, if we add row 1 to row 3 of the new matrix, we get

$$\begin{vmatrix} 2 & 1 & 4 \\ 5 & 0 & 11 \\ 1 & -1 & 2 \end{vmatrix} = \begin{vmatrix} 2 & 1 & 4 \\ 5 & 0 & 11 \\ 3 & 0 & 6 \end{vmatrix}$$

Expanding by minors of column 2,

$$\begin{vmatrix} 2 & 1 & 4 \\ 5 & 0 & 11 \\ 3 & 0 & 6 \end{vmatrix} = (-1)^{1+2} \cdot 1 \cdot |A_{12}| + 0 + 0$$

$$= -\begin{vmatrix} 5 & 11 \\ 3 & 6 \end{vmatrix} = -(30 - 33) = 3.$$

Problem 2. Find $|A|$, where

$$A = \begin{pmatrix} 2 & 3 & 1 & -1 \\ -1 & 1 & 2 & 1 \\ 1 & 2 & -2 & 3 \\ 3 & 1 & -1 & 1 \end{pmatrix}.$$

Solution. The problem is most easily solved by getting three zeros in some row or column. Let us hold fixed row 2 of A, and add multiples of it to the other rows as indicated below.

$$B = \begin{pmatrix} 0 & 5 & 5 & 1 \\ -1 & 1 & 2 & 1 \\ 0 & 3 & 0 & 4 \\ 0 & 4 & 5 & 4 \end{pmatrix} \quad \begin{array}{l} 2(\text{row } 2) + (\text{row } 1) \text{ of} \\ \text{fixed} \\ (\text{row } 2) + (\text{row } 3) \text{ of } A \\ 3(\text{row } 2) + (\text{row } 4) \text{ of } A \end{array}$$

By Property 3 above,

$$|B| = |A|.$$

Now column 1 of B has three zeros, so we expand $|B|$ by minors of column 1.

$$|B| = (-1)^{1+1} \cdot 0 \cdot |B_{11}| + (-1)^{2+1} \cdot (-1) \cdot |B_{21}|$$
$$+ (-1)^{3+1} \cdot 0 \cdot |B_{31}| + (-1)^{4+1} \cdot 0 \cdot |B_{41}|$$
$$= 0 + |B_{21}| + 0 + 0$$

Thus, $|B| = |C|$, where $C = B_{21}$,

$$C = \begin{pmatrix} 5 & 5 & 1 \\ 3 & 0 & 4 \\ 4 & 5 & 4 \end{pmatrix}.$$

If we hold fixed row 1 of C, and add -1 times it to row 3, we get

$$D = \begin{pmatrix} 5 & 5 & 1 \\ 3 & 0 & 4 \\ -1 & 0 & 3 \end{pmatrix} \quad (-1)\,(\text{row } 1) + (\text{row } 3) \text{ of } C$$

Again,

$$|D| = |C| = |B| = |A|.$$

Expanding $|D|$ by minors of column 2, we get

$$|D| = (-1)^{1+2} \cdot 5 \cdot |D_{12}| + (-1)^{2+2} \cdot 0 \cdot |D_{22}| + (-1)^{3+2} \cdot 0 \cdot |D_{32}|$$

$$= -5 \begin{vmatrix} 3 & 4 \\ -1 & 3 \end{vmatrix} + 0 + 0$$

$$= -5(9 + 4) = -65.$$

Thus, $|A| = -65$.

Exercises

1. Find $|A|$ in Problem 1 by finding a 3×3 matrix B having two zeros in column 1 and such that $|B| = |A|$.

2. Find $|A|$ in Problem 2 by finding a 4×4 matrix B having three zeros in column 4 and such that $|B| = |A|$.

3. Verify Property 1 by evaluating the following determinants.

(a) $\begin{vmatrix} 2 & 3 \\ 1 & -4 \end{vmatrix}$ (b) $\begin{vmatrix} 1 & -4 \\ 2 & 3 \end{vmatrix}$

4. Prove Property 1 for determinants of 2×2 matrices by evaluating the determinants $\begin{vmatrix} a & b \\ c & d \end{vmatrix}$ and $\begin{vmatrix} c & d \\ a & b \end{vmatrix}$.

5. Verify Property 2 by evaluating the following determinants.

(a) $\begin{vmatrix} 1 & 2 \\ 4 & 3 \end{vmatrix}$ (b) $\begin{vmatrix} 5 & 10 \\ 4 & 3 \end{vmatrix}$

6. Verify Property 2 by evaluating the following determinants.

(a) $\begin{vmatrix} 2 & 3 \\ -2 & 5 \end{vmatrix}$ (b) $\begin{vmatrix} 2 & 3 \\ -8 & 20 \end{vmatrix}$

7. Verify Property 3 by evaluating the following determinants.

(a) $\begin{vmatrix} 3 & 4 \\ 2 & 3 \end{vmatrix}$ (b) $\begin{vmatrix} 3 & 4 \\ 2+12 & 3+16 \end{vmatrix}$

8. Verify Property 3 by evaluating the following determinants.

(a) $\begin{vmatrix} 1 & -2 \\ 2 & 5 \end{vmatrix}$ (b) $\begin{vmatrix} 1+4 & -2+10 \\ 2 & 5 \end{vmatrix}$

9. Evaluate the following determinants.

(a) $\begin{vmatrix} 1 & 0 & 3 \\ 2 & -2 & 3 \\ 0 & 2 & 4 \end{vmatrix}$ (b) $\begin{vmatrix} 1 & 4 & 3 \\ 0 & -2 & 3 \\ -2 & -2 & -5 \end{vmatrix}$

10. Evaluate the following determinants.

(a) $\begin{vmatrix} 1 & 2 & 0 \\ 3 & 3 & 2 \\ 4 & -3 & 5 \end{vmatrix}$ (b) $\begin{vmatrix} 1 & -2 & 2 \\ -3 & 5 & 2 \\ 0 & 2 & -5 \end{vmatrix}$

11. Evaluate the following determinants.

(a) $\begin{vmatrix} 1 & 1 & -2 \\ 2 & 3 & 4 \\ 5 & 6 & 7 \end{vmatrix}$ (b) $\begin{vmatrix} 1 & 2 & -3 \\ 3 & -3 & 4 \\ 4 & -5 & 4 \end{vmatrix}$

12. Evaluate the following determinants.

(a) $\begin{vmatrix} 1 & -2 & 4 \\ 1 & 3 & 9 \\ 1 & 5 & 25 \end{vmatrix}$ (b) $\begin{vmatrix} 1 & -2 & 3 \\ 3 & 1 & -2 \\ -2 & 3 & 1 \end{vmatrix}$

13. Evaluate the following determinants.

(a) $\begin{vmatrix} 2 & 3 & 4 \\ 1 & -1 & 2 \\ 0 & 2 & 3 \end{vmatrix}$ (b) $\begin{vmatrix} 4 & 5 & 6 \\ 1 & 2 & 3 \\ 7 & 8 & 9 \end{vmatrix}$

14. Evaluate the following determinants.

(a) $\begin{vmatrix} 2 & 0 & 3 \\ 3 & -2 & 1 \\ 1 & 3 & -2 \end{vmatrix}$ (b) $\begin{vmatrix} 1 & 3 & 2 \\ -2 & 7 & -4 \\ 2 & 10 & 4 \end{vmatrix}$

15. Evaluate the following determinants.

(a) $\begin{vmatrix} 1 & 2 & -1 & 0 \\ 3 & 4 & -3 & 2 \\ -2 & 0 & 2 & 1 \\ 3 & -2 & 1 & 0 \end{vmatrix}$
(b) $\begin{vmatrix} 1 & -2 & 2 & 2 \\ 3 & 0 & 4 & 5 \\ 0 & 4 & -5 & -7 \\ -2 & 3 & -2 & -1 \end{vmatrix}$

16. Evaluate the following determinants.

(a) $\begin{vmatrix} 1 & 2 & -2 & 3 \\ 2 & 5 & -2 & 4 \\ 3 & 8 & 1 & 1 \\ 4 & 11 & 2 & 11 \end{vmatrix}$
(b) $\begin{vmatrix} 1 & 2 & -3 & -2 \\ 3 & 8 & -5 & -10 \\ 0 & -1 & 0 & 3 \\ 2 & 8 & 7 & -9 \end{vmatrix}$

17. Prove Property 2 for determinants of 2×2 matrices by evaluating the determinants $\begin{vmatrix} a & b \\ c & d \end{vmatrix}$ and $\begin{vmatrix} ka & kb \\ c & d \end{vmatrix}$.

18. Prove that the determinant of a 2×2 matrix is multiplied by k^2 if every term is multiplied by k.

19. Prove Property 3 for determinants of 2×2 matrices by evaluating the determinants $\begin{vmatrix} a & b \\ c & d \end{vmatrix}$ and $\begin{vmatrix} a & b \\ c + ka & d + kb \end{vmatrix}$.

20. State a column analogue for Property 1 and prove it for determinants of 2×2 matrices by evaluating the determinants
$$\begin{vmatrix} a & b \\ c & d \end{vmatrix} \quad \text{and} \quad \begin{vmatrix} b & a \\ d & c \end{vmatrix}.$$

21. State a column analogue for Property 2 and prove it for determinants of 2×2 matrices by evaluating the determinants
$$\begin{vmatrix} a & b \\ c & d \end{vmatrix} \quad \text{and} \quad \begin{vmatrix} a & kb \\ c & kd \end{vmatrix}.$$

22. State a column analogue for Property 3 and prove it for determinants of 2×2 matrices by evaluating the determinants
$$\begin{vmatrix} a & b \\ c & d \end{vmatrix} \quad \text{and} \quad \begin{vmatrix} a + kb & b \\ c + kd & d \end{vmatrix}.$$

10–9 SOLVING SYSTEMS OF LINEAR EQUATIONS BY DETERMINANTS

If we have a system of two linear equations in two variables x and y, say,

$$\begin{cases} a_1x + b_1y = k_1 \\ a_2x + b_2y = k_2 \end{cases}$$

then the solution can be given in determinants as

$$x = \dfrac{\begin{vmatrix} k_1 & b_1 \\ k_2 & b_2 \end{vmatrix}}{\begin{vmatrix} a_1 & b_1 \\ a_2 & b_2 \end{vmatrix}}, \qquad y = \dfrac{\begin{vmatrix} a_1 & k_1 \\ a_2 & k_2 \end{vmatrix}}{\begin{vmatrix} a_1 & b_1 \\ a_2 & b_2 \end{vmatrix}} \qquad \text{if } \begin{vmatrix} a_1 & b_1 \\ a_2 & b_2 \end{vmatrix} \neq 0.$$

This method of solution, known as Cramer's Rule, can be verified by substitution in the given equations. Note that each denominator is the determinant of the coefficient matrix.

Problem 1.   Use Cramer's Rule to solve the system

$$\begin{cases} 3x - 2y = 4 \\ 2x + 3y = -5. \end{cases}$$

Solution.   Letting $a_1 = 3, b_1 = -2, k_1 = 4, a_2 = 2, b_2 = 3, k_2 = -5$ in the solutions above, we obtain

$$x = \dfrac{\begin{vmatrix} 4 & -2 \\ -5 & 3 \end{vmatrix}}{\begin{vmatrix} 3 & -2 \\ 2 & 3 \end{vmatrix}} = \dfrac{2}{13},$$

$$y = \dfrac{\begin{vmatrix} 3 & 4 \\ 2 & -5 \end{vmatrix}}{13} = \dfrac{-23}{13}.$$

Check.

$$3 \cdot \frac{2}{13} - 2 \cdot \left(-\frac{23}{13}\right) = \frac{6 + 46}{13} \overset{\checkmark}{=} 4$$

$$2 \cdot \frac{2}{13} + 3 \cdot \left(-\frac{23}{13}\right) = \frac{4 - 69}{13} \overset{\checkmark}{=} -5$$

Cramer's Rule can be extended to solve a system of any number of linear equations in the same number of variables. For three equations in three variables, say,

$$\begin{cases} a_1x + b_1y + c_1z = k_1, \\ a_2x + b_2y + c_2z = k_2, \\ a_3x + b_3y + c_3z = k_3, \end{cases}$$

let A be the matrix of coefficients,

$$A = \begin{pmatrix} a_1 & b_1 & c_1 \\ a_2 & b_2 & c_2 \\ a_3 & b_3 & c_3 \end{pmatrix},$$

and A_1, A_2, A_3 be the matrices obtained by replacing each of the columns of A in turn by the column of constants,

$$\begin{pmatrix} k_1 \\ k_2 \\ k_3 \end{pmatrix}.$$

Thus,

$$A_1 = \begin{pmatrix} k_1 & b_1 & c_1 \\ k_2 & b_2 & c_2 \\ k_3 & b_3 & c_3 \end{pmatrix}, \quad A_2 = \begin{pmatrix} a_1 & k_1 & c_1 \\ a_2 & k_2 & c_2 \\ a_3 & k_3 & c_3 \end{pmatrix}, \quad A_3 = \begin{pmatrix} a_1 & b_1 & k_1 \\ a_2 & b_2 & k_2 \\ a_3 & b_3 & k_3 \end{pmatrix}.$$

Then Cramer's Rule states that the solution of the system is

$$x = \frac{|A_1|}{|A|}, \quad y = \frac{|A_2|}{|A|}, \quad z = \frac{|A_3|}{|A|} \quad \text{if } |A| \neq 0.$$

This solution is the obvious extension of the system of two equations in two variables, as you can see.

Problem 2. Use Cramer's Rule to solve the system

$$\begin{cases} 3x + 2y + z = -3 \\ 2x + 3y + 2z = 5 \\ -2x + y - z = 3. \end{cases}$$

Solution. The matrices A, A_1, A_2, A_3 are as follows:

$$A = \begin{pmatrix} 3 & 2 & 1 \\ 2 & 3 & 2 \\ -2 & 1 & -1 \end{pmatrix}, \qquad A_1 = \begin{pmatrix} -3 & 2 & 1 \\ 5 & 3 & 2 \\ 3 & 1 & -1 \end{pmatrix},$$

$$A_2 = \begin{pmatrix} 3 & -3 & 1 \\ 2 & 5 & 2 \\ -2 & 3 & -1 \end{pmatrix}, \qquad A_3 = \begin{pmatrix} 3 & 2 & -3 \\ 2 & 3 & 5 \\ -2 & 1 & 3 \end{pmatrix}.$$

We leave it to you to verify the following determinants.

$$|A| = -11, \quad |A_1| = 33, \quad |A_2| = -11, \quad |A_3| = -44$$

Hence,

$$x = -3, y = 1, z = 4.$$

Check.
$$3 \cdot (-3) + 2 \cdot 1 + 4 \overset{\vee}{=} -3$$
$$2 \cdot (-3) + 3 \cdot 1 + 2 \cdot 4 \overset{\vee}{=} 5$$
$$-2 \cdot (-3) + 1 - 4 \overset{\vee}{=} 3$$

Cramer's Rule has more historical interest than practical use. Although it can be used to solve a system of n linear equations in the same number of variables if the system has a unique solution, it is of no use if the system has no solution or if the system has infinitely many solutions. The echelon method can be used for *any* system of linear equations in any number of variables.

Exercises

1. Solve each of the following systems in two ways, first by Cramer's Rule and then by the echelon method.

(a) $\begin{cases} 2x - y = 1 \\ 3x + 2y = 12 \end{cases}$ (b) $\begin{cases} 3x + y = 0 \\ 2x - 5y = 17 \end{cases}$

2. Solve each of the following systems in two ways, first by Cramer's Rule and then by the echelon method.

(a) $\begin{cases} 4x + y = -1 \\ 2x - 3y = -25 \end{cases}$ (b) $\begin{cases} 3x - 2y = 12 \\ -2x + 5y = -8 \end{cases}$

3. Solve each of the following systems in two ways, first by Cramer's Rule and then by the echelon method.

(a) $\begin{cases} 4x + 2y = 3 \\ 3x - 6y = 1 \end{cases}$ (b) $\begin{cases} 7x + 5y = 9 \\ 2x - y = 5 \end{cases}$

4. Solve each of the following systems in two ways, first by Cramer's Rule and then by the echelon method.

(a) $\begin{cases} 3x - 4y = 1 \\ 2x - 3y = -1 \end{cases}$

(b) $\begin{cases} 6x - 3y = 0 \\ 6x + 5y = 4 \end{cases}$

5. Solve each of the following systems in two ways, first by Cramer's Rule and then by the echelon method.

(a) $\begin{cases} 5x - 2y + z = 4 \\ 2x + 3z = 11 \\ 3x + y + z = 8 \end{cases}$

(b) $\begin{cases} 3x + 4y - z = 1 \\ 2x + 3y + z = 9 \\ 4x - 5y - 2z = -2 \end{cases}$

6. Solve each of the following systems in two ways, first by Cramer's Rule and then by the echelon method.

(a) $\begin{cases} 4x - 3y + 5z = 1 \\ 3y - 2z = 0 \\ 3x + y + 2z = 2 \end{cases}$

(b) $\begin{cases} 4x + 3y + z = 5 \\ 2x + 5y = 13 \\ 3x + y + 2z = 0 \end{cases}$

7. Solve each of the following systems by Cramer's Rule.

(a) $\begin{cases} 3x + 2y + 5z = 3 \\ 2x + 3y + 6z = 3 \\ 5x - 3z = 2 \end{cases}$

(b) $\begin{cases} 2x - 3y - 5z = 8 \\ x + 2z = 10 \\ 2x - 5y + z = 12 \end{cases}$

8. Solve each of the following systems by Cramer's Rule.

(a) $\begin{cases} 3x - y + 3z = 2 \\ 4x + 2y + z = 5 \\ 5y - 3z = 4 \end{cases}$

(b) $\begin{cases} 4x + 2y + 3z = 5 \\ 2x + y + 2z = 4 \\ x + 2z = 6 \end{cases}$

9. Consider the system $\begin{cases} 2x - 3y = 5 \\ 4x - 6y = 10. \end{cases}$

(a) Try to solve this system by Cramer's Rule.
(b) Solve this system by the echelon method.

10. Consider the system $\begin{cases} a_1x + b_1y = k_1 \\ a_2x + b_2y = k_2 \end{cases}$. How many solutions will this sys-

tem have if $\begin{vmatrix} a_1 & b_1 \\ a_2 & b_2 \end{vmatrix} = \begin{vmatrix} k_1 & b_1 \\ k_2 & b_2 \end{vmatrix} = \begin{vmatrix} a_1 & k_1 \\ a_2 & k_2 \end{vmatrix} = 0$?

11. Consider the system $\begin{cases} 4x - 6y = 11 \\ 6x - 9y = 13. \end{cases}$

(a) Try to solve this system by Cramer's Rule.
(b) "Solve" this system by the echelon method.

12. Consider the system $\begin{cases} a_1x + b_1y = k_1 \\ a_2x + b_2y = k_2 \end{cases}$. How many solutions does the

system have if $\begin{vmatrix} a_1 & b_1 \\ a_2 & b_2 \end{vmatrix} = 0,\ \begin{vmatrix} k_1 & b_1 \\ k_2 & b_2 \end{vmatrix} \neq 0$ and $\begin{vmatrix} a_1 & k_1 \\ a_2 & k_2 \end{vmatrix} \neq 0$?

13. What can you say about the solution of a system of n linear equations in n variables if the coefficient matrix of the system is equal to 0?

*10–10 LINEAR PROGRAMMING

The mathematical form of certain practical problems involves a system of linear inequalities. Such a system seldom has a unique solution, but rather has many solutions, as we saw in Section 2–10. However, of all possible solutions of a system of inequalities, some one solution will prove to be the best solution of the practical problem with which we started. The branch of mathematics which solves such problems is called *linear programming*. The following example illustrates the type of problem studied in linear programming.

Consider the problem faced by a manufacturer who has two warehouses, warehouse I containing 40 units of his product and warehouse II containing 50 units. He has two orders to fill, one from town A for 30 units and the other from town B for 40 units. Should he fill the order for town A from one warehouse and that for town B from the other, or is there a more economical distribution?

If we let x designate the number of units shipped from warehouse I to town A, then $30 - x$ units must be shipped from warehouse II to town A. Similarly, if we let y denote the number of units shipped from warehouse I to town B, then $40 - y$ units must be shipped from warehouse II to town B. Each of these four numbers must be greater than or equal to zero:

$$x \geq 0,$$
$$30 - x \geq 0, \quad \text{or } 30 \geq x,$$
$$y \geq 0,$$
$$40 - y \geq 0, \quad \text{or } 40 \geq y.$$

In addition, the number of units the manufacturer ships from each warehouse cannot exceed the number of units stored there:

$$x + y \leq 40,$$
$$(30 - x) + (40 - y) \leq 50, \quad \text{or } 20 \leq x + y.$$

Thus, any ordered pair of *integers* that is a solution of the following system of inequalities is a solution of the manufacturer's problem.

$$\begin{cases} x \geq 0 \\ x \leq 30 \\ y \geq 0 \\ y \leq 40 \\ x + y \leq 40 \\ x + y \geq 20 \end{cases}$$

The graph of this system is the shaded pentagonal region of Fig. 10-1. (This is the intersection of the graphs of the inequalities.) Of course, the boundary of this pentagon is also included in the graph.

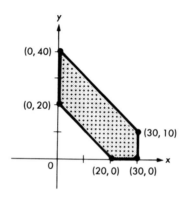

FIGURE 10-1

With what is given, there are many possible solutions of the manufacturer's problem. However, we have not yet taken into account the shipping costs from each warehouse to each town. Suppose that the shipping costs are as follows.

From warehouse	To town	Cost per unit, in dollars	Number of units shipped
I	A	10	x
I	B	14	y
II	A	12	$30 - x$
II	B	15	$40 - y$

Thus, the total shipping costs are

$$10x + 14y + 12(30 - x) + 15(40 - y)$$

dollars. This linear form in x and y reduces to

$$10x + 14y + 360 - 12x + 600 - 15y,$$

or $$960 - 2x - y.$$

Now, our problem is to find the solution of the original problem for which the total shipping costs are smallest. Mathematically speaking, we must find the point with integral coordinates in the pentagonal region of the figure at which the linear form

$$960 - 2x - y$$

has its smallest value.

The linear form has a value for every point in the region, and it would be impossible to compute all these values to find the smallest. Even the task of computing the values at the points with integral co-ordinates would be tedious. However, according to a result proved in the theory of linear programming, the maximum value of the linear form occurs at a vertex of the pentagon, and the minimum value occurs at another vertex.

To find the minimum value, let us compute the value of $960 - 2x - y$ (see the following table) at each of the vertices of the pentagon. According to the theory of linear programming, the maximum value of the linear form is 940, occurring at $(0, 20)$, and the minimum value is 890, occurring at $(30, 10)$. To see that the values are between 890 and 940, let us find the value at some points other than the vertices. At the interior point $(20, 10)$, the value is $960 - (2 \cdot 20) - 10$, or 910; at the boundary point $(15, 25)$, the value is $960 - (2 \cdot 15) - 25$, or 905; at the interior point $(29, 9)$, the value is $960 - (2 \cdot 29) - 9$, or 893.

Vertex	Value of $960 - 2x - y$
$(20, 0)$	$960 - (2 \cdot 20) - 0$, or 920
$(30, 0)$	$960 - (2 \cdot 30) - 0$, or 900
$(30, 10)$	$960 - (2 \cdot 30) - 10$, or 890
$(0, 40)$	$960 - (2 \cdot 0) - 40$, or 920
$(0, 20)$	$960 - (2 \cdot 0) - 20$, or 940

Clearly, the lowest shipping cost is $890, occurring when $x = 30$ and $y = 10$. Thus, the manufacturer is advised to ship all 30 units to town A from warehouse I, and to ship 10 units from warehouse I and 30 units from warehouse II to town B. By doing this, he will make the greatest profit on his two orders.

We have used a theorem from linear programming which states that a linear form defined over a convex polygonal region of the plane assumes its maximum and minimum values at vertices of the region.

Exercises

1. (a) If, in the problem of this section, the shipping costs are $15 per unit from warehouse I to town A, $12 per unit from warehouse I to town B, $14 per unit from warehouse II to town A, and $10 per unit from warehouse II to town B, express the shipping costs as a linear form in x and y.
   (b) Find the value of this linear form at each corner point of the pentagon.
   (c) What shipping advice should be given to the manufacturer if he is to spend as little as possible on shipping?

2. An appliance wholesaler has 8 television sets in his warehouse in Lakeville and 8 sets in his warehouse in Alexandria. He receives orders to ship 6 sets to Central City and 4 sets to Stratford.
   (a) Let x be the number of sets to be shipped from Lakeville to Central City. What represents the number to be shipped from Alexandria to Central City? What is the lower limit of x? What is the upper limit of x?
   (b) Let y be the number of sets to be shipped from Lakeville to Stratford. What will represent the number to be shipped from Alexandria to Stratford? What is the lower limit of y? What is the upper limit of y?
   (c) Write the system of six inequalities describing the problem.
   (d) Graph the system of part (c).
   (e) If shipping costs per television set are $6 from Lakeville to Central City, $5 from Lakeville to Stratford, $7 from Alexandria to Central City, and $8.50 from Alexandria to Stratford, write and simplify a linear form for the total shipping cost.
   (f) Find the value of the linear form of part (e) at each of the six corner points of your graph.
   (g) For maximum profit, what advice should be given to the wholesaler?

3. Two machines A and B produce items at the rate of 50 per hour and 40 per hour, respectively. Under a certain production plan the total number of items needed is at least 1000 items, and the total number of man-hours available for running the machines is at most 24 hours.
   (a) Let x be the number of hours machine A is used and y the number of hours machine B is used, and express the two conditions above as inequalities.
   (b) Add to the system of inequalities in part (a) the two obvious inequalities resulting from the fact that x and y are non-negative numbers, and graph the system of these four inequalities. Find the corner points of the resulting polygon.
   (c) If the hourly cost is $10 for running machine A and $7 for machine B, find the values of x and y which would yield the most economical production program.

(d) In part (c), if the hourly costs for A and B were $10 and $9, respectively, what would be the best plan?

(e) Assuming, in part (c), that the hourly costs for A and B are $10 and $8, respectively, show that two of the corner points give paired values of x and y which minimize the cost. (Actually any point (x, y) on the line segment between these corner points will lead to the same minimal cost.)

4. In the table below, the vitamin and mineral content of two brands of cereals, Soggies ("they sink") and Lumpies ("they clump"), is given in milligrams per ounce. The third column gives the daily minimum requirements of these vitamins and minerals. At the bottom of the first two columns, the cost per ounce of each cereal is listed. Find the number of ounces for each cereal which taken together will satisfy the daily minimum requirements of thiamine, niacin, and iron at lowest cost.

	Soggies	Lumpies	Daily min. requirement
Thiamine	.5	.25	2.00
Niacin	50	150	450
Iron	1.5	2.0	11.0
	$2\frac{1}{2}$¢	2¢	

5. A truck gardener has a plot of 50 acres and decides to plant two different vegetables, B and C. He has a maximum of 185 man-hours of labor to devote to this garden and $205 which he may spend for seed. Let your variables be the number of acres to be planted in B and the number of acres to be planted in C.

(a) Write an inequality which states that he has 50 acres of land available.

(b) If an acre of B requires 4 man-hours for cultivation and an acre of C requires only 1 man-hour, write an inequality stating that he has 185 man-hours of labor at his disposal.

(c) If seed costs $2 an acre for B and $5 an acre for C, write an inequality stating that he has at most $205 to spend for seed.

(d) Write inequalities indicating the minimum number of acres which may be planted in each vegetable.

(e) Graph your system of inequalities.

(f) If labor costs $2.50 a man-hour, an acre's yield of vegetable B sells for $27, and an acre's yield of vegetable C sells for $14, find a linear form which expresses the profit of the gardener.

(g) How many acres should the gardener plant in each vegetable if he wishes to maximize his profit?

6. A couple decides to start a record collection. They can purchase records of musical shows for $5 apiece and records of a vocalist for $2 apiece.

There are only 4 records of musical shows in which they are currently interested, and 6 of their favorite vocalist. They have \$25 to invest and decide that 8 records should be their limit.

(a) Write two inequalities which express the number of records of musical shows which they can buy.

(b) Write two inequalities which express the number of vocalist records which they can buy.

(c) Write an inequality which shows that they have \$25 to invest.

(d) Write an inequality which shows that 8 records should be their limit.

(e) Graph the system of inequalities which you have just written.

(f) They give a popularity rating of 3 to each record of a musical show and of 2 to each record of the vocalist. How many records of each type should they buy to give their collection the highest rating?

CHAPTER REVIEW

Solve the following systems of linear equations by any method of the chapter.

1. $\begin{cases} 3x - y = 5 \\ 2x + y = 3 \end{cases}$ 2. $\begin{cases} x + 3y = 4 \\ 2x - y = 2 \end{cases}$

3. $\begin{cases} 2x - 2y + z = 3 \\ x + 3y = -1 \\ 3x - 3y + 2z = 5 \end{cases}$ 4. $\begin{cases} 2x + 3y + z = 3 \\ -x + 2y + z = 1 \\ y + 3z = -1 \end{cases}$

5. $\begin{cases} 3x + 2y - z = 4 \\ x - 3y - 2z = -3 \\ 2x + 4y + z = 9 \end{cases}$ 6. $\begin{cases} 2x + y - z = 1 \\ -x + 2y + 3z = 7 \\ 3x + y - 2z = 0 \end{cases}$

11 · Concepts in Analytic Geometry

11–1 CIRCLES

The conic sections are plane curves, so named because each of them is the curve of intersection of a plane with a right circular cone. The conic section which is easiest to visualize is the circle, obtained by cutting a cone with a plane perpendicular to the axis of the cone. (See Fig. 11–1.) The circle may be defined equally well as the set of all points in a plane at a given distance from a fixed point in the plane. The given distance is called the *radius* and the fixed point the *center* of the circle.

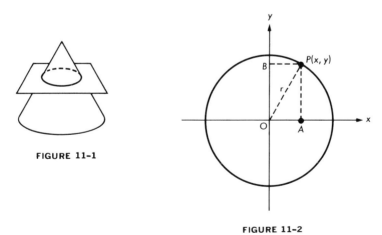

FIGURE 11–1

FIGURE 11–2

Consider a circle of radius r having its center at the origin of a cartesian coordinate system, as shown in Fig. 11–2. If P is a point in the plane with coordinates (x, y), then P is on this circle if, and only if, the distance from O to P is r. The distance from O to P is denoted by OP. Thus, P is on the circle if, and only if,

$$OP = r.$$

If we use the notation of Fig. 11–2, we have, by the pythagorean theorem,

$$(OP)^2 = (OA)^2 + (AP)^2.$$

Regardless of the quadrant in which P lies, $OA = |x|$ and $AP = OB$, or $|y|$. Hence,

$$(OP)^2 = |x|^2 + |y|^2$$
$$= x^2 + y^2.$$

We conclude that the point P with coordinates (x, y) is on the circle if, and only if,

$$x^2 + y^2 = r^2.$$

The graph of the second-degree equation

$$x^2 + y^2 = r^2,$$

in the two variables x and y, is a circle with its center at the origin and radius r.

For example, the graph of the equation

$$x^2 + y^2 = 16$$

is the circle of radius 4 sketched in Fig. 11–3.

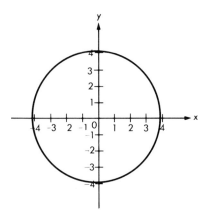

FIGURE 11-3

A circle divides the plane into three sets of points: the sets of points inside the circle, on the circle, and outside the circle. We have just described the set of points on the circle of Fig. 11–3 as the graph of

$$\{(x, y) \mid x^2 + y^2 = 16\}.$$

How do we describe the set of points inside this circle? A point $P(x, y)$ is inside this circle if, and only if, $OP < 4$, or $(OP)^2 < 16$. Since $(OP)^2 = x^2 + y^2$, the graph of

$$\{(x, y) \mid x^2 + y^2 < 16\}$$

is the set of all points inside this circle; similarly, the graph of

$$\{(x, y) \mid x^2 + y^2 > 16\}$$

is the set of all points outside this circle.

Exercises

1. (a) What is the radius of the circle with equation $x^2 + y^2 = 25$?
   (b) What is the radius of the circle with equation $x^2 + y^2 = 49$?

2. (a) Write an equation of a circle with its center at the origin and a radius of 6.
   (b) Write an equation of a circle with its center at the origin and a radius of 8.

3. (a) Write a mathematical statement describing the set of all points in the plane which are at least 4 units from the origin.
   (b) Write a mathematical statement describing the set of all points in the plane which are at least 9 units from the origin.

4. (a) A circle is drawn with its center at the origin of a cartesian coordinate system. The circle passes through the point $(2, 5)$. What is the radius of the circle? Write an equation of the circle.
   (b) A circle is drawn with its center at the origin of a cartesian coordinate system. The circle passes through the point $(-1, 3)$. What is the radius of the circle? Write an equation of the circle.

5. (a) Give three integral solutions of the system of inequalities

$$\begin{cases} x \leq 0, \\ x^2 + y^2 \leq 16. \end{cases}$$

Graph the system.
   (b) Give three solutions, in ordered pairs of integers, of the system of inequalities

$$\begin{cases} x^2 + y^2 \leq 25, \\ y \geq 0. \end{cases}$$

Graph the system.

6. Find a system of inequalities whose graph is the set of all points to the right of the y-axis that are inside the circle with equation

$$x^2 + y^2 = 49.$$

7. Classify the points

$$(2, 3), \quad (1, -1), \quad (1, \tfrac{4}{3}), \quad (-\sqrt{2}, -1), \quad (0, 2)$$

by indicating which are inside, which are outside, and which are on the circle with equation

$$9x^2 + 9y^2 = 25.$$

8. Describe algebraically the set of all points in the plane at a distance of 4 units or less from the origin.

9. The family of concentric circles, with center at the origin, may be characterized by the equation

$$x^2 + y^2 = k.$$

Describe the members of this family for which $k = 10^6$, 10^2, 5^2, 10, 5, 1, 0, and -1, respectively. For what real number values of k does $x^2 + y^2 = k$ represent a circle?

10. Find a system of inequalities whose graph is the set of all points in the region strictly between the circles with equations $x^2 + y^2 - 10 = 0$ and $9x^2 + 9y^2 - 25 = 0$. Graph the region so described.

Preparation for Section 11–2

1. Solve, by substitution, the system

$$\begin{cases} x - y = 4, \\ 3x - 5y = 8. \end{cases}$$

2. Define equivalent systems of equations.

3. Solve

$$x^2 + x - 12 = 0.$$

4. Where does the graph of $y = ax^2 + bx + c$ cross the x-axis if $ax^2 + bx + c = 0$ has no real solution?

11–2 THE INTERSECTION OF A CIRCLE AND A LINE

To find the point of intersection of two lines, we find the solution set of the system composed of the two equations of the lines. In the same way, we can find the points of intersection of a line and a circle by solving the system consisting of the equations of the line and the circle. A circle and a line intersect in two points at most. If the line is tangent to the circle, then they intersect in only one point. Of course, many lines and circles have no points of intersection.

Problem.   Find the points of intersection, if any, of the circle with equation

$$x^2 + y^2 = 25$$

and the line with equation

$$x - y + 1 = 0.$$

Solution. One possible way of finding these points is to graph the circle and the line on the same set of axes. (See Fig.11–4.) Then we can obtain rough approximations of the co-ordinates of the points of inter-section of the two graphs. Stated algebraically, the problem is to solve the following system of equations.

$$\begin{cases} x^2 + y^2 = 25 \\ x - y + 1 = 0 \end{cases}$$

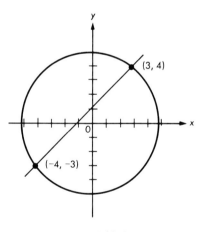

FIGURE 11-4

In other words, we are seeking those, and only those, ordered pairs which are solutions of both equa-tions. We can solve a system con-sisting of one linear and one quadratic equation by essentially the same methods employed with systems of linear equations. For instance, the particular system above can be solved by using the substitution method. Thus, if we solve the linear equation for y and substitute its value in the quadratic equation, we obtain the equivalent system

$$\begin{cases} x^2 + (x + 1)^2 = 25, \\ \qquad\qquad y = x + 1. \end{cases}$$

The quadratic equation of this system is equivalent to each of the following equations.

$$x^2 + x^2 + 2x + 1 = 25$$
$$2x^2 + 2x - 24 = 0$$
$$x^2 + x - 12 = 0$$
$$(x + 4)(x - 3) = 0$$

Therefore, the given system is equivalent to the system

$$\begin{cases} (x + 4)(x - 3) = 0, \\ y = x + 1. \end{cases}$$

The only values of x that make the first equation true are $x = -4$ and $x = 3$. If $x = -4$, then $y = -4 + 1$, or -3; if $x = 3$, $y = 3 + 1$, or 4, from the second equation. Hence,

$$\{(-4, -3), (3, 4)\}$$

is the solution set of the given system.

Check. $\hspace{3cm} (-4, -3)$

$$(-4)^2 + (-3)^2 \stackrel{?}{=} 25 \hspace{1cm} -4 - (-3) + 1 \stackrel{\checkmark}{=} 0$$
$$16 + 9 \stackrel{\checkmark}{=} 25$$

You can verify that the other solution also checks.

Exercises

Use a single set of axes on which to graph the circle and the line in each of the systems. From the graph, find the points of intersection of the circle and the line, if any.

1. (a) $\begin{cases} x^2 + y^2 = 9 \\ x + y = 3 \end{cases}$ $\hspace{2cm}$ (b) $\begin{cases} x^2 + y^2 = 16 \\ x - y = 4 \end{cases}$

2. (a) $\begin{cases} x^2 + y^2 = 36 \\ y - x = 9 \end{cases}$ $\hspace{2cm}$ (b) $\begin{cases} x^2 + y^2 = 25 \\ 3x = 4y + 25 \end{cases}$

3. (a) $\begin{cases} x^2 + y^2 = 20 \\ x - 2y = 10 \end{cases}$ $\hspace{2cm}$ (b) $\begin{cases} x^2 + y^2 - 1 = 0 \\ x + y - 2 = 0 \end{cases}$

4. (a)–6 (a). Solve algebraically each of the systems of equations in Exercises 1(a)–3(a). What does the solution of Exercise 2(a) tell you about the graph of these equations? What do you surmise about the graphs of the equations in Exercise 3(a)?

4. (b)–6 (b). Solve algebraically each of the systems in Exercises 1(b)–3(b). What do you surmise about the graphs of the equations in Exercise 2(b)? What does the solution of Exercise 3(b) tell you about the graphs of these equations?

---

7. In this section, we solved the following system.

$$\begin{cases} x^2 + y^2 = 25 \\ x - y + 1 = 0 \end{cases}$$

We discovered that where the line intersects the circle, x is -4 or 3. Then we found the ordinates of the points of intersection by using the linear equation

$$y = x + 1.$$

What error would occur if we were to find the ordinates of the points of intersection by using the quadratic equation

$$x^2 + y^2 = 25?$$

8. Find a system of inequalities whose graph is the set of all points above the line $x + y = 2$, but inside the circle $x^2 + y^2 = 4$. Graph this set of points.

9. A circle of radius $2\sqrt{5}$ is drawn with its center at the origin. Find the points of intersection of this circle with the line passing through the points $(-1, 7)$ and $(3, 3)$.

Draw the graph of each of the following systems of inequalities.

10. $\begin{cases} x^2 + y^2 \leq 10 \\ 2y \leq x + 5 \end{cases}$ **11.** $\begin{cases} x^2 + y^2 < 8 \\ y < x \\ y > 0 \end{cases}$

12. $\begin{cases} x^2 + y^2 > 4 \\ |x| < 2 \\ |y| < 2 \end{cases}$ **13.** $\begin{cases} x^2 + y^2 < 4 \\ |x| + |y| > 2 \end{cases}$

---

14. Consider the system of equations

$$\begin{cases} x^2 + y^2 = 9, \\ y = k, \end{cases}$$

which consists of a specific circle and a line which varies with k.
(a) For what values of k will the line $y = k$ fail to intersect the circle $x^2 + y^2 = 9$? Give an example.

(b) For what values of k will the line $y = k$ be tangent to the circle? How many such lines are there?

(c) For what values of k will the line $y = k$ intersect the circle in exactly two points? Give an example and check it by finding the points of intersection.

15. For what values of k will the graph of the equation $2x + y = k$ be tangent to the circle with equation $x^2 + y^2 = 4$?

16. What is the largest possible value of the linear form $2x + y$ if (x, y) is restricted so that it is in the set $\{(x, y) \mid x^2 + y^2 \leqq 4\}$?

Preparation for Section 11–3

1. How do x and $|x|$ compare
   (a) for x negative?
   (b) for x zero?
   (c) for x positive?

2. How do x^2 and $|x|^2$ compare
   (a) for x negative?
   (b) for x nonnegative?

3. How far apart are $(-1, 0)$ and $(3, 0)$?

4. How far apart are $(0, 0)$ and $(3, 4)$?

5. How far apart are $(-1, -2)$ and $(2, 2)$?

11–3 THE DISTANCE FORMULA

Before discussing other conic sections, let us derive a formula for the distance between any two points in a plane. Such a formula will be useful in finding equations of conic sections.

Let us assume that a cartesian coordinate system has been drawn on the plane. We now wish to derive a formula for the distance PQ between points P and Q in terms of the coordinates (x_1, y_1) of P and (x_2, y_2) of Q. If point R is chosen as indicated in Fig. 11–5, then $\triangle PRQ$ is a right triangle, and

$$(PQ)^2 = (PR)^2 + (RQ)^2,$$

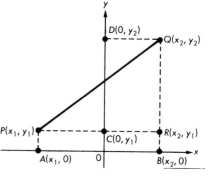

FIGURE 11-5

according to the pythagorean theorem. When we look at Fig. 11–5, we see that

$$PR = AB, \quad \text{or } |x_2 - x_1|,$$
$$RQ = CD, \quad \text{or } |y_2 - y_1|.$$

Hence,

$$(PQ)^2 = |x_2 - x_1|^2 + |y_2 - y_1|^2$$
$$= (x_2 - x_1)^2 + (y_2 - y_1)^2.$$

This proves the following important formula.

DISTANCE FORMULA

The distance between the points $P(x_1, y_1)$ and $Q(x_2, y_2)$ is given by

$$PQ = \sqrt{(x_2 - x_1)^2 + (y_2 - y_1)^2}.$$

The proof of the distance formula must be modified slightly if segment $\overline{PQ}$ is parallel to a coordinate axis, but the formula continues to apply.

Problem 1. Let $\triangle ABC$ be a triangle with vertices $A(9, 6)$, $B(1, -3)$, and $C(-1, 2)$. Find the length of each side of triangle ABC. Is $\triangle ABC$ a right triangle?

Solution. By the distance formula,

$$AB = \sqrt{(1 - 9)^2 + (-3 - 6)^2}$$
$$= \sqrt{8^2 + 9^2}, \quad \text{or } \sqrt{145}.$$
$$BC = \sqrt{(-1 - 1)^2 + [2 - (-3)]^2}$$
$$= \sqrt{2^2 + 5^2}, \quad \text{or } \sqrt{29}.$$
$$AC = \sqrt{(-1 - 9)^2 + (2 - 6)^2}$$
$$= \sqrt{10^2 + 4^2}, \quad \text{or } \sqrt{116}.$$

Thus, $\overline{AB}$ is the longest side. Hence, $\triangle ABC$ is a right triangle if, and only if,

$$(AB)^2 = (AC)^2 + (BC)^2,$$

according to the pythagorean theorem and its converse. The equation

$$(\sqrt{145})^2 = (\sqrt{116})^2 + (\sqrt{29})^2$$

or, equivalently,

$$145 = 116 + 29,$$

is true; therefore, $\triangle ABC$ is a right triangle.

Problem 2. Find an equation of the circle with its center, C, at $(-3, 4)$ and with a radius of 7.

Solution. Point P with coordinates (x, y) is on the circle if, and only if,

$$PC = 7,$$

that is,

$$\sqrt{(x + 3)^2 + (y - 4)^2} = 7.$$

Thus,

$$(x + 3)^2 + (y - 4)^2 = 49,$$

or

$$x^2 + y^2 + 6x - 8y - 24 = 0,$$

is an equation of the circle in Fig. 11–6.

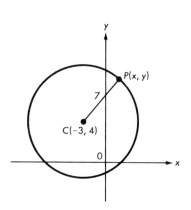

FIGURE 11-6

By the same argument as that used in Problem 2, we see that

$$(x - h)^2 + (y - k)^2 = r^2$$

is an equation of the circle having its center at (h, k) and a radius of r. An equivalent equation is

$$x^2 + y^2 - 2hx - 2ky + (h^2 + k^2 - r^2) = 0.$$

Conversely, if the graph of an equation of the form

$$Ax^2 + Ay^2 + Cx + Dy + E = 0, \quad A \neq 0,$$

consists of more than one point, then the graph is a circle. The following problem illustrates how the circle can be located in the coordinate plane.

Problem 3. Describe the graph of the equation

$$4x^2 + 4y^2 - 16x + 8y + 11 = 0.$$

Solution. We divide each side of this equation by 4, obtaining the equivalent equation

$$x^2 + y^2 - 4x + 2y + \tfrac{11}{4} = 0.$$

Then we proceed by completing the squares separately with the x-terms and the y-terms to get the equivalent equation

$$(x^2 - 4x + 4) + (y^2 + 2y + 1) = -\tfrac{11}{4} + 4 + 1,$$

or

$$(x - 2)^2 + (y + 1)^2 = \tfrac{9}{4}.$$

We recognize this as an equation of the circle with center at $(2, -1)$ and radius $\tfrac{3}{2}$.

It may be shown that the midpoint of a segment of a number line has as its coordinate the arithmetic average of the coordinates of the end-points. In a similar way, it may be shown that the midpoint of the segment having endpoints $P(x_1, y_1)$ and $Q(x_2, y_2)$ has coordinates

$$\left(\frac{x_1 + x_2}{2}, \frac{y_1 + y_2}{2} \right).$$

Exercises

1. (a) How far is the point $(-9, 3)$ from the origin?
   (b) How far is the point $(-3, -4)$ from the point $(3, 4)$?
2. (a) Find an equation of the circle with center at $(2, -5)$ and radius 6. Simplify the equation.
   (b) Find an equation of the circle with center at $(-3, 4)$ and radius 5. Simplify the equation.
3. (a) Find the perimeter of triangle ABC with the following vertices.

   $$A(-1, 3), \quad B(2, 5), \quad C(\tfrac{3}{2}, \tfrac{5}{2})$$

   What type of triangle is ABC? Which angles have the same measure?
   (b) Prove that triangle ABC with the following vertices is a right triangle.

   $$A(-7, 8), \quad B(-1, -4), \quad C(15, 4)$$

4. (a) Prove that triangle CDE with the following vertices is isosceles.

   $$C(2, 3), \quad D(-\tfrac{13}{2}, 3), \quad E(1, 7)$$

   Find the length of the altitude drawn from vertex D to base $\overline{CE}$.

(b) Prove that the angles at R and T are equal in the triangle with the following vertices.

$$R(-1, 5), \quad S(-1, -2), \quad T(6, -2)$$

5. (a) Use the distance formula to verify that the midpoint of the segment having endpoints $A(-1, 6)$ and $B(7, -10)$ has coordinates

$$\left(\frac{-1 + 7}{2}, \frac{6 + (-10)}{2}\right), \quad \text{or } (3, -2).$$

(b) Use the figure to prove that if P has coordinates (x_1, y_1), Q has coordinates (x_2, y_2), and $PM = MQ$, then M has coordinates

$$\left(\frac{x_1 + x_2}{2}, \frac{y_1 + y_2}{2}\right).$$

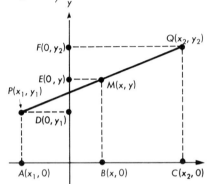

6. (a) A median of a triangle is a line joining a vertex to the midpoint of the opposite side. In triangle CDE with the following vertices, how long is the median drawn from C to the midpoint of DE?

$$C(-8, -5), \quad D(6, 2), \quad E(5, -4)$$

(b) Find the midpoints of the three sides of a triangle with the following vertices.

$$A(4, 4), \quad B(-2, 8), \quad C(2, -6)$$

Find the lengths of the three medians of the triangle. See part (a).

7. (a) Use the distance formula to find RS, ST, and RT, given that R has coordinates $(-1, 2)$, S has coordinates $(2, 3)$, and T has coordinates $(11, 6)$. Compare $RS + ST$ with RT to see whether points R, S, and T are collinear.

(b) Use the distance formula to find PQ, PR, and QR, given that P has coordinates $(-3, 2)$, Q has coordinates $(1, 1)$, and R has coordinates $(5, -2)$. Is $PQ + QR = PR$? Are points P, Q, and R collinear?

---

8. Is $|x_2 - x_1|^2$ always equal to $(x_2 - x_1)^2$? Why?

9. Find the center and radius of the circle having equation

$$x^2 + y^2 + 10x - 4y + 20 = 0.$$

10. If the line segment joining the points $(-3, -7)$ and $(9, 2)$ is a diameter of a circle, find an equation of the circle.

11. Triangle ABC has vertices at $A(7, 8)$, $B(-3, 4)$, and $C(-6, -2)$.
    (a) Find the length of $\overline{BC}$.
    (b) Find the midpoints of $\overline{AB}$ and $\overline{AC}$.
    (c) Find the distance between the midpoints of $\overline{AB}$ and $\overline{AC}$.
    (d) Compare the results of parts (a) and (c). What theorem in geometry does this comparison illustrate?

12. Find an equation of each of the following circles. Simplify each equation.
    (a) A circle of radius 5 with center at $(3, -4)$
    (b) A circle of radius 3 with center at $(-2, 1)$
    (c) A circle tangent to the coordinate axes and having radius 2. (How many such circles are there?)

13. Write the equation of each of the following circles in the form

$$(x - h)^2 + (y - k)^2 = r^2.$$

    In each case, locate the center and give the radius.
    (a) $x^2 + y^2 - 2x - 6y + 6 = 0$
    (b) $x^2 + y^2 + 4x + 2y + 4 = 0$
    (c) $x^2 + y^2 - 6x + 1 = 0$
    (d) $36x^2 + 36y^2 - 36y = 7$

---

14. Two of the vertices of an equilateral triangle are located at $P(1, 2)$ and $Q(4, 5)$. Find the third vertex. Is there more than one possibility?

15. Find the fourth vertex, D, of the parallelogram $ABCD$ if three vertices are located as follows:

$$A(-1, 5), \quad B(-2, 3), \quad C(5, 4).$$

16. A set of points in a coordinate plane is found to have the following property: Every point of the set is twice as far from the point $A(-5, 1)$ as it is from the point $B(3, 8)$. Find an equation for which this set is the graph.

17. A point $P(x, y)$ is on the perpendicular bisector of the line segment joining $A(-3, 5)$ to $B(2, -6)$ if, and only if,

$$PB = PA.$$

    Find an equation of the perpendicular bisector of $\overline{AB}$.

Review for Sections 11–1 through 11–3

Write an equation of each of the following.

1. A circle with its center at the origin and a radius of 7.
2. A circle with its center at the origin and passing through $(-2, -3)$.
3. The set of all points in the plane at a distance of more than 10 units from the origin.
4. The set of all points in the plane at a distance of 9 units or less from the origin.

Solve algebraically and graph each of the following systems of equations.

5. $\begin{cases} x^2 + y^2 = 49 \\ x + y = 7 \end{cases}$

6. $\begin{cases} x^2 + y^2 = 29 \\ y - x = 3 \end{cases}$

7. $\begin{cases} x^2 + y^2 = 50 \\ 2y + x = 9 \end{cases}$

8. $\begin{cases} x^2 + y^2 = 169 \\ y - x = 7 \end{cases}$

Draw the graph of each of the following systems of inequalities.

9. $\begin{cases} x^2 + y^2 \leq 25 \\ 3y - x \leq 3 \end{cases}$

10. $\begin{cases} x^2 + y^2 < 16 \\ x + y < 3 \end{cases}$

In each of the following find the perimeter of the triangle with the given vertices, and tell what type of triangle it is (right, isosceles).

11. $(7, -1)$, $(2, 2)$, $(4, 4)$ 12. $(-5, 5)$, $(5, 3)$, $(1, -1)$
13. $(6, -5)$, $(2, -2)$, $(5, 2)$ 14. $(-6, 0)$, $(3, -8)$, $(6, -1)$

Find the center and radius of the circles having the following equations.

15. $x^2 + y^2 - 6x + 10y + 28 = 0$
16. $x^2 + y^2 + 14x - 2y + 48 = 0$
17. $16x^2 + 16y^2 - 16x + 24y - 131 = 0$
18. $9x^2 + 9y^2 - 12x + 36y + 13 = 0$

Answers to Review for Sections 11–1 through 11–3

1. $x^2 + y^2 = 49$ 2. $x^2 + y^2 = 13$
3. $x^2 + y^2 > 100$ 4. $x^2 + y^2 \leq 81$

5. $\{(0, 7), (7, 0)\}$

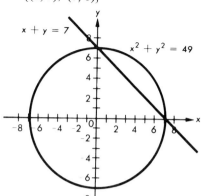

$x + y = 7$

$x^2 + y^2 = 49$

6. $\{(2, 5), (-5, -2)\}$

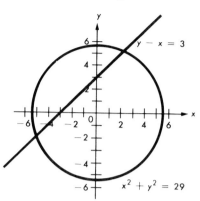

$y - x = 3$

$x^2 + y^2 = 29$

7. $\{(7, 1), (-\frac{17}{5}, \frac{31}{5})\}$

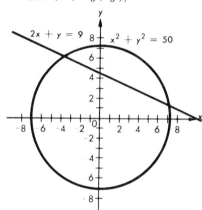

$2x + y = 9$

$x^2 + y^2 = 50$

8. $\{(5, 12), (-12, -5)\}$

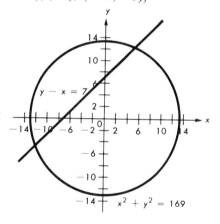

$y - x = 7$

$x^2 + y^2 = 169$

9.

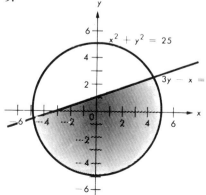

$x^2 + y^2 = 25$

$3y - x = 3$

10.

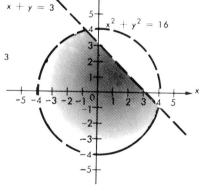

$x + y = 3$

$x^2 + y^2 = 16$

11. $2\sqrt{34} + 2\sqrt{2}$; isosceles   **12.** $2\sqrt{26} + 10\sqrt{2}$; right

13. $10 + 5\sqrt{2}$; right isosceles   **14.** $2\sqrt{145} + \sqrt{58}$; isosceles

15. $(3, -5)$, $\sqrt{6}$ **16.** $(-7, 1)$, $\sqrt{2}$

17. $(\frac{1}{2}, -\frac{3}{4})$, 3 **18.** $(\frac{2}{3}, -2)$, $\sqrt{3}$

11-4   ELLIPSES

An ellipse is obtained when we cut a cone by a plane which is almost perpendicular to the axis of the cone (Fig. 11–7). Thus, if we point our flashlight not quite directly at a wall, the lighted region on the wall has an elliptical shape.

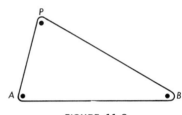

FIGURE 11-7   FIGURE 11-8

An ellipse can be constructed in the following way. Place a piece of paper on a drawing board, and put two thumb tacks into the paper at points A and B. Next, take a loop of thread which is long enough to fit over both tacks, and pull it taut with a pencil point P (Fig. 11–8). Keeping the thread taut, move the point P in a complete turn around points A and B. The figure drawn will be an ellipse (Fig. 11–9). As suggested by this construction, an ellipse consists of all points P such that

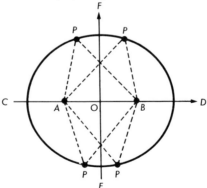

FIGURE 11-9

the sum $AP + BP + AB$ is a constant. Since the distance AB does not change, the ellipse really consists of all points P such that the sum $AP + BP$ is a constant.

Definition of an Ellipse

Given two points A and B in a plane and a positive number k greater than AB, the set consisting of all points P in the plane such that

$$AP + BP = k$$

is called an ellipse. Each of the points A and B is called a focus of the ellipse.

If line $\overleftrightarrow{CD}$ contains the foci A and B, and line $\overleftrightarrow{EF}$ is the perpendicular bisector of segment $\overline{AB}$, then it is reasonably clear from Fig.11–9 that lines $\overleftrightarrow{CD}$ and $\overleftrightarrow{EF}$ are *axes of symmetry* of the ellipse. In other words, if we fold the paper along the line $\overleftrightarrow{CD}$, the upper half and the lower half of the ellipse will coincide. Similarly, if we fold the paper along the line $\overleftrightarrow{EF}$, the right half will coincide with the left half of the ellipse. The point O of intersection of the axes of symmetry is called the *center* of the ellipse.

Each ellipse has an equation which is quite similar to an equation of a circle, as we shall show. To illustrate how an equation of an ellipse can be found, let us place the foci A and B of an ellipse 2 inches apart, and let us choose the number $k = 4$ in the definition of an ellipse. Then point P in the plane is on the ellipse if, and only if,

$$AP + BP = 4. \tag{1}$$

In order to find an equation of this ellipse, we must choose a car- tesian coordinate system in the plane. Although we may choose the axes as we see fit, the only choice that takes advantage of the sym- metry of the ellipse is the pair of axes of symmetry. Thus, let us select the x-axis passing through the foci A and B, and the y-axis perpendicular to the x-axis at the center O of the ellipse (Fig. 11–10). Since the foci are 2 inches apart and equidistant from O, it follows that

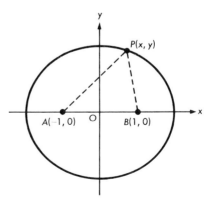

FIGURE 11-10

A has coordinates $(-1, 0)$ and B has coordinates $(1, 0)$. Therefore, if point P has coordinates (x, y),

$$AP = \sqrt{(x + 1)^2 + (y - 0)^2}, \quad \text{or} \quad \sqrt{x^2 + 2x + 1 + y^2},$$

and

$$BP = \sqrt{(x - 1)^2 + (y - 0)^2}, \quad \text{or} \quad \sqrt{x^2 - 2x + 1 + y^2}.$$

In view of Eq. (1), $P(x, y)$ is on the given ellipse if, and only if,

$$\sqrt{x^2 + 2x + 1 + y^2} + \sqrt{x^2 - 2x + 1 + y^2} = 4. \quad (2)$$

This is an *equation of the ellipse.* In other words, the graph of Eq. (2) is the ellipse drawn in Fig. 11–10.

Because Eq. (2) would be awkward to use, we shall simplify it. Equation (2) is equivalent to the equation

$$\sqrt{x^2 - 2x + 1 + y^2} = 4 - \sqrt{x^2 + 2x + 1 + y^2}. \quad (3)$$

This equation is, in turn, equivalent to the equation

$$(\sqrt{x^2 - 2x + 1 + y^2})^2 = (4 - \sqrt{x^2 + 2x + 1 + y^2})^2. \quad (4)$$

Although the equivalency between Eq. (3) and (4) is not as obvious as that between Eq. (1) and (2), it is clear that every solution of Eq. (3) is also a solution of this new equation. Carrying out the indicated operations in this new equation and simplifying, we obtain the following equivalent equations.

$$x^2 - 2x + 1 + y^2 = 16 - 8\sqrt{x^2 + 2x + 1 + y^2}$$
$$+ (x^2 + 2x + 1 + y^2)$$
$$8\sqrt{x^2 + 2x + 1 + y^2} = 16 + 4x$$
$$2\sqrt{x^2 + 2x + 1 + y^2} = 4 + x$$

Each solution of the equations above is also a solution of the equation

$$(2\sqrt{x^2 + 2x + 1 + y^2})^2 = (4 + x)^2.$$

This equation is, in turn, equivalent to each of the following equations.

$$4(x^2 + 2x + 1 + y^2) = 16 + 8x + x^2$$
$$4x^2 + 8x + 4 + 4y^2 = 16 + 8x + x^2$$
$$3x^2 + 4y^2 = 12$$
$$\frac{x^2}{4} + \frac{y^2}{3} = 1 \qquad\qquad (5)$$

Our work above shows only that every solution of Eq. (2) is also a solution of Eq. (5). To show that Eq. (5) is equivalent to Eq. (2), and hence, that Eq. (5) is an equation of the given ellipse, we must show that every solution of Eq. (5) is also a solution of Eq. (2).

If (x, y) is a solution of Eq. (5), (x, y) is a solution of $3x^2 + 4y^2 = 12$. Then $3x^2 \leq 12$, $x^2 \leq 4$, and therefore, $-2 \leq x \leq 2$. By adding 2 to each part of $-2 \leq x \leq 2$, we get $0 \leq 2 + x \leq 4$. However, if $0 \leq 2 + x$, then $0 \leq 4 + x$. Similarly, by adding $-x$ to each part of $-2 \leq x \leq 2$, we get $0 \leq 4 - x$. If $0 \leq 4 + x$ and $0 \leq 4 - x$,

$$\sqrt{(4 + x)^2} = 4 + x$$

and

$$\sqrt{(4 - x)^2} = 4 - x.$$

Consequently,

$$\sqrt{x^2 + 8x + 16} + \sqrt{x^2 - 8x + 16} = 8.$$

Recalling that $12 = 3x^2 + 4y^2$, we also have

$$\sqrt{x^2 + 8x + (4 + 3x^2 + 4y^2)}$$
$$+ \sqrt{x^2 - 8x + (4 + 3x^2 + 4y^2)} = 8,$$
$$\sqrt{4x^2 + 8x + 4 + 4y^2} + \sqrt{4x^2 - 8x + 4 + 4y^2} = 8,$$
$$2\sqrt{x^2 + 2x + 1 + y^2} + 2\sqrt{x^2 - 2x + 1 + y^2} = 8.$$

On dividing each side of this equation by 2, we obtain Eq. (2). Therefore, every solution of Eq. (5) is a solution of Eq. (2).

In the same way, it can be shown that every ellipse whose axes of symmetry are along the coordinate axes has an equation of the form

$$\frac{x^2}{a^2} + \frac{y^2}{b^2} = 1$$

for some positive numbers a and b. If we let $y = 0$ in this equation, we obtain

$$\frac{x^2}{a^2} = 1,$$

$$x^2 = a^2,$$

$$x = a \quad \text{or} \quad x = -a.$$

Thus, the ellipse crosses the x-axis at the points $(a, 0)$ and $(-a, 0)$. For this reason, we call a and $-a$ the x-intercepts of the ellipse. It may be shown in a similar way that the ellipse crosses the y-axis at the points $(0, b)$ and $(0, -b)$. We call b and $-b$ the y-intercepts of the ellipse. It is clear that the ellipse is a circle if, and only if, $a = b$.

Every ellipse has an equation of the form

$$\frac{x^2}{a^2} + \frac{y^2}{b^2} = 1,$$

and the graph of every equation of this form is an ellipse. We make use of this fact in working the following problems.

Problem 1. Describe the graph of the equation $16x^2 + 25y^2 = 400$.

Solution. If we divide each side of this equation by 400, we obtain the equivalent equation

$$\frac{x^2}{25} + \frac{y^2}{16} = 1, \quad \text{or} \quad \frac{x^2}{5^2} + \frac{y^2}{4^2} = 1.$$

Since the equation has the form

$$\frac{x^2}{a^2} + \frac{y^2}{b^2} = 1,$$

the graph is an ellipse with 5 and -5 as its x-intercepts, and 4 and -4 as its y-intercepts. The segments $\overline{CD}$ of the x-axis and $\overline{EF}$ of the y-axis, shown in Fig. 11–11, are called the *axes* of the ellipse. The longer one, $\overline{CD}$ in this case, is called the *major axis* and the shorter one, $\overline{EF}$ in our example, is called the *minor axis* of the ellipse.

The foci of this ellipse, say points A and B, are always on the major axis. If P is any point on the ellipse, then

$$AP + BP = AD + BD$$

since D is also a point on the ellipse. However, $BD = CA$ (Fig. 11–11) so that $AD + BD = AD + CA$, or CD. Hence, $AP + BP = 10$, the length of the major axis, for every point P on the ellipse. Since F is a point on the ellipse and $AF = BF$, it follows that $AF = 5$. Knowing the lengths of two sides of the right triangle, AOF, we find that the length of $\overline{AO}$ is 3 by the pythagorean theorem. Hence, the foci of this ellipse are the points $A(-3, 0)$ and $B(3, 0)$. We can now draw the

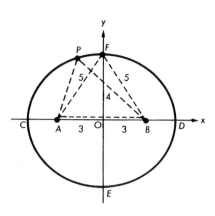

FIGURE 11-11

ellipse by placing thumbtacks at points A and B and taking a loop of string 16 units long.

For the ellipse with equation

$$\frac{x^2}{a^2} + \frac{y^2}{b^2} = 1,$$

the distance, c, from the center of the ellipse to a focus may be found from either

$$c^2 = a^2 - b^2 \quad \text{if} \quad a > b$$

or

$$c^2 = b^2 - a^2 \quad \text{if} \quad b > a.$$

We can think of a circle as a special case of an ellipse when the two foci coincide at the center.

Problem 2. Describe the graph of the equation $9x^2 + 4y^2 = 36$.

Solution. Dividing each side of this equation by 36, we obtain the equivalent equation

$$\frac{x^2}{2^2} + \frac{y^2}{3^2} = 1.$$

Since the equation has the form

$$\frac{x^2}{a^2} + \frac{y^2}{b^2} = 1,$$

the graph is an ellipse with x-intercepts 2 and -2 and y-intercepts 3 and -3. The axis $\overline{CD}$ is shorter than the axis $\overline{EF}$ for this ellipse (Fig. 11–12). Therefore, $\overline{CD}$ is the minor axis and $\overline{EF}$ is the major axis. Since the major axis is on the y-axis, the foci A and B are on the y-axis also. The distance c from the origin to either A or B is given by

$$c^2 = 3^2 - 2^2, \quad \text{or} \quad c = \sqrt{5},$$

according to our statement in Problem 1. Hence, the foci have coordinates $(0, \sqrt{5})$ and $(0, -\sqrt{5})$, as shown in Fig. 11–12.

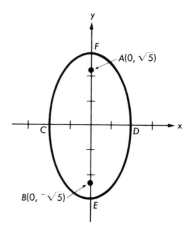

FIGURE 11-12

Given an equation of an ellipse, we can find points on the ellipse by solving the equation either for y in terms of x or for x in terms of y. Then by assigning values to one of the variables, we can easily compute the corresponding values of the other variable.

Exercises

1. (a) Consider the ellipse with equation

$$\frac{x^2}{4} + \frac{y^2}{3} = 1.$$

   (i) Find the x- and y-intercepts.
   (ii) Show that the points $(1, \frac{3}{2})$, $(-1, \frac{3}{2})$, $(1, -\frac{3}{2})$, and $(-1, -\frac{3}{2})$ are on the ellipse.
   (iii) If (x, y) is any point on the ellipse, where $x \neq 0$ and $y \neq 0$, find three other related points on the ellipse.
   (b) An ellipse has equation

$$\frac{x^2}{9} + \frac{y^2}{36} = 1.$$

   (i) Find the x- and y-intercepts and the foci.
   (ii) How long is the major axis? the minor axis?
   (iii) Find the values of x when $y = 3\sqrt{3}$ or when $y = -3\sqrt{3}$.
   (iv) Sketch the graph of the ellipse. Show the points mentioned in parts (i) and (iii). Where do these four points lie on the ellipse with reference to the foci?

2. (a) An ellipse has equation

$$\frac{x^2}{36} + \frac{y^2}{4} = 1.$$

    (i) Find the coordinates of the x- and y-intercepts and of the foci.

    (ii) Give the lengths of the major and minor axes.

    (iii) Find y if $x = 4\sqrt{2}$ or if $x = -4\sqrt{2}$. Where do these four points lie on the ellipse with reference to the foci?

    (iv) Sketch the graph of the ellipse. Show the points mentioned in parts (i) and (iii).

  (b) (i) Describe the graph of the equation $x^2 + 4y^2 = 36$, giving the coordinates of the intercepts and of the foci.

    (ii) A line through either focus perpendicular to the major axis cuts the ellipse in two points. Use the coordinates of the foci and the equation of the ellipse to find these four points.

    (iii) Graph the ellipse, showing all points mentioned in parts (i) and (ii).

Write an equation of the ellipses with foci at points A and B, given that P is on the ellipse. Simplify each equation.

3. (a) $A(2, 0)$, $B(-2, 0)$; $AP + BP = 6$

    (b) $A(0, 3)$, $B(0, -3)$; $AP + BP = 8$

4. (a) $A(4, 0)$, $B(-4, 0)$; $AP + BP = 11$

    (b) $A(0, 5)$, $B(0, -5)$; $AP + BP = 13$

5. (a) Draw the graph of the equation $x^2 + 2y^2 = 18$. List the coordinates of the intercepts and of the foci. Find the coordinates of the points on the ellipse that are vertically above or below the foci. Give the lengths of the major and minor axes.

  (b) Draw the graph of the equation $9x^2 + y^2 = 36$. List the coordinates of the intercepts and of the foci. Find the coordinates of the points on the ellipse that are horizontally to the right or to the left of the foci. Give the length of the major axis.

6. (a) Tell which of the following points are inside, which are outside, and which are on the ellipse with equation $4x^2 + 9y^2 = 36$.

$(1, 1)$, $(1, 2)$, $(1, \frac{4}{3}\sqrt{2})$, $(1, \sqrt{3})$, $(1, -2)$, $(-2, \frac{5}{4})$, $(-1, -2)$

Write an algebraic expression describing the points inside the ellipse. Write an algebraic expression describing the points outside the ellipse.

  (b) Draw and describe the graph of the equation $4x^2 + 18y^2 = 36$. Write a mathematical statement describing the points that are inside the ellipse. Write a mathematical statement describing the points that are on or outside the ellipse.

7. (a) Describe the graph of the inequality

$$\frac{x^2}{4} + \frac{y^2}{3} < 1.$$

Find all integral solutions.

(b) Draw the graph of the equation $64x^2 + 9y^2 = 16$. Give the coordinates and plot the intercepts, foci, and points on the ellipse that are horizontally to the right or to the left of the foci.

8. (a) The foci of an ellipse are at points $A(4, 0)$ and $B(-4, 0)$. A point is on the ellipse if, and only if, the sum of its distances from A and B is equal to 16. Find an equation of the ellipse and sketch it.

(b) Find an equation of the ellipse with foci $A(0, -1)$, and $B(0, 1)$, given that point P is on the ellipse if, and only if, $AP + BP = 3$. What are the coordinates of the x- and y-intercepts?

---

9. Find the intersections of the ellipse $3x^2 + 4y^2 = 9$ with the straight line $x = k$ for each of the following values of k.

$$-4, \quad -\sqrt{3}, \quad 1, \quad \sqrt{3}, \quad 5$$

10. Consider the system of equations

$$\begin{cases} x^2 + 3y^2 = 12, \\ x + 3y = 6. \end{cases}$$

(a) Find the solution set by graphing each member of the system and observing their points of intersection.

(b) Use the substitution method to find the solution set.

11. Consider the system of equations

$$\begin{cases} x^2 + y^2 = 13, \\ 2x^2 + 3y^2 = 35. \end{cases}$$

(a) Describe the graph of each equation of this system.

(b) Solve the system.

(Hint: The *method of addition* used on a system of linear equations in x and y is applicable here.)

12. Graph the solution set of the system of inequalities

$$\begin{cases} x^2 + 3y^2 \geq 3, \\ x^2 + y^2 \leq 5. \end{cases}$$

13. An equation of the family of ellipses with center at the origin and axes along the coordinate axes is

$$\frac{x^2}{a^2} + \frac{y^2}{b^2} = 1.$$

(a) Write an equation of the member of this family with y-intercepts 1 and -1, and x-intercepts 2 and -2.

(b) How many members of this family have x-intercepts 8 and -8? Write an equation of this set of ellipses. Write an equation of the ellipse which has these x-intercepts and also passes through the point $(4, 3)$.

(c) How many members of this family have y-intercepts 4 and -4? Write an equation of this set of ellipses. Write an equation of the ellipse which has these y-intercepts and also passes through the point with coordinates $(-3, 2)$. Through what other three points does this ellipse automatically pass because of its two axes of symmetry?

14. (a) Graph each of the following equations on a single set of axes.

$$\frac{x^2}{25} + \frac{y^2}{1} = 1, \quad \frac{x^2}{25} + \frac{y^2}{4} = 1, \quad \frac{x^2}{25} + \frac{y^2}{9} = 1,$$

$$\frac{x^2}{25} + \frac{y^2}{16} = 1, \quad \frac{x^2}{25} + \frac{y^2}{25} = 1$$

(b) Find c and c/a for each of the ellipses you just graphed, where c is half the distance between the foci and a is half the length of the major axis. Tell how the appearance of the ellipse changes as c/a changes. Is there a maximum value for c/a? What is the minimum value for c/a?

(c) The quotient c/a is called the *eccentricity* of the ellipse. Two ellipses are drawn, each with major axis 20 units long. How do their appearances compare if the eccentricity of one is $\frac{1}{20}$ and that of the other $\frac{19}{20}$?

Preparation for Section 11–5

1. Find the distance AP from $A(-5, 0)$ to $P(x, y)$.

2. Find the distance BP from $B(5, 0)$ to $P(x, y)$.

3. Find the difference, $AP - BP$.

4. Set the difference in Exercise 3 equal to 8.

5. Simplify the equation in Exercise 4 by squaring until you have no more radicals in the equation.

6. Find the difference, $BP - AP$.

7. Set the difference in Exercise 6 equal to 8.

8. Simplify the equation in Exercise 7 in the same way you did that in Exercise 4.

9. What relation, if any, exists between the equations in Exercises 4, 5, 7. and 8? Are any of them equivalent?

11–5 HYPERBOLAS

To visualize a hyperbola completely, we must start with a cone that has two *nappes* (see Fig. 11–13 at the bottom of the page). Then any plane which cuts both nappes without passing through the vertex intersects the cone in a hyperbola. Thus, the hyperbola has two separate parts, or branches, each extending indefinitely far. The following is a description of the hyperbola relative to its focal points.

Definition of a Hyperbola

Given two points A and B in a plane and a positive number k less than AB, the set consisting of every point P in the plane such that either

$$AP - BP = k \quad or \quad BP - AP = k$$

is called a hyperbola. Each of the points A and B is called a focus of the hyperbola.

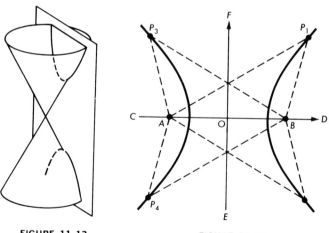

FIGURE 11–13   FIGURE 11–14

In Fig.11–14, we have sketched the hyperbola for $AB = 6$ and $k = 4$. The figure shows four symmetrically placed points of the hyperbola: P_1, P_2, P_3, and P_4. Points P_1 and P_2 are closer to B, so that

$$AP_1 - BP_1 = 4, \quad AP_2 - BP_2 = 4.$$

Points P_3 and P_4 are closer to A, so that

$$BP_3 - AP_3 = 4, \quad BP_4 - AP_4 = 4.$$

The points closer to B form the right-hand branch of the hyperbola of Fig. 11–14, and the points closer to A form the left-hand branch.

The hyperbola, like the ellipse, has two axes of symmetry, the line $\overleftrightarrow{CD}$ through the foci and the line $\overleftrightarrow{EF}$ which is the perpendicular bisector of segment $\overline{AB}$, as shown in Fig. 11–14. The point O, in which these two axes intersect, is called the center of the hyperbola.

To find an equation of the hyperbola of Fig.11–14, we naturally select our coordinate axes as the axes of symmetry described above. Since $AB = 6$ by assumption, A has coordinates $(-3, 0)$ and B has coordinates $(3, 0)$. Point P of the plane (Fig.11–15) is on the right-hand branch if, and only if,

$$AP - BP = 4.$$

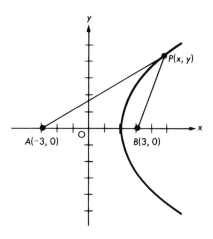

FIGURE 11-15

If P has coordinates (x, y) then

$$AP = \sqrt{(x + 3)^2 + (y - 0)^2}$$

and

$$BP = \sqrt{(x - 3)^2 + (y - 0)^2}$$

so that P is on the right-hand branch of the hyperbola if, and only if,

$$\sqrt{x^2 + 6x + 9 + y^2} - \sqrt{x^2 - 6x + 9 + y^2} = 4. \quad (1)$$

Thus, Eq. (1) is an *equation of the right-hand branch* and

$$\sqrt{x^2 - 6x + 9 + y^2} - \sqrt{x^2 + 6x + 9 + y^2} = 4 \quad (2)$$

is an *equation of the left-hand branch* of this hyperbola.

Let us simplify Eq. (1) as we did the equation of the ellipse. We proceed in the following manner.

$$\sqrt{x^2 + 6x + 9 + y^2} = 4 + \sqrt{x^2 - 6x + 9 + y^2}$$

$$x^2 + 6x + 9 + y^2 = 16 + 8\sqrt{x^2 - 6x + 9 + y^2}$$

$$+ (x^2 - 6x + 9 + y^2)$$

$$12x - 16 = 8\sqrt{x^2 - 6x + 9 + y^2}$$

$$3x - 4 = 2\sqrt{x^2 - 6x + 9 + y^2}$$

$$9x^2 - 24x + 16 = 4(x^2 - 6x + 9 + y^2)$$

$$5x^2 - 4y^2 = 20$$

$$\frac{x^2}{4} - \frac{y^2}{5} = 1 \quad (3)$$

We leave it to you to verify that Eq. (2) also simplifies to Eq. (3). Thus, the graph of Eq. (3) contains both branches of the hyperbola.

To show that the graph of Eq. (3) is the hyperbola of Fig.11–14, we must show that every solution of Eq. (3) is also a solution of either Eq. (1) or Eq. (2). With this in mind, let (x, y) be a solution of Eq. (3). Then $5x^2 = 20 + 4y^2$, $5x^2 \geq 20$, and $x^2 \geq 4$. Hence, either

$$x \geq 2 \quad \text{or} \quad x \leq -2.$$

If (x, y) is a solution of (3) for which $x \geq 2$, then $3x + 4 \geq 0$ and $3x - 4 \geq 0$. Furthermore,

$$\sqrt{(3x + 4)^2} = 3x + 4, \quad \sqrt{(3x - 4)^2} = 3x - 4.$$

Hence,

$$\sqrt{9x^2 + 24x + 16} - \sqrt{9x^2 - 24x + 16} = 8.$$

Now $9x^2 = 4x^2 + 5x^2$ and $5x^2 = 20 + 4y^2$, or $9x^2 = 4x^2 + 20 + 4y^2$.

Therefore,

$$\sqrt{4x^2 + 20 + 4y^2 + 24x + 16}$$
$$- \sqrt{4x^2 + 20 + 4y^2 - 24x + 16} = 8,$$

or

$$\sqrt{4x^2 + 24x + 36 + 4y^2} - \sqrt{4x^2 - 24x + 36 + 4y^2} = 8,$$
$$2\sqrt{x^2 + 6x + 9 + y^2} - 2\sqrt{x^2 - 6x + 9 + y^2} = 8.$$

On dividing each side of this equation by 2, we obtain Eq. (1). Thus, every solution of Eq. (3) for which $x \geq 2$ is also a solution of Eq. (1).

It may be shown in exactly the same way that every solution (x, y) of Eq. (3) for which $x \leq -2$ is also a solution of Eq. (2). Consequently, the graph of Eq. (3) is the hyperbola of Fig. 11–14.

In Eq. (3), what significance do the numbers 4 and 5 have in relation to the hyperbola? If we let $y = 0$, we obtain the equation

$$\frac{x^2}{4} = 1, \quad x^2 = 4,$$

and finally,

$$x = 2 \quad \text{or} \quad x = -2.$$

Thus, the x-intercepts of this hyperbola are 2 and -2. If we let $x = 0$ in the equation above, we obtain the equation

$$\frac{-y^2}{5} = 1, \quad \text{or} \quad y^2 = -5.$$

The solutions of this equation are the complex numbers $\sqrt{5}i$ and $-\sqrt{5}i$. Since the graph consists of only the real solutions of Eq. (3), we conclude that the hyperbola has no y-intercepts. We note that the sum of 4 and 5 is the square of the distance from the center of the hyperbola to each focus. Thus, 3, the positive square root of 9, is this distance.

It can be shown that every hyperbola with the coordinate axes as its axes of symmetry has an equation either of the form

$$\frac{x^2}{a^2} - \frac{y^2}{b^2} = 1$$

or of the form

$$\frac{y^2}{a^2} - \frac{x^2}{b^2} = 1.$$

Conversely, it may be shown that every equation of either form has a hyperbola as its graph. If we let

$$c^2 = a^2 + b^2,$$

then the hyperbola

$$\frac{x^2}{a^2} - \frac{y^2}{b^2} = 1 \quad \text{has foci at } (c, 0) \text{ and } (-c, 0).$$

$$\frac{y^2}{a^2} - \frac{x^2}{b^2} = 1 \quad \text{has foci at } (0, c) \text{ and } (0, -c).$$

Problem 1. Discuss the graph of the equation $16y^2 = 9x^2 + 144$.

Solution. This equation is equivalent to each of the following equations.

$$16y^2 - 9x^2 = 144$$

$$\frac{16y^2}{144} - \frac{9x^2}{144} = 1$$

$$\frac{y^2}{9} - \frac{x^2}{16} = 1$$

$$\frac{y^2}{3^2} - \frac{x^2}{4^2} = 1$$

Since this equation has form

$$\frac{y^2}{a^2} - \frac{x^2}{b^2} = 1,$$

its graph is a hyperbola. The y-intercepts are 3 and -3. There are no x-intercepts. Since

$$3^2 + 4^2 = 5^2,$$

the foci are 5 units below and above the center. Hence, $(0, 5)$ and $(0, -5)$ are the foci.

We may find points on this hyperbola if we solve its equation for y in terms of x or for x in terms of y. We solve for y in terms of x as follows:

$$\frac{y^2}{3^2} = \frac{x^2}{4^2} + 1,$$

$$y^2 = \frac{3^2}{4^2}(x^2 + 4^2),$$

$$y = \tfrac{3}{4}\sqrt{x^2 + 16} \quad \text{or} \quad y = -\tfrac{3}{4}\sqrt{x^2 + 16}.$$

Hence,

$$y = \tfrac{3}{4}\sqrt{x^2 + 16}$$

is an equation of the upper branch, and

$$y = -\tfrac{3}{4}\sqrt{x^2 + 16}$$

is an equation of the lower branch of the hyperbola. You can verify that the following points are on the upper branch by letting x equal 0, 2, 3, and 8 in the equation of the upper branch.

$$(0, 3), \quad \left(2, \frac{3\sqrt{5}}{2}\right), \quad \left(3, \frac{15}{4}\right), \quad (8, 3\sqrt{5})$$

We used the approximation $\sqrt{5} \doteq 2.2$ to plot points in Fig. 11–16. The other points plotted in the figure were obtained by considering the symmetry of the hyperbola about the coordinate axes.

The points $C(0, -3)$ and $D(0, 3)$ are called the *vertices* of the hyperbola, and the segment $\overline{CD}$, which joins them, is called the *transverse axis* of the hyperbola. The branches of a hyperbola extend indefinitely far from the axes. In other words, the curve is unbounded.

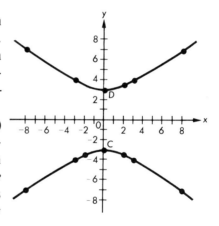

FIGURE 11-16

If two conic sections are drawn in the same plane, then they might have several points of intersection. It is intuitively clear that an ellipse and a hyperbola might have as many as four points of intersection. The following problem illustrates an algebraic method of finding the points of intersection of two conic sections.

Problem 2. Find the points of intersection of the circle with equation

$$x^2 + y^2 = 16$$

and the hyperbola with equation

$$4x^2 - y^2 = 4.$$

Solution. Algebraically, the problem is to find all solutions of the system of equations

$$\begin{cases} x^2 + y^2 = 16, \\ 4x^2 - y^2 = 4. \end{cases}$$

If we solve the system by the addition method, we obtain the equivalent system

$$\begin{cases} x^2 + y^2 = 16, \\ 5x^2 = 20. \end{cases}$$

The latter equation is easily solved, yielding $x = 2$ or $x = -2$. Letting $x = 2$ in the first equation, we get the equation

$$y^2 = 12,$$

which is solved to yield $y = 2\sqrt{3}$ or $y = -2\sqrt{3}$. Thus, $(2, 2\sqrt{3})$ and $(2, -2\sqrt{3})$ are solutions of the system. If we let $x = -2$ in the first equation, we again obtain $y = 2\sqrt{3}$ or $y = -2\sqrt{3}$. Thus, $(-2, 2\sqrt{3})$ and $(-2, -2\sqrt{3})$ are also solutions. Therefore, the four points of intersection of the circle and the hyperbola have coordinates

$$(2, 2\sqrt{3}), \quad (2, -2\sqrt{3}),$$
$$(-2, 2\sqrt{3}), \quad (-2, -2\sqrt{3}).$$

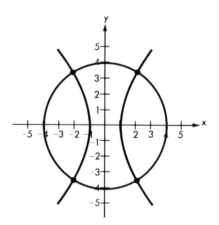

These four points are identified in Fig. 11–17.

FIGURE 11-17

Exercises

1. (a) A hyperbola has equation $x^2/25 - y^2/16 = 1$.
   (i) Find the x-intercepts and show that there are no y-intercepts.
   (ii) Find the coordinates of the foci.
   (iii) Find the points of the hyperbola directly above and below the foci by substituting $x = \pm\sqrt{41}$ in the equation of the hyperbola and solving for y.
   (iv) Solve the equation for y in terms of x and find y when $x = \pm6, \pm7,$ and ±10.
   (v) Graph the hyperbola showing all the points found in parts (i) through (iv).

(b) A hyperbola has equation $y^2/16 - x^2/9 = 1$.

   (i) Find the y-intercepts and show that there are no x-intercepts.

   (ii) Find the coordinates of the foci.

   (iii) Find the points horizontally directly to the right and left of the foci by substituting $y = \pm 5$ in the equation of the hyperbola and solving for x.

   (iv) Solve the equation for x in terms of y and find x when $y = \pm 6, \pm 7,$ and ± 10.

   (v) Graph the hyperbola, showing all the points found in parts (i) through (iv).

2. (a) Sketch the graph of $16y^2 - 25x^2 = 400$.

   (b) Sketch the graph of $9x^2 - 16y^2 = 144$.

In Exercises 3 and 4 the foci of a hyperbola are at points A and B with coordinates $(-4, 0)$ and $(4, 0)$, respectively. A point is on the hyperbola if the difference of its distances from these two points is 6.

3. (a) Using the distance formula, write the equation which says that $PA - PB = 6$ where $P(x, y)$ is a point on the hyperbola.

   (b) Using the distance formula, write the equation which says that $PB - PA = 6$ where $P(x, y)$ is a point on the hyperbola.

4. (a) Find the x-intercepts of this hyperbola. Sketch the hyperbola.

   (b) Show that this hyperbola does not have y-intercepts.

5. Find an equation, in simplified form, of a hyperbola if the foci are at points A and B with coordinates as given, and if point P on the hyperbola has the given number as the difference of its distances from A and B.

   (a) $A(1, 0)$, $B(-1, 0)$; 1   (b) $A(0, 2)$, $B(0, -2)$; 3

For each of the following equations, find the intercepts of the hyperbola. Also, use the Table of Squares and Square Roots to approximate the coordinates of eight other points on the hyperbola. Sketch each graph.

6. (a) $\dfrac{x^2}{4} - \dfrac{y^2}{9} = 1$ (b) $\dfrac{x^2}{9} - \dfrac{y^2}{9} = 1$

7. (a) $\dfrac{y^2}{9} - \dfrac{x^2}{16} = 1$ (b) $25y^2 - 4x^2 = 100$

---

8. Use algebraic methods to find the points of intersection of the hyperbola $y^2 - 3x^2 = 6$ and each of the lines given below. In each case, sketch the graph of the hyperbola and the line.

   (a) $x + y - 4 = 0$

   (b) $x - y + 2 = 0$

   (c) $x - y - 1 = 0$

9. Solve the system of equations

$$\begin{cases} 4x^2 - 5y^2 = 20, \\ 16x^2 + 25y^2 = 400, \end{cases}$$

and sketch the graph of each conic section.

10. Use algebraic methods to find the solution set of the systems of equations

$$\begin{cases} x^2 - 3y^2 + 12 = 0, \\ 4x^2 + 3y^2 - 192 = 0. \end{cases}$$

Check your solutions by graphing.

11. Use algebraic methods to find the points of intersection of the two conic sections $x^2 + 4y^2 = 16$ and $x^2 - y^2 = 16$. Check your answer by sketching a graph.

---

12. (a) Solve the equation $x^2/4 - y^2/5 = 1$ for y in terms of x. What values of x lead to real values for y?
   (b) Solve the equation $x^2/4 - y^2/5 = 1$ for x in terms of y. Are there any real values for y that lead to complex values for x?

13. A hyperbola is drawn with focus B at $(c, 0)$ and focus A at $(-c, 0)$. For every point $P(x, y)$ on the hyperbola, it is true that $PA - PB = 2a$, or $-2a$, depending on which branch of the hyperbola is being considered. Use the distance formula to find an equation of this hyperbola. Your equation contains the constants a and c. Show that $c^2 - a^2$ is positive and then replace it by b^2 to obtain an equation containing the constants a and b. You should see now why we said in this section that $c^2 = a^2 + b^2$.

Preparation for Section 11–6

1. Graph the equation $y = x^2 - 5x - 6$.
2. What is the lowest point on the graph in Exercise 1?
3. Use your graph in Exercise 1 to estimate the real solutions of each of the following quadratic equations.
   (a) $x^2 - 5x - 6 = 0$
   (b) $x^2 - 5x - 6 = 3$
   (c) $x^2 - 5x - 6 = -7$
4. What is the distance AP from $A(3, 0)$ to $P(x, y)$?
5. What is the distance from $P(x, y)$ to the line $x = -3$?
6. Set the distances in Exercises 4 and 5 equal to each other and simplify the resulting equation.

11-6 PARABOLAS

The conic sections studied so far have been *central conics;* that is, each has had two axes of symmetry and a center. The final conic section to be studied, the parabola, is not a central conic. The parabola is the curve of intersection of a plane with a cone; the plane is parallel to an edge of the cone. (See Fig. 11–18.)

The parabola may be described relative to a point and a line in the following way.

Definition of a parabola

Given a point F and a line L not containing F, the set consisting of every point P in the plane such that

$$PF = PQ,$$

where Q is the foot of the perpendicular drawn from P to line L (Fig.11-19), is called a parabola. The point F is called the focus and the line L the directrix of the parabola.

FIGURE 11-18

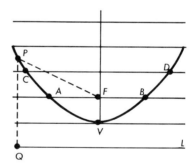

FIGURE 11-19

With a piece of graph paper and a compass, it is easy to find as many points on a parabola as you wish. Let the directrix L be along one of the lines of the paper and let F also be on a line. In Fig.11–19, F is two units above L. Clearly one point of the parabola is the point V halfway between F and L, that is, one unit directly under F. Incidentally, V is called the *vertex* of the parabola. Now open the compass to a radius of two units, place the point of the compass at F, and mark off points A and B on the line two units above L. Next, open the compass to a radius of three units, place the point of the compass at F, and mark off points C and D on the line three units above L, and so on.

The line through the focus of a parabola and perpendicular to the directrix is called the *axis* of the parabola. From Fig. 11–19, it can be seen that the axis of the parabola is also the axis of symmetry of the parabola.

Let us find an equation of a parabola. The axis of the parabola is an obvious choice for one coordinate axis, say the y-axis. While it might seem plausible to select the directrix L as the x-axis, a still better choice for the x-axis is the line through the vertex V, as indicated in Fig. 11–20.

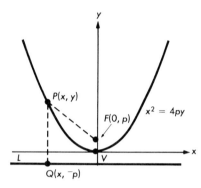

FIGURE 11-20

Let p be the distance from the vertex V to the focus F. Then F has coordinates $(0, p)$, and the directrix L has equation $y = -p$. A point P in the plane is on the parabola if, and only if,

$$PF = PQ,$$

where Q is the point at the foot of the perpendicular drawn from P to line L. If P has coordinates (x, y), it follows that Q then has coordinates $(x, -p)$. Since

$$PF = \sqrt{(x - 0)^2 + (y - p)^2}$$

and

$$PQ = \sqrt{(x - x)^2 + (y + p)^2},$$

$P(x, y)$ is on the parabola if, and only if,

$$\sqrt{x^2 + (y - p)^2} = \sqrt{(y + p)^2}.$$

The equation above is equivalent to the equation

$$x^2 + (y - p)^2 = (y + p)^2$$

for the reason that, if b and c are positive numbers, then $\sqrt{b} = \sqrt{c}$ if, and only if, $b = c$. In turn, this equation is equivalent to the equation

$$x^2 + y^2 - 2py + p^2 = y^2 + 2py + p^2,$$

which simplifies to

$$x^2 = 4py.$$

Thus, this simple quadratic equation is an equation of the given parabola.

Problem 1. Find an equation of the parabola with focus $(0, 3)$ and directrix $y = -3$.

Solution. We need only let $p = 3$ in $x^2 = 4py$ to find

$$x^2 = 12y$$

as an equation of the parabola.

If we choose the x-axis on the axis of the parabola and the y-axis through the vertex V, as shown in Fig. 11–21, then we shall obtain the same equation for the parabola except that x and y will be interchanged. Thus,

$$y^2 = 4px$$

is an equation of the parabola under consideration.

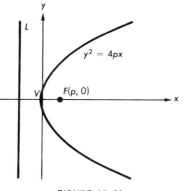

FIGURE 11–21

Problem 2. Find an equation of the parabola with focus $(\frac{1}{4}, 0)$ and directrix $x = -\frac{1}{4}$.

Solution. We let $p = \frac{1}{4}$ in $y^2 = 4px$ obtaining

$$y^2 = 4 \cdot \tfrac{1}{4}x, \quad \text{or } y^2 = x,$$

as an equation of this parabola.

Problem 3. Find the coordinates of the points of intersection, if any, of the parabola with equation

$$x^2 = 4y$$

and the line with equation

$$x + 2y - 4 = 0.$$

Solution. We are asked to solve the system of equations

$$\begin{cases} x^2 = 4y, \\ x + 2y - 4 = 0. \end{cases}$$

If we solve the second equation for $2y$ and substitute its value in the first equation, we obtain the equivalent system

$$\begin{cases} x^2 = 2(4 - x), \\ 2y = 4 - x. \end{cases}$$

The first equation of this system may be solved as follows:

$$x^2 = 8 - 2x,$$
$$x^2 + 2x - 8 = 0,$$
$$(x + 4)(x - 2) = 0,$$
$$x = -4 \quad \text{or} \quad x = 2.$$

If we let $x = -4$ in the second equation, we obtain

$$2y = 4 - (-4), \quad \text{or } y = 4.$$

If we let $x = 2$, we obtain

$$2y = 4 - 2, \text{ or } y = 1.$$

Thus,

$$\{(-4, 4), (2, 1)\}$$

is the solution set of the system that we were asked to solve.

Figure 11–22 shows the two points of intersection of the given parabola and the given line.

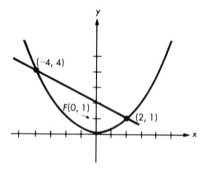

FIGURE 11-22

Exercises

1. Find an equation of the parabola with
   (a) focus $(0, -3)$ and directrix $y = 3$.
   (b) focus $(-\frac{1}{4}, 0)$ and directrix $x = \frac{1}{4}$.

2. (a) Find the points on the parabola $x^2 = 12y$ for which $y = 3$. How long is the line segment joining these points?
   (b) Find the points where the line $x = \frac{1}{4}$ intersects the parabola $y^2 = x$. How long is the line segment joining these points?

The line segment through the focus perpendicular to the axis, terminating in two points on the parabola, is called the *latus rectum* of the parabola. Find the length of this line and the coordinates of its endpoints for each of the following parabolas.

3. (a) $x^2 = 16y$ (b) $3x^2 = 20y$

4. (a) $y^2 = 12x$ (b) $5y^2 = 16x$

Draw the graph of each of the following parabolas, showing vertex, focus, directrix, and *latus rectum*. List the coordinates of vertex, focus, and of the endpoints of the *latus rectum*. Write the equation of the directrix and of the axis of symmetry.

5. (a) $x^2 = 8y$ (b) $x^2 = -8y$

6. (a) $y^2 = 10x$ (b) $y^2 = -10x$

Graph each of the following equations. List the coordinates of vertex, the focus, and the endpoints of *latus rectum* for each parabola. Also give the equations of the directrix and the axis of symmetry of each parabola.

7. (a) $x^2 = 20y$ (b) $y^2 = 24x$

8. (a) $x^2 + 6y = 0$ (b) $3y^2 + 4x = 0$

In each exercise, find an equation of the parabola with focus and directrix as given below.

9. (a) $(0, \frac{1}{2})$; $y = -\frac{1}{2}$ (b) $(5, 0)$; $x = -5$

10. (a) $(-3, 0)$; $x = 3$ (b) $(0, -\frac{5}{2})$; $y = \frac{5}{2}$

---

11. If the focus of a parabola is at $(0, 4)$ and the directrix is the x-axis, does the origin lie on the parabola? Is $(0, 0)$ a solution of the equation of the parabola? Could an equation of the parabola be of the form $x^2 = 4py$?

12. Graph the set $\{(x, y) \mid x = y^2 - 6y + 7\}$ by finding the points corresponding to $y = 0, 1, 2, 3, 4, 5,$ and 6 and drawing a smooth curve through them.

13. (a) Solve the system

$$\begin{cases} x^2 = 4y, \\ x + y = 1. \end{cases}$$

(b) Sketch the graph of each equation of the system.

Find the points of intersection of the parabola and the line. Draw the appropriate graph.

14. $\begin{cases} y^2 = 4x \\ x + 2y + 3 = 0 \end{cases}$ **15.** $\begin{cases} x^2 + y = 0 \\ 2x - y - 3 = 0 \end{cases}$

16. $\begin{cases} 2x^2 - 3y = 0 \\ 4x - y - 6 = 0 \end{cases}$ **17.** $\begin{cases} y^2 + x = 0 \\ x - y = 4 \end{cases}$

Graph the solution set of each system of inequalities.

18. $\begin{cases} y^2 \le 4x \\ y + 2x \le 4 \end{cases}$

19. $\begin{cases} y^2 - x^2 \ge 8 \\ y^2 \le 9x \end{cases}$

20. $\begin{cases} y^2 \ge 2x + 10 \\ x^2 + y^2 \le 25 \end{cases}$

21. Using the definition of a parabola, find an equation of the parabola with
   (a) focus $(0, 0)$ and directrix $y = -4$.
   (b) focus $(0, 0)$ and directrix $y = 2$.
   (c) focus $(0, 3)$ and directrix $y = 1$.
   (d) focus $(0, -2)$ and directrix $y + 1 = 0$.

   Study these four equations to observe the effect when the vertex is not placed at the origin, the directrix is kept parallel to the x-axis, and the focus is on the y-axis. In each case, locate the vertex, and try to put the equation in a form which shows the coordinates of the vertex.

Graph each of the following parabolas, showing its vertex, focus, and directrix.

22. $x^2 = 4(y - 1)$

23. $x^2 = -4(y - 1)$

24. $x^2 = 6(y + 2)$

25. $x^2 = -6(y + 2)$.

CHAPTER REVIEW

1. (a) Show that the following points are the vertices of an equilateral triangle.
$$A(0, 0), \quad B(6, 0), \quad C(3, 3\sqrt{3})$$
   (b) Find the coordinates of the midpoints of $\overline{AC}$ and $\overline{BC}$.
   (c) Find the length of the segment joining the midpoints of part (b).

2. Write an equation of a circle having
   (a) its center at the origin and radius $5\sqrt{2}$.
   (b) its center at $(-4, 3)$ and radius 9.

Discuss and sketch the graph of each of the following.

3. (a) $4x^2 + 25y^2 = 100$ (b) $4x^2 + 25y^2 > 100$

4. (a) $25x^2 - 4y^2 = 100$ (b) $25x^2 - 4y^2 > 100$

5. (a) $y^2 - 4x^2 = 4$ (b) $y^2 - 4x^2 < 4$

6. Discuss the graph of each of the following equations. Give the coordinates of the vertex and the focus, an equation of the directrix, and an equation of the axis of symmetry.
   (a) $x^2 = 6y$ (b) $y^2 + 7x = 0$

7. Solve algebraically and graphically the system of equations

$$\begin{cases} y^2 - x^2 = 1, \\ x^2 + y^2 = 1. \end{cases}$$

8. Use algebraic methods to find the intersections of the following pairs of conic sections. Sketch graphs to check your answers.
   (a) $\begin{cases} y^2 - 3x - 19 = 0 \\ x^2 + y^2 - 29 = 0 \end{cases}$ (b) $\begin{cases} 4x^2 + 5y - 10 = 0 \\ 5y^2 - 4x^2 = 20 \end{cases}$

9. Using the definition of a parabola, find an equation of the parabola with
   (a) focus $(0, 2)$ and directrix $y = -2$.
   (b) focus $(-1, 0)$ and directrix $x = 1$.

10. A square with sides parallel to the coordinate axes is inscribed in the ellipse $4x^2 + y^2 = 20$. Find its area.

11. Graph each of the following systems of inequalities.
    (a) $\begin{cases} 3y^2 \leq 4x \\ 4x^2 + 9y^2 \leq 72 \end{cases}$ (b) $\begin{cases} x^2 > 4y \\ x + 2y < 4 \end{cases}$

12. Solve each of the following systems algebraically.
    (a) $\begin{cases} x + y = 1 \\ 4x^2 + 4y^2 = 1 \end{cases}$ (b) $\begin{cases} 3x^2 - y^2 = 7 \\ 2x^2 + 3y^2 = 23 \end{cases}$

13. Find the center and/or vertices of each of the following conic sections.
    (a) $x^2 + y^2 - 6x + 8y = 0$ (b) $y = x^2 - 2x - 3$
    (c) $x = 3y^2 - 6y - 2$ (d) $3x^2 + 2y^2 - 12x + 6y - 3 = 0$

Appendix

Axioms of Algebra

The axioms of the real number system are divided into two groups: those concerning addition and multiplication and those concerning order. In the first group, we have such familiar axioms as the commutative axioms, associative axioms, and the distributive axiom. Also in this group are the axioms concerning 0 and 1, and the axioms of negatives and reciprocals. The order axioms of the real number system are concerned with the relative sizes of numbers.

ADDITION AND MULTIPLICATION AXIOMS

The real number system is closed with respect to addition and multiplication. In other words, if x and y are real numbers, then $x + y$ and xy are also real numbers. Addition and multiplication are unique in the following way.

ADDITIVE AXIOM

If $a = b$ and $c = d$, then $a + c = b + d$.

In other words, if a and b have the same value and c and d have the same value, then $a + c$ has the same value as $b + d$.

MULTIPLICATIVE AXIOM

If $a = b$ and $c = d$, then $ac = bd$.

The Additive and Multiplicative Axioms are commonly called *Axioms of Equality*.

Addition and multiplication have the following five fundamental properties.

COMMUTATIVE AXIOMS OF ADDITION AND MULTIPLICATION

The equations

$$x + y = y + x,$$
$$x \cdot y = y \cdot x$$

are true for all real numbers x and y.

ASSOCIATIVE AXIOMS OF ADDITION AND MULTIPLICATION

The equations

$$(x + y) + z = x + (y + z),$$
$$(x \cdot y) \cdot z = x \cdot (y \cdot z)$$

are true for all real numbers x, y, and z.

DISTRIBUTIVE AXIOM

The equations

$$x \cdot (y + z) = (x \cdot y) + (x \cdot z),$$
$$(y + z) \cdot x = (y \cdot x) + (z \cdot x)$$

are true for all real numbers x, y, and z.

ADDITIVE AND MULTIPLICATIVE IDENTITY AXIOMS

The equations

$$x + 0 = x, \quad 0 + x = x,$$
$$x \cdot 1 = x, \quad 1 \cdot x = x$$

are true for every real number x.

ADDITIVE AND MULTIPLICATIVE INVERSE AXIOMS

Each real number x has a unique additive inverse, $-x$, called the negative of x such that

$$x + -x = 0,$$
$$-x + x = 0.$$

Each nonzero real number x has a unique multiplicative inverse, $1/x$, called the reciprocal of x such that

$$x \cdot \frac{1}{x} = 1,$$

$$\frac{1}{x} \cdot x = 1, \quad x \neq 0.$$

These five axioms are assumptions that we make about the real number system, and they are not to be proved.

The following basic assumptions about the use of the equals sign, $=$, are also *Axioms of Equality*.

REFLEXIVE AXIOM

$$x = x \text{ for every real number } x$$

SYMMETRIC AXIOM

If $x = y$, then $y = x$ for every pair x, y of real numbers.

TRANSITIVE AXIOM

If $x = y$ and $y = z$, then $x = z$ for every triple x, y and z of real numbers.

Another property, the *substitution principle*, is so elementary that it is used almost without mention. For example, in the equation $3x + 11 - 6 = 7$, we can write $3x + 5 = 7$ instead of $3x + 11 - 6 = 7$; 5 and $11 - 6$ are numerals for the same number and hence either can be *substituted* for the other.

So far, we have discussed only the operations of addition and multiplication. The other common operations of arithmetic, subtraction and division, may be defined in terms of addition and multiplication. Hence, the properties of subtraction and division may be derived from the five axioms already given. We define subtraction and division in the following way.

Definition of subtraction

The equation

$$x - y = x + {}^-y$$

is true for all real numbers x and y.

Definition of division

The equation

$$x \div y = x \cdot \frac{1}{y}$$

is true for all real numbers x and y if y $\neq$ *0.*

The notations

$$\frac{x}{y} \quad \text{and} \quad x/y$$

are also used for $x \div y$.

The following are examples of the way in which we use the definitions of subtraction and division.

$$7 - 4 = 7 + (-4), \quad \text{or } 3$$
$$13 - 17 = 13 + (-17), \quad \text{or } -4$$
$$9 \div 6 = 9 \cdot \tfrac{1}{6}, \quad \text{or } \tfrac{3}{2}$$
$$\tfrac{1}{3} \div \tfrac{7}{9} = \tfrac{1}{3} \cdot \tfrac{9}{7}, \quad \text{or } \tfrac{3}{7}$$

The real number system is also closed with respect to the operations of subtraction and division, with the exception that division by zero is not defined. Since subtraction is defined in terms of addition and division is defined in terms of multiplication, the additive and multiplicative axioms are valid for subtraction and division.

In the process of finding a sum of several numbers, we may make repeated use of the associative and commutative laws to change the grouping of addends in any way we wish. For example,

$$a + (b + c) = a + (c + b)$$
$$= (a + c) + b$$
$$= (c + a) + b$$
$$= c + (a + b)$$
$$= c + (b + a).$$

It is common practice to write

$$a + b + c$$

for either $a + (b + c)$ or $(a + b) + c$. Hence,

$$a + b + c = a + c + b = c + a + b = c + b + a,$$

and so on, by our argument above. If we continue our argument to include four or more addends, we can prove the following property.

REARRANGEMENT PROPERTY OF ADDITION

The terms of a sum may be rearranged in any way.

Since the commutative and associative axioms are also true for multiplication, the rearrangement property is true for multiplication.

REARRANGEMENT PROPERTY OF MULTIPLICATION

The factors of a product may be rearranged in any way.

The *cancellation laws* are, in a sense, converses of the additive and multiplicative axioms.

CANCELLATION LAW OF ADDITION

If $x + z = y + z$, then $x = y$.

Proof.

$$x + z = y + z \qquad \text{(hypothesis)}$$
$$x + z + (-z) = y + z + (-z) \qquad (\text{add} - z \text{ to both sides})$$
$$x + [z + (-z)] = y + [z + (-z)] \qquad \text{(rearranging)}$$
$$x + 0 = y + 0 \qquad \text{(substituting)}$$
$$x = y$$

This proves that the cancellation law of addition is valid for all real numbers x, y, and z. The *cancellation law of multiplication* can be proved in a similar manner.

CANCELLATION LAW OF MULTIPLICATION

$$\textit{If } x \cdot z = y \cdot z \textit{ and } z \neq 0, \textit{ then } x = y.$$

According to the following property, the product of any number and zero is always zero.

ZERO MULTIPLICATION

$$x \cdot 0 = 0 \quad \textit{for every real number } x$$

Proof. Since $0 + 0 = 0$,

$$
\begin{array}{ll}
x \cdot (0 + 0) = x \cdot 0, & \text{(multiply by } x\text{)} \\
(x \cdot 0) + (x \cdot 0) = x \cdot 0, & \text{(distrib. law)} \\
(x \cdot 0) + (x \cdot 0) = (x \cdot 0) + 0, & (x \cdot 0 = x \cdot 0 + 0) \\
x \cdot 0 = 0. & \text{(cancel } x \cdot 0\text{)}
\end{array}
$$

From an earlier algebra course, we recall that the product of a positive number and a negative number is a negative number. This is one example of the following property, which we shall not prove.

NEGATIVE MULTIPLICATION

$$x \cdot (-y) = -(x \cdot y)$$

Some examples of the use of negative multiplication are given below.

$$
\begin{array}{l}
-5 \cdot 4 = -(5 \cdot 4), \quad \text{or } -20 \\
\tfrac{2}{3} \cdot (-9) = -(\tfrac{2}{3} \cdot 9), \quad \text{or } -6
\end{array}
$$

Using the inverse axiom of addition, we can show that $-(-x) = x$. By this axiom, $-x + [-(-x)] = 0$. However, $-x + x = 0$, also, by the inverse axiom of addition. Hence,

$$-x + [-(-x)] = -x + x$$

and

$$-(-x) = x.$$

In other words,

$$-(-x) = x \quad \text{for every real number } x.$$

For example, $-(-8) = 8$ and $-[-(-3)] = -3$.
If we use negative multiplication, we see that

$$
\begin{aligned}
(-8) \cdot (-5) &= -(-8 \cdot 5) \\
&= -(5 \cdot -8) \\
&= -[-(5 \cdot 8)] \\
&= 5 \cdot 8, \quad \text{or } 40.
\end{aligned}
$$

Every nonzero real number is either a *positive number* or a *negative number*. For example, 7 and $\pi - 3$ are positive numbers, and -5 and $\sqrt{15} - 4$ are negative numbers. There are three additional fundamental axioms of the real number system that apply to the set of all positive real numbers. They are called the *order axioms*. The order axioms, like the five fundamental axioms above, are basic assumptions which cannot be proved. If we denote the set of all positive real numbers by *P*, we can state these properties in the following manner.

CLOSURE OF P UNDER ADDITION

For every pair x, y of positive real numbers, $x + y$ is also a positive real number.

CLOSURE OF P UNDER MULTIPLICATION

For every pair x, y of positive real numbers, $x \cdot y$ is also a positive real number.

TRICHOTOMY AXIOM

For every real number x, one, and only one, of the following three statements is true:

$$x = 0, \quad x \text{ is positive}, \quad -x \text{ is positive}.$$

According to the trichotomy axiom, the system of real numbers consists of three kinds of numbers: positive numbers, negative numbers, and zero. If x is a positive number, then $-x$ is a negative number; if x is a negative number, then $-x$ is a positive number; if x is neither a positive number nor a negative number, then $x = 0$.

The order relations *greater than*, designated by $>$, and *less than*, designated by $<$, are defined in the following way.

Definition of greater than

   $x > y$ if, and only if, $x - y$ is a positive number

Definition of less than

        $x < y$ if, and only if, $y > x$

For example,

$$11 > 9, \quad \text{since } 11 - 9 = 2, \text{ and 2 is positive;}$$
$$-7 < -4, \text{ or } -4 > -7, \quad \text{since } -4 - (-7) = 3 \text{ and 3 is positive.}$$

Since $x - 0 = x$,

$$x > 0 \quad \text{if, and only if, } x \text{ is a positive number.}$$

Similarly,

$$x < 0 \quad \text{if, and only if, } x \text{ is a negative number.}$$

Using the order relations, we may express closure of P under addition, closure of P under multiplication, and the trichotomy axiom in the following condensed form.

   If $x > 0$ and $y > 0$, then $x + y > 0$.
   If $x > 0$ and $y > 0$, then $xy > 0$.
   If x is a real number, then $x = 0$, $x > 0$, or $x < 0$.

We may derive other useful order properties of the real number system from the basic assumptions. The following are three such properties.

TRANSITIVE LAW OF INEQUALITIES

If $x > y$ and $y > z$, then $x > z$.

ADDITIVE PROPERTY OF INEQUALITIES

If $x > y$, then $x + z > y + z$ for every real number z.

MULTIPLICATIVE PROPERTIES OF INEQUALITIES

If $x > y$, then $xz > yz$ for every positive number z.
If $x > y$, then $xz < yz$ for every negative number z.

We shall indicate how these might be proven by proving the transitive law.

Proof.

$x > y$ and $y > z$	(hypothesis)
$x - y$, $y - z$ positive	(definition of $>$)
$(x - y) + (y - z)$ positive	(closure of P under $+$)
$x + (-y + y) - z$ positive	(rearranging)
$x - z$ positive	($x + 0 - z = x - z$)
$x > z$	(definition of $>$)

The three properties above are true if every "$>$" is replaced by "$<$" and every "$<$" by "$>$". For example, if $x < y$, then $x + z < y + z$ for every real number z.

The rules for multiplying positive and negative numbers may be summarized using "$>$" and "$<$".

If $x > 0$ and $y > 0$, then $xy > 0$.
If $x > 0$ and $y < 0$, or $x < 0$ and $y > 0$, then $xy < 0$.
If $x < 0$ and $y < 0$, then $xy > 0$.

The order relation *greater than or equal to* is denoted by $\geq$.

Definition of greater than or equal to

$$x \geq y, \quad \textit{if and only if,} \quad \textit{either } x > y \quad x = y$$

Similarly, the order relation *less than or equal to* is denoted by $\leq$.

Definition of less than or equal to

$$x \leq y \quad \textit{if, and only if,} \quad y \geq x$$

For example,

$$7 \geq 3 \quad \text{because} \quad 7 > 3,$$
$$-3 \geq -3 \quad \text{because} \quad -3 = -3,$$
$$-4 \leq -1 \quad \text{because} \quad -4 < -1,$$
$$\frac{1}{\sqrt{2}} \leq \frac{\sqrt{2}}{2} \quad \text{because} \quad \frac{1}{\sqrt{2}} = \frac{\sqrt{2}}{2}.$$

If x, y, and z are three numbers such that $x < y$ and $y < z$, then we write

$$x < y < z.$$

This shows that y is a number *between* x and z. For example,

$$-1 < 2 < 5 \quad \text{because} \quad -1 < 2 \text{ and } 2 < 5.$$

Statements such as

$$x > y > z, \quad x \leq y < z, \quad x < y \leq z,$$

and so on, are also meaningful and are often used in mathematics.

We shall never contract a statement such as $0 < 2$ and $2 > -1$ to $0 < 2 > -1$, or $5 > 1$ and $1 < 3$ to $5 > 1 < 3$. We contract only when two order relations are of the same type and the contraction shows us at a glance that the middle number is between the two end numbers. Thus $0 < 27 - 1$ is meaningless because 2 is not between 0 and -1.

Table of Squares and Square Roots

N	N^2	$\sqrt{N}$	N	N^2	$\sqrt{N}$
1	1	1	51	2,601	7.141
2	4	1.414	52	2,704	7.211
3	9	1.732	53	2,809	7.280
4	16	2	54	2,916	7.348
5	25	2.236	55	3,025	7.416
6	36	2.449	56	3,136	7.483
7	49	2.646	57	3,249	7.550
8	64	2.828	58	3,364	7.616
9	81	3	59	3,481	7.681
10	100	3.162	60	3,600	7.746
11	121	3.317	61	3,721	7.810
12	144	3.464	62	3,844	7.874
13	169	3.606	63	3,969	7.937
14	196	3.742	64	4,096	8
15	225	3.873	65	4,225	8.062
16	256	4	66	4,356	8.124
17	289	4.123	67	4,489	8.185
18	324	4.243	68	4,624	8.246
19	361	4.359	69	4,761	8.307
20	400	4.472	70	4,900	8.367
21	441	4.583	71	5,041	8.426
22	484	4.690	72	5,184	8.485
23	529	4.796	73	5,329	8.544
24	576	4.899	74	5,476	8.602
25	625	5	75	5,625	8.660
26	676	5.099	76	5,776	8.718
27	729	5.196	77	5,929	8.775
28	784	5.292	78	6,084	8.832
29	841	5.385	79	6,241	8.888
30	900	5.477	80	6,400	8.944
31	961	5.568	81	6,561	9
32	1,024	5.657	82	6,724	9.055
33	1,089	5.745	83	6,889	9.110
34	1,156	5.831	84	7,056	9.165
35	1,225	5.916	85	7,225	9.220
36	1,296	6	86	7,396	9.274
37	1,369	6.083	87	7,569	9.327
38	1,444	6.164	88	7,744	9.381
39	1,521	6.245	89	7,921	9.434
40	1,600	6.325	90	8,100	9.487
41	1,681	6.403	91	8,281	9.539
42	1,764	6.481	92	8,464	9.592
43	1,849	6.557	93	8,649	9.644
44	1,936	6.633	94	8,836	9.695
45	2,025	6.708	95	9,025	9.747
46	2,116	6.782	96	9,216	9.798
47	2,209	6.856	97	9,409	9.849
48	2,304	6.928	98	9,604	9.899
49	2,401	7	99	9,801	9.950
50	2,500	7.071	100	10,000	10

Table of Common Logarithms

N	0	1	2	3	4	5	6	7	8	9
10	.0000	.0043	.0086	.0128	.0170	.0212	.0253	.0294	.0334	.0374
11	.0414	.0453	.0492	.0531	.0569	.0607	.0645	.0682	.0719	.0755
12	.0792	.0828	.0864	.0899	.0934	.0969	.1004	.1038	.1072	.1106
13	.1139	.1173	.1206	.1239	.1271	.1303	.1335	.1367	.1399	.1430
14	.1461	.1492	.1523	.1553	.1584	.1614	.1644	.1673	.1703	.1732
15	.1761	.1790	.1818	.1847	.1875	.1903	.1931	.1959	.1987	.2014
16	.2041	.2068	.2095	.2122	.2148	.2175	.2201	.2227	.2253	.2279
17	.2304	.2330	.2355	.2380	.2405	.2430	.2455	.2480	.2504	.2529
18	.2553	.2577	.2601	.2625	.2648	.2672	.2695	.2718	.2742	.2765
19	.2788	.2810	.2833	.2856	.2878	.2900	.2923	.2945	.2967	.2989
20	.3010	.3032	.3054	.3075	.3096	.3118	.3139	.3160	.3181	.3201
21	.3222	.3243	.3263	.3284	.3304	.3324	.3345	.3365	.3385	.3404
22	.3424	.3444	.3464	.3483	.3502	.3522	.3541	.3560	.3579	.3598
23	.3617	.3636	.3655	.3674	.3692	.3711	.3729	.3747	.3766	.3784
24	.3802	.3820	.3838	.3856	.3874	.3892	.3909	.3927	.3945	.3962
25	.3979	.3997	.4014	.4031	.4048	.4065	.4082	.4099	.4116	.4133
26	.4150	.4166	.4183	.4200	.4216	.4232	.4249	.4265	.4281	.4298
27	.4314	.4330	.4346	.4362	.4378	.4393	.4409	.4425	.4440	.4456
28	.4472	.4487	.4502	.4518	.4533	.4548	.4564	.4579	.4594	.4609
29	.4624	.4639	.4654	.4669	.4683	.4698	.4713	.4728	.4742	.4757
30	.4771	.4786	.4800	.4814	.4829	.4843	.4857	.4871	.4886	.4900
31	.4914	.4928	.4942	.4955	.4969	.4983	.4997	.5011	.5024	.5038
32	.5051	.5065	.5079	.5092	.5105	.5119	.5132	.5145	.5159	.5172
33	.5185	.5198	.5211	.5224	.5237	.5250	.5263	.5276	.5289	.5302
34	.5315	.5328	.5340	.5353	.5366	.5378	.5391	.5403	.5416	.5428
35	.5441	.5453	.5465	.5478	.5490	.5502	.5514	.5527	.5539	.5551
36	.5563	.5575	.5587	.5599	.5611	.5623	.5635	.5647	.5658	.5670
37	.5682	.5694	.5705	.5717	.5729	.5740	.5752	.5763	.5775	.5786
38	.5798	.5809	.5821	.5832	.5843	.5855	.5866	.5877	.5888	.5899
39	.5911	.5922	.5933	.5944	.5955	.5966	.5977	.5988	.5999	.6010
40	.6021	.6031	.6042	.6053	.6064	.6075	.6085	.6096	.6107	.6117
41	.6128	.6138	.6149	.6160	.6170	.6180	.6191	.6201	.6212	.6222
42	.6232	.6243	.6253	.6263	.6274	.6284	.6294	.6304	.6314	.6325
43	.6335	.6345	.6355	.6365	.6375	.6385	.6395	.6405	.6415	.6425
44	.6435	.6444	.6454	.6464	.6474	.6484	.6493	.6503	.6513	.6522
45	.6532	.6542	.6551	.6561	.6571	.6580	.6590	.6599	.6609	.6618
46	.6628	.6637	.6646	.6656	.6665	.6675	.6684	.6693	.6702	.6712
47	.6721	.6730	.6739	.6749	.6758	.6767	.6776	.6785	.6794	.6803
48	.6812	.6821	.6830	.6839	.6848	.6857	.6866	.6875	.6884	.6893
49	.6902	.6911	.6920	.6928	.6937	.6946	.6955	.6964	.6972	.6981
50	.6990	.6998	.7007	.7016	.7024	.7033	.7042	.7050	.7059	.7067
51	.7076	.7084	.7093	.7101	.7110	.7118	.7126	.7135	.7143	.7152
52	.7160	.7168	.7177	.7185	.7193	.7202	.7210	.7218	.7226	.7235
53	.7243	.7251	.7259	.7267	.7275	.7284	.7292	.7300	.7308	.7316
54	.7324	.7332	.7340	.7348	.7356	.7364	.7372	.7380	.7388	.7396

Table of Common Logarithms (*Continued*)

N	0	1	2	3	4	5	6	7	8	9
55	.7404	.7412	.7419	.7427	.7435	.7443	.7451	.7459	.7466	.7474
56	.7482	.7490	.7497	.7505	.7513	.7520	.7528	.7536	.7543	.7551
57	.7559	.7566	.7574	.7582	.7589	.7597	.7604	.7612	.7619	.7627
58	.7634	.7642	.7649	.7657	.7664	.7672	.7679	.7686	.7694	.7701
59	.7709	.7716	.7723	.7731	.7738	.7745	.7752	.7760	.7767	.7774
60	.7782	.7789	.7796	.7803	.7810	.7818	.7825	.7832	.7839	.7846
61	.7853	.7860	.7868	.7875	.7882	.7889	.7896	.7903	.7910	.7917
62	.7924	.7931	.7938	.7945	.7952	.7959	.7966	.7973	.7980	.7987
63	.7993	.8000	.8007	.8014	.8021	.8028	.8035	.8041	.8048	.8055
64	.8062	.8069	.8075	.8082	.8089	.8096	.8102	.8109	.8116	.8122
65	.8129	.8136	.8142	.8149	.8156	.8162	.8169	.8176	.8182	.8189
66	.8195	.8202	.8209	.8215	.8222	.8228	.8235	.8241	.8248	.8254
67	.8261	.8267	.8274	.8280	.8287	.8293	.8299	.8306	.8312	.8319
68	.8325	.8331	.8338	.8344	.8351	.8357	.8363	.8370	.8376	.8382
69	.8388	.8395	.8401	.8407	.8414	.8420	.8426	.8432	.8439	.8445
70	.8451	.8457	.8463	.8470	.8476	.8482	.8488	.8494	.8500	.8506
71	.8513	.8519	.8525	.8531	.8537	.8543	.8549	.8555	.8561	.8567
72	.8573	.8579	.8585	.8591	.8597	.8603	.8609	.8615	.8621	.8627
73	.8633	.8639	.8645	.8651	.8657	.8663	.8669	.8675	.8681	.8686
74	.8692	.8698	.8704	.8710	.8716	.8722	.8727	.8733	.8739	.8745
75	.8751	.8756	.8762	.8768	.8774	.8779	.8785	.8791	.8797	.8802
76	.8808	.8814	.8820	.8825	.8831	.8837	.8842	.8848	.8854	.8859
77	.8865	.8871	.8876	.8882	.8887	.8893	.8899	.8904	.8910	.8915
78	.8921	.8927	.8932	.8938	.8943	.8949	.8954	.8960	.8965	.8971
79	.8976	.8982	.8987	.8993	.8998	.9004	.9009	.9015	.9020	.9025
80	.9031	.9036	.9042	.9047	.9053	.9058	.9063	.9069	.9074	.9079
81	.9085	.9090	.9096	.9101	.9106	.9112	.9117	.9122	.9128	.9133
82	.9138	.9143	.9149	.9154	.9159	.9165	.9170	.9175	.9180	.9186
83	.9191	.9196	.9201	.9206	.9212	.9217	.9222	.9227	.9232	.9238
84	.9243	.9248	.9253	.9258	.9263	.9269	.9274	.9279	.9284	.9289
85	.9294	.9299	.9304	.9309	.9315	.9320	.9325	.9330	.9335	.9340
86	.9345	.9350	.9355	.9360	.9365	.9370	.9375	.9380	.9385	.9390
87	.9395	.9400	.9405	.9410	.9415	.9420	.9425	.9430	.9435	.9440
88	.9445	.9450	.9455	.9460	.9465	.9469	.9474	.9479	.9484	.9489
89	.9494	.9499	.9504	.9509	.9513	.9518	.9523	.9528	.9533	.9538
90	.9542	.9547	.9552	.9557	.9562	.9566	.9571	.9576	.9581	.9586
91	.9590	.9595	.9600	.9605	.9609	.9614	.9619	.9624	.9628	.9633
92	.9638	.9643	.9647	.9652	.9657	.9661	.9666	.9671	.9675	.9680
93	.9685	.9689	.9694	.9699	.9703	.9708	.9713	.9717	.9722	.9727
94	.9731	.9736	.9741	.9745	.9750	.9754	.9759	.9763	.9768	.9773
95	.9777	.9782	.9786	.9791	.9795	.9800	.9805	.9809	.9814	.9818
96	.9823	.9827	.9832	.9836	.9841	.9845	.9850	.9854	.9859	.9863
97	.9868	.9872	.9877	.9881	.9886	.9890	.9894	.9899	.9903	.9908
98	.9912	.9917	.9921	.9926	.9930	.9934	.9939	.9943	.9948	.9952
99	.9956	.9961	.9965	.9969	.9974	.9978	.9983	.9987	.9991	.9996

SELECTED ANSWERS FOR EXERCISES

1–2   **1.** (a) $\frac{3}{8}$ (b) $\frac{7}{72}$ **3.** (a) .375 (b) .833 or .8$\overline{3}$ **5.** (a) $\frac{1}{12}$ (b) $-\frac{1}{12}$
7. (a) $-\frac{9}{8}$ (b) $-\frac{28}{27}$ **9.** (a) $-\frac{9}{5}$ (b) $\frac{13}{48}$ **11.** (a) 0 (b) 0 **13.** Yes
15. No **17.** Yes **19.** Yes **21.** Yes **23.** No **25.** Yes **27.** (a) 2 (b) 3 (c) 2
29. Yes, multiplication **31.** Yes, multiplication **33.** q is the product of
non-negative powers of 2 and non-negative powers of 5.

1–3   **1.** $\frac{25}{16}$, $\frac{5}{45}$, $\left(\frac{2}{3}\right)^2$, .0121, $\sqrt{16}$ **3.** (a) $(4.2)^2 = 17.64$, $(4.3)^2 = 18.49$; $4.2 < \sqrt{18} < 4.3$
(b) $(-5)^2 = 25$, $(-5.1)^2 = 26.01$; $-5.1 < -\sqrt{26} < -5$ **5.** (a) $(3.5)^2 = 12.25$,
$4^2 = 16$; $3.5 < \sqrt{13} < 4$; $\sqrt{13}$ is closer to 4 than it is to 3 (b) $6^2 = 36$ and
$(6.5)^2 = 42.25$; $\sqrt{42}$ is closer to 6 than it is to 7. **7.** (a) $1^2 = 1$, $2^2 = 4$;
$1 < \sqrt{3} < 2$ (b) $17^2 = 289$, $18^2 = 324$; $17 < \sqrt{300} < 18$; $17 < 10\sqrt{3} < 18$
(c) $(173)^2 = 29{,}929$; $(174)^2 = 30{,}276$; $173 < \sqrt{30{,}000} < 174$; $173 < 100\sqrt{3} < 174$
9. (a) $(-4)^3 = -64$, $(-5)^3 = -125$; $-5 < -\sqrt[3]{100} < -4$ (b) -5 (c) No
11. (a) $2\sqrt{6}$ (b) 0 **13.** (a) 22 (b) 11 **15.** Yes; $+$, $-$, $\times$ $(a + b\sqrt{7}) \pm$
$(c + d\sqrt{7}) = (a \pm c) + (b \pm d)\sqrt{7}$ $(a + b\sqrt{7})(c + d\sqrt{7}) = (ac + 7bd) +$
$(ad + bc)\sqrt{7}$

1–4   **1.** (a) 16 (b) 13 (c) 29 (d) 3 **3.** (a) 1 (b) 55 (c) 1 (d) 121
5. $15 + 6b - 9a$, -21 **7.** $-a^2 + 3ab + 2b^2$, -4 **9.** $11x + 3y - 1$
11. $2x + 8y + 6$ **13.** $10x - 2y - 12$ **15.** $3x^2 - 8xy + 2y^2$

1–5   **1.** $x \cdot x^8 = x^9$ **3.** $(x^5)^2 = x^{10}$ **5.** $(3x^4)^2 = 9x^8$ **7.** $-2x(7x - 3y) = -14x^2 + 6xy$
9. $(3x - 5y)(2x + 7y) = 6x^2 + 11xy - 35y^2$ **11.** $10x^4y^6$ **13.** $9x^2y^2$ **15.** x^{18}
17. 7^9 **19.** x^7 **21.** $-32x^5y^5$ **23.** $125x^3y^{12}$ **25.** $-a^{35}b^{21}$ **27.** $6x^2y - 21xy^2$
29. $6x^2 + 5xy + y^2$ **31.** $6x^2 + 5xy + y^2$ **33.** $14x^2 - 29xy - 15y^2$
35. $16x^2 - 81y^2$ **37.** $16x^2 - 72xy + 81y^2$

1–6   **1.** 1 **3.** $\dfrac{1}{x^2}$ **5.** $\dfrac{1}{x^4}$ **7.** $\dfrac{4y}{x^3}$ **9.** $\dfrac{1}{3x^3}$ **11.** $5^2 \cdot 2$ or 50 **13.** $4xy^2 - 3x^2$

      15. $-1 + \dfrac{3x}{4y^2}$

1–7   **1.** $\frac{5}{7}$ **3.** $\dfrac{5x^2 + x}{6}$ **5.** $\dfrac{6x + 7}{x^2}$ **7.** $\dfrac{8x^2 + 5y^3}{12xy^2}$ **9.** $\dfrac{2y + 3xy + 4x}{x^2y}$

      11. $\dfrac{x^2 + 6xy + y^2}{2xy}$ **13.** x any real number except 0, 1 **15.** None

1–8   **1.** (a) 3^7 (b) $(-2)^3$ or -8 **3.** (a) 3^0 or 1   (b) 2^0 or 1   **5.** (a) 3   (b) 3

7. (a) $\dfrac{81x^2}{16y^{12}}$ (b) $\dfrac{4a^4}{9b^8}$ **9.** (a) x^8 (b) $7x^{-3}$ **11.** (a) $\frac{1}{9}x^{-8}$ (b) $16x^{12}$ **13.** (a) $\dfrac{1}{y^3}$

(b) 0   **15.** (a) 3^4 or 81   (b) $\frac{1}{2}$ **17.** (a) $4^8 = 2^{16}$; ? = 16   (b) $9^6 = 3^{12}$; ? = 12

19. (a) $2^7 \cdot 4^3 = 2^{13}$; ? = 13   (b) $3^6 \cdot 81^2 = 3^{14}$; ? = 14   **21.** (a) 3^{46} (b) $\frac{2}{9}$

23. (a) $\dfrac{x^2 + y^2}{x^2 y^2}$ (b) $\dfrac{y - z^3}{yz^3}$ **25.** (a) $\dfrac{b^4}{a^8}$ (b) 1

1–9   **1.** (a) $\sqrt{20x^5} = \sqrt{4x^4 \cdot 5x} = \sqrt{4x^4} \cdot \sqrt{5x} = 2x^2 \cdot \sqrt{5x}$?'s: $5x$, $5x$, $\sqrt{5x}$

(b) $\sqrt{75x^7} = \sqrt{25x^6 \cdot 3x} = \sqrt{25x^6} \cdot \sqrt{3x} = 5x^3 \sqrt{3x}$?'s: $25x^6$, $25x^6$, $5x^3$

3. (a) $3\sqrt{5}$ (b) $2\sqrt{5}$ **5.** (a) $2\sqrt{3}$ (b) $3\sqrt{3}$ **7.** (a) $7\sqrt{2}$ (b) $11\sqrt{7}$

9. (a) $15\sqrt{11}$ (b) $44\sqrt{2}$ **11.** (a) 7   (b) -3 **13.** (a) $-2xy\sqrt[5]{3x^2}$ (b) -3

15. (a) $2x^2y^2\sqrt[4]{3y^2}$ (b) $3xy^3\sqrt[4]{2x^2}$ **17.** (a) $\frac{1}{5}\sqrt{5}$ (b) $\frac{1}{6}\sqrt{6}$ **19.** (a) $\frac{1}{4}\sqrt{6}$

(b) $\frac{1}{9}\sqrt{6}$ **21.** (a) $\frac{1}{10}\sqrt{35}$ (b) $\frac{1}{6}\sqrt{210}$ **23.** (a) $\dfrac{x}{5}\sqrt{10x}$ (b) $\dfrac{1}{3x}\sqrt[3]{6x^2}$

1–10   **1.** (a) $8\sqrt{2}$ (b) $11\sqrt{5}$ **3.** (a) $2\sqrt{3} + 27\sqrt{2}$ (b) $-\sqrt{7} - 15\sqrt{3}$

5. (a) $\frac{47}{15}\sqrt{15}$ (b) $-\frac{1}{2}\sqrt{2}$ **7.** (a) $(2 + x)\sqrt{2x}$ (b) $-3x^2\sqrt{5x}$

9. Let $x = 25$, $y = 16$

1–11   **1.** (a) $\sqrt{15}$ (b) $\sqrt{6}$ **3.** (a) $\sqrt{6}$ (b) $\sqrt{2}$ **5.** (a) $3\sqrt{2}$ (b) $7\sqrt{5}$ **7.** (a) 30

(b) 48   **9.** $10x^5\sqrt{6}$ (b) $2x^4\sqrt[3]{5x^2}$ **11.** (a) 2   (b) $\sqrt[5]{2}$ **13.** (a) 22

(b) $30 + 12\sqrt{6}$ **15.** (a) $\dfrac{28 + 10\sqrt{3}}{22}$ or $\dfrac{14 + 5\sqrt{3}}{11}$ (b) $\dfrac{17 - 4\sqrt{15}}{7}$

17. (a) $4(\sqrt{7} + \sqrt{3})$ (b) $\dfrac{9 - 2\sqrt{14}}{5}$

1–12   **1.** (a) 3   (b) 9   **3.** (a) 32   (b) $\frac{1}{4}$ **5.** (a) 9   (b) $\frac{80}{81}$ **7.** (a) $3(4x^3y)^{1/4}$ or $18^{1/2}x^{3/4}y^{1/4}$

(b) $2(2x^2y)^{1/3}$ or $2^{4/3}x^{2/3}y^{1/3}$ **9.** (a) $\sqrt[5]{2x^4}$ or $\sqrt[5]{16x^4}$ (b) $\sqrt[3]{y^2}$ **11.** (a) $\sqrt[4]{x} - \sqrt[4]{y}$

(b) $\sqrt[3]{x + y}$ **13.** 100.01   **15.** 2^5 or 32   **17.** $\dfrac{1}{216x^3}$ or $\dfrac{1}{6x^3}$ **19.** $e^{2x} - 2 + e^{-2x}$ or

$\dfrac{e^{4x} - 2e^{2x} + 1}{e^{2x}}$ **21.** $x + 2\sqrt{xy} + y$ **23.** $\dfrac{1}{b^2}\sqrt[6]{ab^5}$ **25.** (a) $\sqrt[4]{2}$ (b) $\sqrt{x}$

27. $\sqrt[6]{x^3} = (x^3)^{1/6} = x^{3/6} = x^{1/2} = x^{2/4} = \sqrt[4]{x^2}$; $\sqrt{x}$ **29.** (a) $\sqrt{5}$ (b) $\sqrt[3]{2}$

31. $\frac{1}{5}\sqrt{10}$ **33.** $\sqrt[5]{4}$

1–13   **1.** (a) False $|3 - \pi| = \pi - 3$ (b) True   **3.** (a) True   (b) True   **5.** (a) 1

(b) -1 **7.** (a) $\sqrt{2} - 1.41$ (b) $4 - \sqrt{15}$ **9.** (a) 3   (b) 21   **11.** (a) $\{4, -4\}$

(b) $\{7, -7\}$ **13.** (a) $\{-4, -3, -2, -1, 0, 1, 2, 3, 4\}$ (b) $\{\cdots -8, -7, -6, 6,$

$7, 8, \cdots\}$ Infinite set   **15.** (a) $\{-11, -10, -9, -8, -7, -6, -5, -4, -3, -2,$

$-1, 0, 1, 2, 3, 4, 5, 6, 7, 8, 9, 10\}$ (b) $\{\cdots -14, -13, -12, 11, 12, 13, \cdots\}$

Infinite set   **17.** (a) $\{-5, -4, -3, -2, -1, 0, 1, 2, 3, 4, 5, 6, 7, 8, 9\}$

(b) Infinite set $\{\cdots -8, -7, -6, 10, 11, 12, \cdots\}$ **19.** (a) 3   (b) 8   (c) 4   (d) 9

(e) 5   (f) 12   (g) 17   (h) 5   **21.** The coordinate of P is the arithmetic average

(one-half the sum) of the coordinates of A and B.   **23.** (a) $|5| \cdot |6| = |5 \cdot 6| = 30$

(b) $|-4| \cdot |3| = |-4 \cdot 3| = 12$ (c) $|7| \cdot |-8| = |7 \cdot (-8)| = 56$

(d) $|-2| \cdot |-10| = |-2 \cdot (-10)| = 20$ (e) Equal to (always)

Chapter   **1.** (a) $5\sqrt{5} - 2$ (b) $-\sqrt{18} + 2\sqrt{2}$ **3.** (a) 7   (b) 3   **5.** $-x + 7y + 2$

Review   **7.** $2a - 4b + 8$ **9.** (a) $12x^4y^9$ (b) $3x^6y^6$ **11.** (a) $16x^{12}y^{20}$ (b) $27x^{33}y^6$

13. (a) $2x^2 + xy - 15y^2$ (b) $3x^2 - 2xy - 5y^2$ **15.** (a) $3a - 2a^2b$

(b) $\frac{1}{3}a^5 + a^2b^5$ **17.** (a) $\frac{1}{35}$ (b) $\frac{11}{8}$ **19.** (a) $(3 - 4a + 2a^2)/a^2$

(b) $(-5a^2 + 7a - 2)/a^2$ **21.** (a) $6x^3y^{-2}$ (b) $256x^2y^2$ **23.** (a) $16/(x^4y^4)$
(b) $27x^9/y^{12}$ **25.** (a) $3xy\sqrt{2x}$ (b) $2x^2y\sqrt{2y}$ **27.** (a) $\frac{1}{10}\sqrt{6}$ (b) $\frac{6}{7}\sqrt{35}$
29. (a) $(2x + y)\sqrt{y}$ (b) $(xy - 3)\sqrt{2x}$ **31.** (a) $4\sqrt{14}$ (b) 70   **33.** (a) $(\sqrt{2x})/(2y)$
(b) $\frac{x}{5y}\sqrt{5x}$ **35.** (a) $(16 + 5\sqrt{15})/17$ (b) $(49 - 10\sqrt{22})/67$ **37.** (a) x^4y^{10}
(b) xy^6 **39.** (a) 6   (b) 0   **41.** (a) 9   (b) 3   **43.** (a) 4   (b) 24
45. (a) $\{-4, -3, -2, \ldots, 9, 10\}$ (b) $\{-9, -8, -7, \ldots, 4, 5\}$
47. (a) $\frac{1}{108}$ (b) $\frac{1}{75}$

2–1   **1.** (a) Equivalent   **3.** (a) $\{4\}$ **5.** (a) $\{-\frac{16}{11}\}$ **7.** (a) $\{\frac{11}{10}\}$ **9.** Equivalent
11. Not equivalent, change second equation to $3x - 6 - 5 = 8 - 2x + 8$
13. $\{2\}$ **15.** $\{5\}$ **17.** $\{-4\}$ **19.** $\{-\frac{21}{10}\}$ **21.** $\{\frac{1}{8}\}$ **23.** $\{-4\}$ **25.** (a) 0, 0;
12, 12; 6, 6; 5, 5   (b) Infinite number of values

2–2   **1.** (a) $4x + 6$ **3.** (a) $8x$ **5.** (a) $8x + 11(100 - x)$ **7.** (a) $|2\frac{1}{2}h - 3\frac{1}{2}(h - 3)|$ mi
9. (a) $2(x + 3)$ **11.** (a) $.65x + .75(15)$ (in ounces)   **13.** 40, 42, 44   **15.** -6
17. 12 quarters, 16 dimes, 34 nickels   **19.** 7 yrs, 37 yrs   **21.** 15 lbs
23. $3\frac{3}{4}$ hr; $13\frac{1}{8}$ mi   **25.** 2.4 gal

Preparation   **1.** $3 > 1$ **2.** $-3 > -5$ **3.** $-21 < -5$ **4.** $10 > 7$ **5.** $-7 < 3$
Exercises   **6.** $2 < 12$

2–3   **1.** (a) 8, 3, 10, 1.6   **3.** (a) 5   **5.** (a) $x > -1$ **7.** (a) $x \geq -6$
9. (a) $x > -\frac{14}{3}$ **17.** (b) $x < 3$ and $-2x > -6$ **19.** $x > 5, x > 1,$
$\{x \mid x > 5\}$ **21.** $x > 4, x < \frac{4}{5}, \emptyset$ **23.** E.g., $A = \{0, 1, 2\}, B = \{-1, -2, -3\}$;
$A \cup B =$ number line   **25.** E.g., $A = \{2, 3, 3.5\}, B = \{1, 0, -2\}$;
$A \cup B =$ number lines   **27.** $x \geq 2$

2–4   **1.** (a) $(\frac{1}{3}, -4)$, $(0, -5)$, $(\frac{5}{3}, 0)$ **3.** (a) $x = \frac{1}{4}(7y + 5)$ **5.** (a) E.g., $(0, -4)$,
$(2, -3)$, $(8, 0)$ **7.** (a) $y = -\frac{8}{5}x + \frac{6}{5}$ **9.** (a) Yes   **11.** (a) Yes, no, yes
(f) $M = R \cup S$ **13.** $2x - 3y = 10, 2x - 3y = -10$ **15.** (a) $x \leq 2; y \leq 2$
(b) $x + y = 2$ (c) $-x - y = 2$ (d) $-x + y = 2$ (e) $x - y = 2$

2–5   **1.** (a) $\frac{4}{3}$ **3.** (a) $\frac{3}{4}$ **5.** (a) No. Use of the formula would entail division by zero.
7. (a) $-\frac{2}{5}, 2$ **9.** (a) No slope, no y-intercept   **11.** (b) They are parallel with
slope 2   (c) Each, solved for y, has a coefficient of 2 for x.

2–6   **1.** 7, $y = 7x + 47$ **3.** $y + 2 = -\frac{1}{3}(x + 3)$ **5.** $y = 3$ **9.** (a) $y = -2$
(b) $x = \frac{3}{2}$ **11.** Slope between any two points $= -\frac{5}{4}$ **13.** (b) 2,3; 4,-6; $-3,5$
(c) a is x-intercept, b is y-intercept   (d) $\dfrac{x}{-2} + \dfrac{y}{2} = 1$ **15.** (c) They have the same
y-intercept -1 **17.** (b) They all pass through the point $(-1, -1)$; they have
different slopes.   **19.** (a) $y = \frac{3}{4}x + b$ (b) $y = \frac{3}{4}x + \frac{23}{4}$

2–7   **1.** (a) 0, 3   **3.** (a) $-1, 2$ **5.** (a) $\{(x, y) \mid y > 3x - 2\}$ **7.** (a) $\{(x, y) \mid y < \frac{x}{3}\}$
9. $y \leq 2$ **11.** $y > -4x$ **13.** (b) $(2, 0)$, $(4, 1)$, and $(-2, -2)$ lie to the left of
the line $x = 2y + 3$ **15.** $-1 \geq -3b + 6, 3b \geq 7$

Chapter   **1.** $\{4\}$ **3.** $\{x \mid x < -3\}$ **5.** $\{\frac{2}{3}\}$ **7.** $\{\frac{5}{8}\}$ **9.** $\{-\frac{1}{2}\}$ **11.** $\{y \mid y > -\frac{1}{5}\}$
Review   **13.** $\{n \mid n < -\frac{4}{3}\}$ **15.** $\{k \mid k > \frac{3}{8}\}$ **17.** $2m(2m + 2)$ **19.** $.06m + .12(12 - m)$ or
$.12m + .06(12 - m)$ **21.** $x + (x + 1) + (x + 2) + (x + 3) = 90$;
$x = 21, x + 1 = 22, x + 2 = 23, x + 3 = 24$ **23.** $.05x + .10(30 - x) = \$2.15$;
there are 17 nickels and 13 dimes.   **25.**
27. $y = \dfrac{x + 2}{4}$; $(2, 1), (-6, -1)$ **29.** $y = 3x - 4$; $(1, -1), (2, 2)$

31. (a) slope 3, y-int. 2   (b) slope -2, y-int. 3   **33.** (a) no slope, no y-int.
(b) no slope, no y-int.   **35.** (a) slope 2, $y = 2x - 1$ (b) $\frac{1}{2}$, $x - 2y + 4 = 0$
37. (a) no slope, $x = 2$ (b) slope 0, $y = 1$ **39.** (a) half-plane on and below line
$y = 3$ (b) half-plane on and above line $y = -1$ **41.** (a) half-plane below the
line $y = \frac{1}{2}x - \frac{3}{2}$ (b) half-plane below the line $y = -\frac{1}{3}x + 1$

3–1   **1.** (a) $\{(3, 4)\}$ **3.** (a) $\{(-1, 3)\}$ **5.** Inconsistent   **7.** Dependent
9. Independent   **11.** $\{(\frac{39}{7}, \frac{1}{7})\}$ **13.** $\{(1, 1)\}$ **15.** $\{(5, 10)\}$ **17.** $\{(0, 0)\}$
19. (b) $0 = 0$. For any k, the two equations are equivalent and thus, any
solution of the first equation is a solution of the second one also.

3–2   **1.** (a) $\{(\frac{21}{7}, 5)\}$ **3.** (a) $\{(8, 17)\}$ **5.** (a) $\begin{cases} 8x - 20y = 36 \\ 15x + 20y = 40 \end{cases}$ **7.** (a) $\{(0, 4)\}$
9. (a) $\{(3, 2)\}$ **11.** (a) $\{(\frac{1}{2}, \frac{1}{3})\}$

3–3   **1.** (a) 2650 mi and back   **3.** (a) 15 quarters   **5.** (a) The numbers l and p will
both be integers if, and only if, $d + s$ and $s - d$ are both even.   **7.** (a) $a = 5$
and $b = 3$

3–4   **1.** (a) Quarter-plane   **3.** (a) Infinite strip   **5.** (a) $(1, 1)$, $(1, 2)$
7. $\begin{cases} x - 2y + 6 > 0, \\ x - 2y < 4. \end{cases}$ **9.** Pentagon, $(8, 22)$, $(3, 22)$, $(15, 15)$, $(3, 0)$, $(15, 0)$
11. Pentagon, $(0, 8)$, $(9, 8)$, $(2, 4)$, $(6, 1)$, $(9, 0)$ **13.** Quadrilateral, $(-7, 5)$,
$(-3, 3)$, $(-3, -3)$, $(\frac{3}{2}, -\frac{3}{2})$ **15.** (e) Triangle, $(0, 4)$, $(0, -8)$, $(3, -2)$
17. $S = \{(x, y) \mid 5x - 3y - 9 < 0\} \cap \{(x, y) \mid 2x + 3y - 12 > 0\}$
Quarter-plane; No, because the graph is a quarter-plane with no edge.

Chapter
Review   **1.** (a) $\{(2, 2)\}$ (b) $\{(-1, 8)\}$ **3.** (a) $\varnothing$ (b) $\varnothing$

5. (a)   (b)

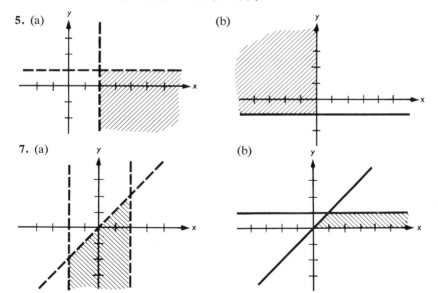

7. (a)   (b)

9. 39 dimes, 13 quarters   **11.** Jane must earn $60 and Joe $90; Jane must earn
at least $80 and Joe at least $130.

4-1   **1.** (a) $D = \{n \mid n,$ a nonnegative integer$\}$ **3.** (a) $D = \{t \mid 0 \le t \le 2\}$
5. (a) $D = \{x \mid x = 7, 8, 9\}$; $R = \{y \mid y = -3, 2, 0\}$ **7.** (a) (i) $y =$
$-\frac{5}{2}x + 5$ (ii) Yes   (iii) $x = -\frac{2}{5}y + 2$ (iv) Yes   **9.** (a) (2, 3) and (2, 4)
have the same first element.   **11.** (a) $D = \{n \mid 0 < n \le 16\}$ **13.** $A = x(x + 3)$;
$D = \{x \mid x > 0\}$; $R = \{A \mid A > 0\}$ **15.** $B = \dfrac{100}{h}$; $D = \{h \mid h > 0\}$;
$R = \{B \mid B > 0\}$ **17.** $A = (12 - 2x)(14 - 2x)$; $D = \{x \mid 0 < x < 6\}$;
$R = \{A \mid 0 < A < 168\}$

4-2   **1.** (a) $0, 1 - 5\sqrt{2}, -\frac{49}{8} - 3$ **3.** (a) $x \ne -4$ **5.** (a) $x \ne 2$ **7.** (a) $\frac{5}{6}, \frac{5}{3}, \frac{10}{11}$;
$\sqrt{3}, 0, \frac{1}{2}\sqrt{5}$; indeterminant, $-1, -6; 4, 4, 4$ **9.** (a) $3, 4, 1, \sqrt{2}$;
$R = \{y \mid y \ge 1\}$ **11.** (a) $9, 25, 225$; equal   **13.** (a) $k = 132$ (b) $N(p) = \dfrac{132}{p}$;
$D = \{p \mid p$ integer, $p > 0\}$ (c) $12, 22, 33$ **15.** (a) $O(x) = 10x$ (b) $O(x) =$
$x + 7$ (c) $O(x) = \dfrac{x}{3}$ (d) $O(x) = x$ (e) $O(x) = 1$ **17.** $g(x) = \dfrac{1}{\sqrt{x + 2}}$,
$x > 0$

Preparation Exercise   **1.** (a) $2; -3$ (b) $x = \frac{3}{2}$ (c) Yes, no, yes, yes, no, yes

4-3   **4.** (a) $D = \{x \mid -3 \le x \le 3\}$ **5.** (a) $D = \{v \mid v > 0\}$ **8.** $-3, -6,$
$-12, -30, 3, 6, 12, 30, .3, .03, .003, -3, -.03, -.003$

Preparation   **1.** $\frac{1}{8}, \frac{1}{2}, \frac{1}{5}, 3, 216, \frac{1}{32}, 8$ **2.** $.18, .35, .71, 1.41, 2.83, 5.66$ **3.** $(2^4)^{\frac{1}{8}} = 2^{\frac{1}{2}} = \sqrt{2}$;
Exercise $(3^2)^{\frac{1}{4}} = \sqrt{3}; (3^3)^{-\frac{1}{9}} = 3^{-\frac{1}{3}} = \dfrac{1}{\sqrt[3]{3}}$

4-4   **3.** (a) $150; 37.5; t = 1500$; No, since $2^{-.002t} > 0$ for all real t.   **5.** 1 hr
7. 212.1 mg   **9.** (a) $\{x \mid x \le 4\}$ (b) $\{x \mid x > \frac{3}{2}\}$ (c) $\{x \mid x < \frac{3}{2}\}$
(d) $\{x \mid x > 0\}$

Chapter   **1.** (a) $F(C) = \frac{9}{5}C + 32$ (b) $32, 212, -40$ (c) Linear
Review   **3.** (a) $D = \{x \mid x \ne -2\}$ (b) $D = \{x \mid -4 \le x \le 4\}$ (c) $D = \{$all reals$\}$
(d) $D = \{x \mid x \ge 0\}$ **7.** $0, 0, 0, \frac{7}{4}, \sqrt{5}, 6, \pi$ **9.** 500 yrs

5-1   **1.** (a) $x^2 + 5x + 3$ (b) $x^3 + 2x^2 - 4x + 12$ **3.** (a) $-x^3 + 4x^2 - 2$ (b) $2x$
5. (a) $-x^3 + 5x^2 + 6$ (b) $x^3 - 3x^2 + 3x + 5$ **7.** (a) $3x^2 + 4x$ (b) 0
9. (a) $2x^3 - 25x^2 - 17x - 2$ (b) $2x^3 - 9x^2 + 6x - 8$ **11.** (a) $x^4 + x^2 + 1$
(b) $9x^4 + 12x^3 + 4x^2 - 1$ **13.** (a) $-5x^6 + x^5 + 10x^4 - 23x^3 + 4x^2 + 2x - 1$
(b) $x^5 - x^4 + 2x^3 + x - 1$ **15.** (a) $x^6 - x^2 - \frac{3}{8}$ (b) $x^6 + x^4 + \frac{1}{4}x^2 - \frac{1}{9}$

5-2   **1.** (a) $(4x^2 - 9x + 12)(x + 1) - 14$ **3.** (a) $1 \cdot (x^2 + x - 2) + (-3x + 5)$
5. (a) $(5x + 25)(x^3 - 5x^2 + 2x - 1) + (115x^2 - 48x + 33)$
7. (a) $(-x^3 - x^2)(1 - x) + 1$ (b) $(x^3 - x^2)(x + 1)x + 1$
9. $(x^2 + 2x + 1)(x^2 + 4) = (x + 1)^2(x^2 + 4)$ **11.** $(x + 1)(x + 2)^2$
13. $(x + 2)(x^2 - 2x + 4)(x + 3)^2$ **15.** (a) $R = 0$ (b) $f(1) = 0$
17. (a) $f(3) = 11$ (b) $R = 11$

5-3   **1.** (a) $(x + 2)(2x^2 - 5x + 14) - 33$ **3.** (a) $(x^2 - 4x + 8)(x + 1)$
5. (a) $(x^4 + x^3 + x^2 + x + 1)(x - 1) + 2$
7. (a) $(3x^3 - 3x^2 + 6)(x - \frac{1}{3}) + 19$ **9.** $a = -5, b = 10$
11. (a) $(x - 2)(x - 1) - x$

Preparation   **1.** $-4; -8; \sqrt{3} - 6; -7; -5\frac{1}{2}$ **2.** $13; 1; 3\sqrt{3} + 7; 4; 8\frac{1}{2}$ **3.** $3; 3; 2; 0; -\frac{3}{4}$
Exercises   **4.** $17; 5; 10 + 3\sqrt{3}; 5; 8\frac{3}{4}$ **5.** $18; 6; 7 + 3\sqrt{3}; -6; -5\frac{1}{4}$ **6.** $25 - 2\sqrt{2}$;
$25 + 2\sqrt{2}; 23 + \sqrt{6}; 19 + \sqrt{2}; 17\frac{1}{2} - \frac{1}{2}\sqrt{2}$ **7.** $31; 11; 17 + 4\sqrt{3}; 7; 6\frac{5}{8}$
8. $-1; 27; 6 - 4\sqrt{3}; -4; -\frac{13}{16}$

5-4   **1.** (a) $-3, -39, 192, -195$ **3.** (a) $-1, 0, 1$ **5.** (a) $-3, -1, 1$ **7.** (a) $(x - 1)$, $(x + 3), (x - 4)$ **9.** (a) $\pm\sqrt{2}$ **11.** (a) $8, 8; 32, 32; k^4 + 3k^2 + 4$, $k^4 + 3k^2 + 4$; even function   **13.** (a) $1, -3; 60, -68; 2k^5 - k^2, -2k^5 - k^2$; neither   **15.** (a) No   **17.** No; yes

5-5   **1.** (a) $\pm1, \pm\frac{1}{2}; 1, \frac{1}{2}, -1$ (b) $\pm1, \pm2; 2$ **3.** (a) $\pm1, \pm2, \pm\frac{1}{2}; -1, -1, -1, \frac{1}{2}$ (b) $\pm1, \pm2, \pm4, \pm\frac{1}{5}, \pm\frac{2}{5}, \pm\frac{4}{5}, 1, 2, \frac{2}{5}$ **5.** (a) $-\frac{1}{2}$ (b) -1 **7.** (a) $\frac{1}{2}$ (b) $\frac{1}{3}$ **9.** (a) no rational zeros   (b) $\frac{3}{2}$ **11.** The rational zeros must be of the form $\pm(a_0/1) = \pm a_0$ **13.** 2, 3, 4   **15.** 5   **17.** $-1, \frac{5}{3}, -\frac{2}{3}; (x + 1)(3x - 5(3x + 2)$ **19.** $0, -\frac{1}{7}; x(7x + 1)(x^2 + 3x + 5)$ **21.** $\frac{5}{6}, -\frac{1}{5}; (6x - 5)(5x + 1)(x^2 + x + 1)$ **23.** They are reciprocals.   **25.** (a) $\sqrt{2}$ is a zero of $x^2 - 2$ which has no rational zero (b) $\sqrt{5}$ is a zero of $x^2 - 5$ which has no rational zero   (c) $\sqrt[3]{4}$ is a zero of $x^3 - 4$ which has no rational zero

Chapter   **1.** $x^3 + 3x^2 + 7x + 1$ **3.** $x - 1 + (x + 6)/(x^2 + 1)$ **5.** $-30, 0, 50, 120$
Review   **7.** $2x - 2, 2x - 8, 2x + 6$ **9.** None   **11.** $(x - 1)(x - 2)(x - 4)(x + 7)$ **13.** $x(x - 1)(x + 1)(3x - 1)$ **15.** $2, -\frac{1}{2}, \frac{1}{3}$ (b) no rational zeros   **17.** $3, -2, \frac{5}{2}$ **19.** $1, -1, 3, -\frac{3}{2}$ **21.** $(x - 1)(x + 1)(x^2 - 2)$ **23.** $(2x + 1)(x + 1)(3x - 5)$ **25.** $\sqrt{2}/\sqrt{3}$ is a zero of $3x^2 - 2$ which has no rational zeros.

6-1   **1.** (a) $\log_2 32 = 5$ **3.** (a) $\log_{16}\frac{1}{64} = -\frac{3}{2}$ **5.** (a) $10^2 = 100$ **7.** (a) $8^0 = 1$ **9.** (a) $n^4 = 9$ **11.** (a) 4   **13.** (a) -2 **15.** (a) -2 **17.** $\frac{1}{216}$ **19.** -3 **21.** 100   **23.** 128   **25.** 0   **27.** $\frac{1}{64}$ **29.** $\frac{3}{2}$

6-2   **1.** (a) $y = x$. By interchanging x and y.   **3.** (a) $-1 < \log_{10} .375 < 0$ **5.** If $M > N$, $\log_{10} M > \log_{10} N$.   **15.** (b) For $x < 0$ **17.** $x > -1$; $y = \log_2 x$ is one unit to the right.

Preparation Exercises   **1.** $b^r = x$ **2.** $b^s = y$ **3.** $b^{r+s} = y$ **4.** $\log_b xy = \log_b x + \log_b y$

6-3   **1.** (a) $\frac{5}{3}$ **3.** (a) 5   **5.** (a) $\frac{11}{2}$ **7.** (a) $\log_3 400$ **9.** $p - q$ **11.** $-p$ **13.** $-q$ **15.** $s - r$ **17.** $3s - 2r$ **19.** $3rs - 3r$ **21.** $\frac{1}{2}(s - r)$ **23.** $x = 42$ **25.** $x = \frac{9}{2}$ **27.** $x = \dfrac{12 + 5^{20}}{8}$ **32.** $x = 2$ **34.** (a) 6   (b) 12   (c) 20   (d) -56

6-4   **1.** (a) 5.87×10^{12} mi   **3.** (a) 2.6990   **5.** (a) $10^3; 2$ **7.** (a) $0 < \log 1.56 < 1$ **9.** (a) -2 **11.** (a) $2.051 \times 10^1; 1$ **13.** (a) $3.1875; 10^{3.1875}$ **15.** (a) $-3.3947; 10^{-3.3947}$ **17.** $-.5918$ **19.** -1.5918 **21.** -3.5918 **23.** 1.5105   **25.** 6.5105   **27.** .9304   **29.** 3.3139   **31.** 4.3139   **33.** (a) -1 and 0; -1 (b) -2 and -1; -2 (c) -3 (d) $-k$

6-5   **1.** (a) 324   **3.** (a) 1080   **5.** (a) .705   **7.** (a) 29.9   **9.** (a) .00145   **11.** 18.0 **13.** 4.03   **15.** 9.40   **17.** 617   **19.** 82,800   **21.** 1.85   **23.** 1.92 sec   **25.** (a) $2210 (b) $2210   (c) $1200   **27.** 415 mg   **29.** 1180 sq in.

Chapter   **1.** F, $2^r > 2^s$ **3.** F, $\log rs = \log r + \log s$ **5.** T   **7.** F, $\log x^n = n \log x$
Review   **9.** T   **11.** 20   **13.** $\frac{1}{3}$ or 1   **15.** $\frac{8}{3}$ **17.** 16   **19.** .05259   **21.** 16.55   **23.** $x > 0$ **25.** $x > -2$ **27.** (a) .8993   (b) .09434   **29.** 1.46×10^3 cm

7-1   **1.**

	30°	45°	60°
sine	$\frac{1}{2}$	$\frac{1}{2}\sqrt{2}$	$\frac{1}{2}\sqrt{3}$
cosine	$\frac{1}{2}\sqrt{3}$	$\frac{1}{2}\sqrt{2}$	$\frac{1}{2}$
tangent	$\frac{1}{3}\sqrt{3}$	1	$\sqrt{3}$

3. $\sin \alpha = \frac{12}{145}\sqrt{145}$, $\cos \alpha = \frac{1}{145}\sqrt{145}$ **5.** $\sin 30° = \frac{1}{2}$, $\cos 30° = \frac{1}{2}\sqrt{3}$, $\tan 30° = \frac{1}{3}\sqrt{3}$ **7.** $\sin \alpha = .2$, $\cos \alpha = \frac{2}{5}\sqrt{6}$, $\tan \alpha = \frac{1}{12}\sqrt{6}$ **9.** $\cos \alpha = \frac{1}{100}\sqrt{199}$, $\tan \alpha = \frac{99}{199}\sqrt{199}$ **11.** $\sin \alpha = \frac{9}{130}\sqrt{130}$,. $\cos \alpha = \frac{7}{130}\sqrt{130}$, $\tan \alpha = \frac{9}{7}$

7-2

1.

s	0	$\frac{1}{6}\pi$	$\frac{1}{4}\pi$	$\frac{1}{3}\pi$	$\frac{1}{2}\pi$
$W(s)$	$(1, 0)$	$(\frac{1}{2}\sqrt{3}, \frac{1}{2})$	$(\frac{1}{2}\sqrt{2}, \frac{1}{2}\sqrt{2})$	$(\frac{1}{2}, \frac{1}{2}\sqrt{3})$	$(0, 1)$

s	$\frac{2}{3}\pi$	$\frac{3}{4}\pi$	$\frac{5}{6}\pi$	π
$W(s)$	$(-\frac{1}{2}, \frac{1}{2}\sqrt{3})$	$(-\frac{1}{2}\sqrt{2}, \frac{1}{2}\sqrt{2})$	$(-\frac{1}{2}\sqrt{3}, \frac{1}{2})$	$(-1, 0)$

s	$\frac{7}{6}\pi$	$\frac{5}{4}\pi$	$\frac{4}{3}\pi$
$W(s)$	$(-\frac{1}{2}\sqrt{3}, -\frac{1}{2})$	$(-\frac{1}{2}\sqrt{2}, -\frac{1}{2}\sqrt{2})$	$(-\frac{1}{2}, -\frac{1}{2}\sqrt{3})$

s	$\frac{3}{2}\pi$	$\frac{5}{3}\pi$	$\frac{7}{4}\pi$	$\frac{11}{2}\pi$	2π
$W(s)$	$(0, -1)$	$(\frac{1}{2}, -\frac{1}{2}\sqrt{3})$	$(\frac{1}{2}\sqrt{2}, -\frac{1}{2}\sqrt{2})$	$(\frac{1}{2}\sqrt{3}, -\frac{1}{2})$	$(1, 0)$

3.

s	3π	$\frac{7}{2}\pi$	4π	$\frac{11}{2}\pi$	7π	10π
$W(s)$	$(-1, 0)$	$(0, -1)$	$(1, 0)$	$(0, -1)$	$(-1, 0)$	$(1, 0)$

s	-2π	$-\frac{5}{2}\pi$	-3π	-5π	-7π	$-\frac{15}{2}\pi$
$W(s)$	$(1, 0)$	$(0, -1)$	$(-1, 0)$	$(-1, 0)$	$(-1, 0)$	$(0, 1)$

5. $\frac{7}{6}\pi$ **7.** $\frac{2}{3}\pi$ **9.** $\frac{1}{4}\pi$ **11.** $(-\frac{1}{2}, -\frac{1}{2}\sqrt{3})$ **13.** $(-\frac{1}{2}\sqrt{2}, \frac{1}{2}\sqrt{2})$ **15.** $(-\frac{1}{2}\sqrt{3}, \frac{1}{2})$ **17.** $(\frac{1}{2}\sqrt{2}, -\frac{1}{2}\sqrt{2})$ **19.** $(\frac{1}{2}, \frac{1}{2}\sqrt{3})$ **21.** $(\frac{1}{2}\sqrt{3}, -\frac{1}{2})$

7-3

1. $(-\frac{1}{2}\sqrt{2}, \frac{1}{2}\sqrt{2})$, $(-\frac{1}{2}\sqrt{2}, \frac{1}{2}\sqrt{2})$
3. $(-\frac{1}{2}\sqrt{3}, -\frac{1}{2})$, $(-\frac{1}{2}\sqrt{3}, -\frac{1}{2})$ **5.** $(1, 0)$, $(-1, 0)$

7.

s	0	$\frac{1}{6}\pi$	$\frac{1}{4}\pi$	$\frac{1}{3}\pi$
$W(s)$	$(1, 0)$	$(\frac{1}{2}\sqrt{3}, \frac{1}{2})$	$(\frac{1}{2}\sqrt{2}, \frac{1}{2}\sqrt{2})$	$(\frac{1}{2}, \frac{1}{2}\sqrt{3})$
$W(-s)$	$(1, 0)$	$(\frac{1}{2}\sqrt{3}, -\frac{1}{2})$	$(\frac{1}{2}\sqrt{2}, -\frac{1}{2}\sqrt{2})$	$(\frac{1}{2}, -\frac{1}{2}\sqrt{3})$
$s + \frac{1}{2}\pi$	$\frac{1}{2}\pi$	$\frac{2}{3}\pi$	$\frac{3}{4}\pi$	$\frac{5}{6}\pi$
$W(s + \frac{1}{2}\pi)$	$(0, 1)$	$(-\frac{1}{2}, \frac{1}{2}\sqrt{3})$	$(-\frac{1}{2}\sqrt{2}, \frac{1}{2}\sqrt{2})$	$(-\frac{1}{2}\sqrt{3}, \frac{1}{2})$

s	$\frac{1}{2}\pi$	$\frac{2}{3}\pi$	$\frac{5}{6}\pi$	$\frac{3}{4}\pi$
$W(s)$	$(0, 1)$	$(-\frac{1}{2}, \frac{1}{2}\sqrt{3})$	$(-\frac{1}{2}\sqrt{3}, \frac{1}{2})$	$(-\frac{1}{2}\sqrt{2}, \frac{1}{2}\sqrt{2})$
$W(-s)$	$(0, -1)$	$(-\frac{1}{2}, -\frac{1}{2}\sqrt{3})$	$(-\frac{1}{2}\sqrt{3}, -\frac{1}{2})$	$(-\frac{1}{2}\sqrt{2}, -\frac{1}{2}\sqrt{2})$
$s + \frac{1}{2}\pi$	π	$\frac{7}{6}\pi$	$\frac{4}{3}\pi$	$\frac{5}{4}\pi$
$W(s + \frac{1}{2}\pi)$	$(-1, 0)$	$(-\frac{1}{2}\sqrt{3}, -\frac{1}{2})$	$(-\frac{1}{2}, -\frac{1}{2}\sqrt{3})$	$(-\frac{1}{2}\sqrt{2}, -\frac{1}{2}\sqrt{2})$

7-4

1.

	I	II	III	IV
$\sin s$	$+$	$+$	$-$	$-$
$\cos s$	$+$	$-$	$-$	$+$

3. $W\left(\dfrac{4\pi}{3}\right) = \left(-\dfrac{1}{2}, -\dfrac{\sqrt{3}}{2}\right)$, $\sin\left(\dfrac{4\pi}{3}\right) = -\dfrac{\sqrt{3}}{2}$, $\cos\left(\dfrac{4\pi}{3}\right) = -\dfrac{1}{2}$

5. $W(7\pi) = (-1, 0)$, $\sin 7\pi = 0$, $\cos 7\pi = -1$

7. $W\left(\dfrac{23\pi}{6}\right) = \left(\dfrac{\sqrt{3}}{2}, -\dfrac{1}{2}\right)$, $\sin\dfrac{23\pi}{6} = -\dfrac{1}{2}$, $\cos\dfrac{23\pi}{6} = \dfrac{\sqrt{3}}{2}$

9. $W\left(-\dfrac{16\pi}{3}\right) = \left(-\dfrac{1}{2}, \dfrac{\sqrt{3}}{2}\right)$, $\sin\left(-\dfrac{16\pi}{3}\right) = \dfrac{\sqrt{3}}{2}$, $\cos\left(-\dfrac{16\pi}{3}\right) = -\dfrac{1}{2}$

11. $-\frac{1}{2}\sqrt{3}$ **13.** $-\frac{1}{2}\sqrt{2}$ **15.** $-\frac{1}{2}\sqrt{3}$ **17.** 0 **19.** 1 **21.** (a) $s = 0$ (b) $s = \frac{1}{2}\pi$
23. (a) $\cos s = \frac{1}{2}\sqrt{3}$ or $-\frac{1}{2}\sqrt{3}$ (b) The sine is the ordinate of a point and only points in the first or second quadrants have positive ordinates.
(c) $-\frac{1}{2}\sqrt{3}$ (d) $s = \frac{5}{6}\pi$ **25.** $\cos s = \frac{1}{10}\sqrt{51}$

7–5 **1.** $-\frac{1}{2}\sqrt{3}$ **3.** -1 **5.** $\frac{1}{2}$ **7.** $-\frac{1}{2}\sqrt{3}$ **9.** $-\frac{1}{2}\sqrt{2}$ **11.** $-\frac{1}{2}\sqrt{3}$ **13.** $-\frac{1}{2}\sqrt{3}$ **15.** $\frac{1}{2}$

7–6 **1.** $\sin s = \frac{1}{2}\sqrt{2}$, $\tan s = 1$, $\cot s = 1$, $\sec s = \sqrt{2}$,
$\csc s = \sqrt{2}$ **3.** $\sin s = -\frac{2}{5}\sqrt{5}$, $\cos s = \frac{1}{5}\sqrt{5}$, $\cot s = -\frac{1}{2}$, $\sec s = \sqrt{5}$,
$\csc s = -\frac{1}{2}\sqrt{5}$ **5.** $\sin s = \frac{1}{2}\sqrt{2}$, $\cos s = -\frac{1}{2}\sqrt{2}$, $\tan s = -1$,
$\cot s = -1$, $\csc s = \sqrt{2}$ **7.** $\sin s = -\frac{1}{2}\sqrt{2}$, $\cos s = -\frac{1}{2}\sqrt{2}$, $\cot s = 1$,
$\sec s = -\sqrt{2}$, $\csc s = -\sqrt{2}$ **9.** Values decrease from 1 to 0
11. (a) $\{y \mid -1 \leq y \leq 1\}$ (b) $\{x \mid -1 \leq x \leq 1\}$

13.

	I	II	III	IV
tan	+	−	+	−
cot	+	−	+	−
sec	+	−	−	+
cos	+	+	−	−

15. Increases through all negative real numbers to 0 **17.** (a) $s = n\pi$,
n an integer (b) $\{s \mid s \neq n\pi, n$ an integer$\}$

7–7 **1.** $160°$ **3.** $\left(\dfrac{360}{\pi}\right)°$ **5.** $-300°$ **7.** $-10°$ **9.** $\left(-\dfrac{540}{\pi}\right)°$

11. $\dfrac{10\pi}{9}$ radians **13.** $\dfrac{11\pi}{6}$ radians **15.** $\dfrac{8\pi}{9}$ radians **17.** 5π radians

19. $-\dfrac{5\pi}{3}$ radians **21.** $\sin 45° = \frac{1}{2}\sqrt{2}$, $\cos 45° = \frac{1}{2}\sqrt{2}$, $\tan 45° = 1$

23. $\sin(-60°) = -\frac{1}{2}\sqrt{3}$, $\cos(-60°) = \frac{1}{2}$, $\tan(-60°) = -\sqrt{3}$
25. $\sin(-210°) = \frac{1}{2}$, $\cos(-210°) = -\frac{1}{2}\sqrt{3}$, $\tan(-210°) = -\frac{1}{3}\sqrt{3}$
27. $\sin 370° = .174$, $\cos 370° = .985$, $\tan 370° = .176$
29. $\sin 756° = .588$, $\cos 756° = .809$, $\tan 756° = .727$
31. $\sin .942 = .809$, $\cos .942 = .588$ **33.** $\sin .401 = .391$, $\cos .401 = .921$
35. $\sin 1.501 = .998$, $\cos 1.501 = .070$ **37.** $\sin .314 = .309$, $\cos .314 = .951$

7–8 Ex, p. 296 **1.** $\frac{1}{2}$ **3.** 0 **5.** $-\sqrt{2}$ **7.** $-.087$ **9.** -4.331 **11.** $-.087$

13. $\sin\dfrac{\pi}{4} = \cos\dfrac{\pi}{4}$ **15.** $\sec\dfrac{\pi}{3} = \csc\dfrac{\pi}{6}$ **17.** $\csc 46° = \sec 44°$

19. $\cos \dfrac{\pi}{10} = \sin \dfrac{2\pi}{5}$ **21.** $\tan 48° = \cot 42°$ **23.** $\cot \dfrac{3\pi}{4} = \tan -\dfrac{\pi}{4}$
25. Ex. 13, $\tfrac{1}{2}\sqrt{2}$; Ex. 14, 0.510; Ex. 15, 2; Ex. 16, $\tfrac{1}{3}\sqrt{3}$; Ex. 17, 1.39;
Ex. 18, 0.946; Ex. 19, 0.951; Ex. 20, 1.15 or $\tfrac{2}{3}\sqrt{3}$; Ex. 21, 1.111;
Ex. 22, 0.961; Ex. 23, -1; Ex. 24, 1.661; **27.** Complement $= 0.367$
29. Complement $= 0.925$ **31.** Complement $= 0.262$

Chapter Review **1.** 0 **3.** 0 **5.** 0 **7.** -1 **9.** -1 **11.** 1 **13.** -1 **15.** $\tfrac{1}{2}\sqrt{3}$
17. $(\tfrac{1}{2}\sqrt{2}, \tfrac{1}{2}\sqrt{2})$ **21.** $\sin^2 s$ **23.** $\cos^2 s$ **25.** $\tan^2 s$
31. $\cos(-\tfrac{1}{3}\pi) = \cos(-60°) = \tfrac{1}{2}$ **33.** $\tan(-\tfrac{3}{4}\pi) = \tan(-135) = 1$
35. $\cos s$ **37.** $-\sin s$ **39.** $-\sin s$ **41.** $\tan s$ **43.** Even **45.** Odd

8-1 **1.** $x \doteq 78.3$ **3.** $x \doteq 95.9$ **5.** $x \doteq 46.2$ **7.** $\alpha \doteq 55°$ **9.** $\alpha \doteq 47°$ **11.** $\alpha \doteq 14°$
13. 39.4 inches **15.** 83.5 meters

8-2 **1.** 5.57 **3.** 5 **5.** 29° **7.** 26° **9.** 2.65 **11.** 105 feet **13.** 36°

8-3 **1.** 10 **3.** 90° **5.** $\gamma \doteq 56°$, $\gamma' \doteq 124°$; $\alpha \doteq 94^0$, $\alpha' \doteq 26°$;
$a = 17.96$, $a' = 7.88$ **7.** 8.26 **9.** 99.7 **11.** $b = 11.27$, $\alpha \doteq 72°$
13. 48.1 **15.** 14° **17.** 1072 ft **19.** 73°, 60°, 47° **21. (a)** $A = bc \sin \alpha$
(b) 132,614.4 **23.** $p = 2nr \sin (180/n)°$

8-4 **1.** $\tfrac{1}{4}(\sqrt{6} - \sqrt{2})$ **3.** $\tfrac{1}{4}(\sqrt{6} + \sqrt{2})$ **5.** $2 + \sqrt{3}$
7. $\tfrac{1}{4}(\sqrt{2} - \sqrt{6})$ **9.** $2 + \sqrt{3}$ **11.** $-\tfrac{56}{65}$ **13.** $\tfrac{33}{56}$ **15.** $\tfrac{44}{125}$
17. $\tfrac{6}{91}\sqrt{13}(1 - \sqrt{10})$ **19.** $\tfrac{6}{79}(49 - 13\sqrt{10})$ **21.** $-\sin u$ **23.** $\sin u$

8-5 **1.** $-\tfrac{12}{13}$ **3.** $-\tfrac{120}{119}$ **5.** $\tfrac{4}{5}$ **7.** $\tfrac{24}{25}$ **9.** $-\tfrac{24}{7}$ **11.** $\tfrac{2}{5}\sqrt{5}$ **13.** $-\tfrac{24}{25}$
15. $-\tfrac{527}{625}$ **17.** $-\tfrac{2}{7}\sqrt{6}$ **19.** $-\tfrac{1}{6}\sqrt{6}$

8-6 **1.** $\left\{\dfrac{\pi}{6}, \dfrac{5\pi}{6}\right\}$ **3.** $\left\{\dfrac{\pi}{3}, \dfrac{2\pi}{3}, \dfrac{4\pi}{3}, \dfrac{5\pi}{3}\right\}$ **5.** $\left\{\dfrac{\pi}{12}, \dfrac{5\pi}{12}, \dfrac{13\pi}{12}, \dfrac{17\pi}{12}\right\}$

7. $\left\{0, \dfrac{4\pi}{3}\right\}$ **9.** $\left\{\dfrac{5\pi}{6}, \dfrac{7\pi}{6}\right\}$ **11.** $\left\{1.107, 4.249, \dfrac{\pi}{4}, \dfrac{5\pi}{4}\right\}$ **13.** $\left\{\dfrac{\pi}{3}, \dfrac{5\pi}{3}, \pi\right\}$

8-8 **1.** Period, 2π; amplitude, 4 **3.** Period, π; amplitude, 2
5. Period, π; amplitude, 1 **7.** Period, 2; amplitude, 2
9. Period, 2π; amplitude, 1 **11.** Period, 3π; amplitude, 4
13. Period, π; amplitude, 2

8-9 **1.** $\dfrac{\pi}{3}$ **3.** π **5.** 0 **7.** 2.496 **9.** $\dfrac{\pi}{4}$ **11.** $\dfrac{\pi}{4}$ **13.** $\dfrac{-\pi}{4}$ **15.** 2 **17.** $\tfrac{7}{24}$

Chapter Review **1.** 4.36 **3.** $5\sqrt{2}$ **5.** $\tfrac{1}{77}(-21\sqrt{5} + 12\sqrt{2})$
7. $\dfrac{14 + 18\sqrt{10}}{12\sqrt{2} - 21\sqrt{5}}$ **9.** $\dfrac{-51 + 10\sqrt{91}}{10\sqrt{389}}$

11. $\sin \dfrac{\pi}{8} = \dfrac{1}{2}\sqrt{2 - \sqrt{2}}$, $\cos \dfrac{\pi}{8} = \dfrac{1}{2}\sqrt{2 + \sqrt{2}}$, $\tan \dfrac{\pi}{8} = \sqrt{2} - 1$

13. $\sin \dfrac{2\pi}{3} = \dfrac{\sqrt{3}}{2}$, $\cos \dfrac{2\pi}{3} = -\dfrac{1}{2}$, $\tan \dfrac{2\pi}{3} = -\sqrt{3}$

15. $-\tfrac{4}{9}\sqrt{5}$ **17.** $\cos x - \sin x$ **19.** 1 **21.** $\{7/6\pi, 11/6\pi\}$ **23.** $\{0, \tfrac{1}{4}\pi, \pi, 5/4\pi\}$
25. Period, π; amplitude, 3 **27.** Does not exist **29.** $-\tfrac{1}{4}\pi$ **31.** π **33.** $\tfrac{2}{3}\sqrt{3}$

9-1   **1.** (a) $4i$ (b) $\sqrt{7}i$ (c) $4\sqrt{2}i$ **3.** $\sqrt{5}i, -\sqrt{5}i$ **5.** $[3i, -3i]$
7. $[-3 + 4i, -3 - 4i]$ **9.** (a) $7 + 4i$; 7, $4i$ (b) 4; 4, $0i$ **11.** (a) $1 - 2\sqrt{2}i$;
$1, -2\sqrt{2}i$ (b) $-2 - 2\sqrt{3}i$; $-2, -2\sqrt{3}i$ **13.** (a) 0 (b) $30 + 36i$ **15.** (a) i
(b) $\dfrac{\sqrt{2}}{2} + \dfrac{\sqrt{2i}}{2}, -\dfrac{\sqrt{2}}{2} - \dfrac{\sqrt{2}}{2} - \dfrac{\sqrt{2i}}{2}$ (c) $\dfrac{\sqrt{2}}{2} - \dfrac{\sqrt{2i}}{2}, -\dfrac{\sqrt{2}}{2} + \dfrac{\sqrt{2i}}{2}$

9-2   **1.** (a) $4 - 2i$; 8; 20 **3.** (a) $\frac{1}{2} + \frac{1}{2}\sqrt{3}i$; 1; 1 **5.** (a) $\frac{1}{2} - \frac{1}{2}i$ **7.** (a) $-\frac{2}{29} + \frac{5}{29}i$
9. $\frac{2}{5} - \frac{1}{5}i$ **11.** $\frac{3}{2} - 3i$ **13.** i **15.** $\frac{5}{7} + \frac{6}{7}\sqrt{3}i$ **17.** $-\frac{1}{5} - \frac{9}{10}i$ **19.** $\frac{33}{85} - \frac{89}{85}i$
21. (a) $a - bi, c - di$; $(ac - bd) - i(bc + ad)$ (b) $(ac - bd) + i(bc + ad)$;
$(ac - bd) - i(bc + ad)$ (c) Equal **23.** $x = -5, y = 4$ **25.** $x = 5, y = 2$

9-3   **1.** (a) $\{3 + i, 3 - i\}$ **3.** (a) $\{2 + 5i, 2 - 5i\}$ **5.** (a) $\{\sqrt{3} + i, \sqrt{3} - i\}$
9. (a) $x^2 - \frac{1}{6}x - \frac{1}{6} = 0$ **11.** (a) $x^2 + 6x + 25 = 0$
13. $-2 + 4i, -2 - 4i$; $(x + 2 - 4i)(x + 2 + 4i)$ **15.** $1 + \sqrt{3}i, 1 - \sqrt{3}i$;
$(x - 1 - \sqrt{3}i)(x - 1 + \sqrt{3}i)$ **17.** $\frac{3}{8} + \frac{1}{24}\sqrt{321}, \frac{3}{8} - \frac{1}{24}\sqrt{321}$;
$(x - \frac{3}{8} - \frac{1}{24}\sqrt{321})(x - \frac{3}{8} + \frac{1}{24}\sqrt{321})$ **19.** $(ac - bd) + (ad + bc)i = r + 0i$
So $ad + bc = 0$ **21.** The sum and product of the two roots must both be real
numbers (cf exercise 6)

9-4   **1.** (a) $\{1 + \sqrt{6}, 1 - \sqrt{6}\}$ (b) $\left\{\dfrac{-1 + i\sqrt{11}}{6}, \dfrac{-1 - i\sqrt{11}}{6}\right\}$
3. (a) $\left\{\dfrac{3 + i\sqrt{15}}{2}, \dfrac{3 - i\sqrt{15}}{2}\right\}$ (b) $\left\{\dfrac{-1 + i\sqrt{3}}{2}, \dfrac{-1 - i\sqrt{3}}{2}\right\}$ **5.** (a) $\{3i, -3i\}$
(b) $\{10i, -10i\}$ **7.** (a) $\left\{\dfrac{-1 + \sqrt{13}}{6}, \dfrac{-1 - \sqrt{13}}{6}\right\}$ (b) $\{2 + \sqrt{2}, 2 - \sqrt{2}\}$
9. (a) $\left\{\dfrac{2 + \sqrt{14}}{3}, \dfrac{2 - \sqrt{14}}{3}\right\}$ (b) $\left\{\dfrac{-5 + \sqrt{505}}{12}, \dfrac{-5 - \sqrt{505}}{12}\right\}$
11. $x^2 - 2x - 2 = 0$ **13.** $2x^2 - x - 6 = 0$ **15.** $x^2 - x - 1 = 0$
17. $x^2 + x + 1 = 0$ **19.** (a) $\{3, -3, 2, -2\}$ (b) $\{2, -2\}$ **21.** (a) $\{1\}$
(b) $\{1, \frac{1}{2}\}$ **23.** $\frac{9}{4}$ **25.** $-4, 8$

9-5   **1.** $m < \frac{9}{4}$ **3.** $m > \frac{9}{4}$ **5.** $k > 4$ or $k < -4$ **7.** no real zeros; 8; $(-2, 4)$ lowest
point **9.** $[1, -3]$; 3; $(-1, 4)$ highest point **11.** $[-\frac{3}{2}]$; $9 - (-\frac{3}{2}, 0)$ lowest point

Chapter   **1.** $-2\sqrt{2}i$ **3.** $34 - 13i$ **5.** $\frac{3}{4}$ **7.** $\frac{7}{11}, -\frac{6}{11}\sqrt{2}i$ **9.** $x = \frac{23}{5}, y = \frac{3}{5}$
Review   **11.** $[-1 + \sqrt{2}i, -1 - \sqrt{2}i]$ **13.** $[3 + \sqrt{2}, 3 - \sqrt{2}]$ **15.** $[2 + \sqrt{3}i, 2 - \sqrt{3}i]$
17. $[-\frac{2}{3} + \frac{1}{3}\sqrt{11}i, -\frac{2}{3} - \frac{1}{3}\sqrt{11}i]$ **19.** $x^2 - 6x + 14 = 0$ **21.** $x^2 + 4x + 13 = 0$
23. (a) $m < 9$ (b) $m > 9$ **25.** $(2, 1)$ lowest point

10-1   **1.** (a) 2×2 row 1 = (1 2), row 2 = (3 4) (b) 2×2 row 1 = (0 0),
row 2 = (0 0) (c) 2×2 row 1 = (1 0), row 2 = (0 1) (d) 3×2
row 1 = (1 0), row 2 = (-3 2), row 3 = (4 2) (e) 2×3 row 1 =
(-2 0 3), row 2 = (1 5 -3) (f) 2×3 row 1 = (1 0 2), row 2 =
(0 1 -3) **3.** (a) $\begin{pmatrix} 3 & 2 \\ 7 & 4 \end{pmatrix}$ (b) $\begin{pmatrix} 0 & 1 & 2 \\ 3 & 4 & 5 \end{pmatrix}$ (c) $\begin{pmatrix} 3 & 0 \\ 1 & -1 \\ -4 & 3 \\ 2 & 5 \end{pmatrix}$

5. (a) $\begin{pmatrix} 2 & -1 \\ 1 & 3 \end{pmatrix}$ and $\begin{pmatrix} 2 & -1 & 3 \\ 1 & 3 & 5 \end{pmatrix}$ (b) $\begin{pmatrix} 2 & 3 \\ -1 & 2 \end{pmatrix}$ and $\begin{pmatrix} 2 & 3 & -5 \\ -1 & 2 & 3 \end{pmatrix}$

(c) $\begin{pmatrix} 1 & -1 \\ 0 & 1 \end{pmatrix}$ and $\begin{pmatrix} 1 & -1 & 2 \\ 0 & 1 & 7 \end{pmatrix}$ (d) $\begin{pmatrix} 1 & 2 & -3 \\ 2 & 0 & 1 \\ 3 & -1 & 0 \end{pmatrix}$ and $\begin{pmatrix} 1 & 2 & -3 & 4 \\ 2 & 0 & 1 & 8 \\ 3 & -1 & 0 & 9 \end{pmatrix}$

(e) $\begin{pmatrix} 0 & 1 & 2 \\ 3 & 2 & -1 \\ 7 & 1 & 0 \end{pmatrix}$ and $\begin{pmatrix} 0 & 1 & 2 & -1 \\ 3 & 2 & -1 & 0 \\ 7 & 1 & 0 & 3 \end{pmatrix}$ **7.** (a) $\begin{cases} x + 2y = 3 \\ 4x + 5y = 6 \end{cases}$

(b) $\begin{cases} x \quad = 1 \\ \quad y = 2 \end{cases}$ (c) $\begin{cases} -x + 2y = 2 \\ 2x + 4y = 6 \end{cases}$ (d) $\begin{cases} x \quad + z = 3 \\ 3x + 2y - 3z = 7 \\ \quad y + 2z = 6 \end{cases}$

(e) $\begin{cases} -x + y + 3z = 3 \\ 4x + 2y \quad = 2 \\ 3x - 2y - z = 0 \end{cases}$ **9.** $\begin{cases} 3x - y = 6 \\ -2x + 4y = 13 \end{cases}$ and $\begin{cases} 3x - y = a \\ -2x + 4y = b \end{cases}$

Infinitely many, since a and b may take on any values.

10–2   **1.** (a) $\begin{pmatrix} 3 & 4 \\ 1 & 2 \end{pmatrix}$ (b) $\begin{pmatrix} 3 & 6 \\ 3 & 4 \end{pmatrix}$ (c) $\begin{pmatrix} 1 & 2 \\ 1 & 0 \end{pmatrix}$ **3.** (a) $\begin{pmatrix} 2 & -1 & 0 \\ 3 & 5 & 2 \\ 0 & 2 & -1 \end{pmatrix}$

(b) $\begin{pmatrix} -4 & 2 & 0 \\ 0 & 2 & -1 \\ 3 & 5 & 2 \end{pmatrix}$ (c) $\begin{pmatrix} 2 & -1 & 0 \\ 4 & 0 & -1 \\ 3 & 5 & 2 \end{pmatrix}$ (d) $\begin{pmatrix} 2 & -1 & 0 \\ 0 & 2 & -1 \\ 3 & 9 & 0 \end{pmatrix}$

5. $\begin{pmatrix} c & d \\ a & b \end{pmatrix}$, $\begin{pmatrix} ka & kb \\ c & d \end{pmatrix}$, $\begin{pmatrix} a & b \\ mc & md \end{pmatrix}$, $\begin{pmatrix} a & b \\ c + na & d + nb \end{pmatrix}$, $\begin{pmatrix} a + pc & b + pd \\ c & d \end{pmatrix}$.

7. (a) $\begin{pmatrix} 1 & -2 & 8 \\ 3 & 2 & 0 \end{pmatrix}$ (b) $\begin{pmatrix} 1 & -2 & 8 \\ 0 & 8 & -24 \end{pmatrix}$ (c) $\begin{pmatrix} 1 & -2 & 8 \\ 0 & 1 & -3 \end{pmatrix}$

(d) $\begin{pmatrix} 1 & 0 & 2 \\ 0 & 1 & -3 \end{pmatrix}$ (e) $\begin{cases} x = 2 \\ y = -3 \end{cases}$ **9.** (a) $x = 3, y = \frac{1}{2}$ (b) $x = -2, y = 2$

(c) $x = \frac{1}{2}, y = \frac{1}{4}$ **11.** (a) $x = -2, y = 3$ (b) $x = \frac{4}{5}, y = \frac{2}{5}$ (c) $x = -1, y = 4$

10–3   **1.** (a) $\begin{pmatrix} 1 & 2 \\ 0 & -2 \end{pmatrix}$ (b) $\begin{pmatrix} 1 & 0 \\ 0 & 3 \end{pmatrix}$ (c) $\begin{pmatrix} 1 & -1 \\ 0 & 9 \end{pmatrix}$ **3.** (a) $\begin{pmatrix} 1 & 2 & 3 \\ 0 & -3 & -6 \end{pmatrix}$

(b) $\begin{pmatrix} 1 & 0 & 2 \\ 0 & 1 & 4 \end{pmatrix}$ (c) $\begin{pmatrix} 1 & 0 & 3 & 4 \\ 0 & 0 & -4 & -6 \end{pmatrix}$ **5.** (a) $\begin{pmatrix} 2 & 1 \\ 0 & -\frac{1}{2} \end{pmatrix}$ (b) $\begin{pmatrix} 3 & 0 \\ 0 & 2 \end{pmatrix}$

(c) $\begin{pmatrix} 2 & 2 \\ 0 & 1 \end{pmatrix}$ **7.** (a) $\begin{pmatrix} 2 & 3 & 4 \\ 0 & -6 & -6 \end{pmatrix}$ (b) $\begin{pmatrix} 2 & -2 & 3 \\ 0 & 0 & -4 \end{pmatrix}$

(c) $\begin{pmatrix} 4 & 2 & 5 & 0 & 2 \\ 0 & -\frac{3}{2} & -\frac{3}{4} & 0 & \frac{3}{2} \end{pmatrix}$ **9.** (a) $\begin{pmatrix} 1 & 0 & 2 \\ 0 & 2 & 7 \\ 0 & 0 & -15 \end{pmatrix}$ (b) $\begin{pmatrix} 1 & 2 & 3 \\ 0 & -1 & 4 \\ 0 & 0 & -12 \end{pmatrix}$

(c) $\begin{pmatrix} 1 & -2 & 2 \\ 0 & 0 & -1 \\ 0 & 0 & 0 \end{pmatrix}$ **11.** (a) $\begin{pmatrix} 2 & 2 & 4 \\ 0 & -4 & -6 \\ 0 & 0 & 2 \end{pmatrix}$ (b) $\begin{pmatrix} -2 & 4 & 1 \\ 0 & 8 & 5 \\ 0 & 0 & 3 \end{pmatrix}$

(c) $\begin{pmatrix} 3 & -6 & 6 \\ 0 & 3 & -3 \\ 0 & 0 & 9 \end{pmatrix}$ **13.** (a) $\begin{pmatrix} 1 & 2 & 2 & 4 \\ 0 & -2 & -3 & -6 \\ 0 & 0 & 2 & -7 \\ 0 & 0 & 0 & -19 \end{pmatrix}$ (b) $\begin{pmatrix} 1 & 0 & 4 & 2 & -3 \\ 0 & 1 & 5 & 1 & -1 \\ 0 & 0 & -12 & -3 & -1 \\ 0 & 0 & 0 & 0 & 11 \end{pmatrix}$

10–4   **1.** (a) $x = 1, y = 2$ (b) $x = -1, y = 2$ **3.** (a) $x = -1, y = 4$ (b) $x = 2,$ $y = -2$ **5.** (a) $x = \frac{3}{2}, y = \frac{2}{3}$ (b) $x = 2, y = \frac{1}{5}$ **7.** (a) $x = \frac{3}{2} - (5k)/2,$ $y = k$ for all values of k (b) no solution **9.** (a) $x = 1, y = 2, z = -2$ (b) $x = 2, y = 0, z = 3$ **11.** (a) $p = -3, q = 0, r = 4$ (b) $x = \frac{5}{4}, y = -\frac{1}{2},$ $z = -\frac{1}{4}$

10-5   **1.** (a) -7 (b) 5   (c) 3   (d) -6 **3.** (a) 0   (b) $\begin{pmatrix} -6 & 9 \\ 4 & 6 \end{pmatrix}$ **5.** (a) 6   (b) 2

(c) 6   (d) -1 **7.** (a) 0   (b) $\begin{pmatrix} -2 & 0 & -1 \\ 4 & 0 & 2 \\ 4 & 0 & 2 \end{pmatrix}$ **9.** (a) (7   4)   (b) (3   6)

(c) (1   2)   (d) $(-1 \quad 2)$ **11.** (a) $(-1 \quad 2)$ (b) (0   3   3)   (c) (5 -3)

(d) (1 -8 -4)   **13.** (a) $(ac \quad bc)$ (b) $(a \quad b)$ (c) $\begin{pmatrix} c \\ d \end{pmatrix}$ **15.** (a) $\begin{pmatrix} 7 & -9 & 4 \\ 4 & -6 & 3 \end{pmatrix}$

(b) $\begin{pmatrix} 0 & 4 & 4 \\ 5 & -1 & 10 \end{pmatrix}$ (c) $\begin{pmatrix} 2 & 0 & -1 \\ 1 & -3 & 2 \end{pmatrix}$ (d) $\begin{pmatrix} 1 & 2 & 2 \\ 0 & 1 & -1 \\ 2 & 0 & 2 \end{pmatrix}$ (e) $\begin{pmatrix} 1 & 2 & 3 \\ 0 & 1 & -1 \\ 2 & 0 & 2 \end{pmatrix}$

17. (a) $\begin{pmatrix} 1 & 0 \\ 0 & 1 \end{pmatrix}$ (b) $\begin{pmatrix} 0 & 1 \\ -1 & 0 \end{pmatrix}$ (c) $\begin{pmatrix} 0 & 1 \\ -1 & 0 \end{pmatrix}$ (d) $\begin{pmatrix} -1 & 0 \\ 0 & -1 \end{pmatrix}$ (e) $\begin{pmatrix} 1 & 0 \\ 0 & 1 \end{pmatrix}$

19. (a) $\begin{pmatrix} a_{11} & a_{12} & a_{13} \\ a_{21} & a_{22} & a_{23} \\ a_{31} & a_{32} & a_{33} \end{pmatrix}$ (b) $\begin{pmatrix} a_{11} & a_{12} & a_{13} \\ a_{21} & a_{22} & a_{23} \\ a_{31} & a_{32} & a_{33} \end{pmatrix}$ (c) $\begin{pmatrix} 1 & 0 & 0 \\ 0 & 1 & 0 \\ 0 & 0 & 1 \end{pmatrix}$

21. (a) $\begin{pmatrix} 1 & 0 \\ 0 & 1 \end{pmatrix}$ (b) $\begin{pmatrix} 1 & 0 \\ 0 & 1 \end{pmatrix}$ **23.** (a) $\begin{pmatrix} 0 & 0 \\ 0 & 0 \end{pmatrix}$ (b) $\begin{pmatrix} -30 & -45 \\ 20 & 30 \end{pmatrix}$

25. (a) $\begin{pmatrix} 1 & 0 & 0 \\ 0 & 1 & 0 \\ 0 & 0 & 1 \end{pmatrix}$ (b) $\begin{pmatrix} 1 & 0 & 0 \\ 0 & 1 & 0 \\ 0 & 0 & 1 \end{pmatrix}$

Preparation   **1.** (a) $\begin{pmatrix} ad - bc & 0 \\ 0 & ad - bc \end{pmatrix}$ (b) $\begin{pmatrix} ad - bc & 0 \\ 0 & ad - bc \end{pmatrix}$
Exercises

10-6   **1.** (a) $\begin{pmatrix} a \\ b \end{pmatrix}$ (b) $(c \quad d)$ **3.** (a) $\begin{pmatrix} 3 & 2 \\ 4 & 3 \end{pmatrix}$ (b) $x = 12$, $y = 17$ (c) $x = 14$, $y = 19$

5. (a) $\begin{pmatrix} \dfrac{d}{ad - bc} & \dfrac{-b}{ad - bc} \\ \dfrac{-c}{ad - bc} & \dfrac{a}{ad - bc} \end{pmatrix}$ (b) $ad - bc$ must not be equal to zero   (c) $ad - bc$

must not be equal to zero and it must be a divisor (or factor) of each of the four
integers: a, b, c, and d.   **7.** (a) $\begin{pmatrix} \frac{1}{11} & -\frac{2}{11} \\ \frac{4}{11} & \frac{3}{11} \end{pmatrix}$ (b) $x = \frac{2}{11}$, $y = \frac{41}{11}$ (c) $x = \frac{7}{11}$,

$y = \frac{28}{11}$ **9.** (a) $\begin{pmatrix} 1 & 1 & -1 \\ -2 & -1 & 0 \\ 4 & 2 & 2 \end{pmatrix}$ (b) $x = 0$, $y = 5$, $z = 14$ (c) $x = 4$, $y = -2$,

$z = -2$ **11.** (a) $\begin{pmatrix} -3 & 5 & 6 \\ -1 & 2 & 2 \\ 1 & -1 & -1 \end{pmatrix}$ (b) $x = 25$, $y = 11$, $z = -4$ (c) $x = -6$,

$y = -2$, $z = 3$

10-7   **3.** (a) 1   (b) -1 **5.** (a) -1 (b) -1 **7.** (a) $ps - qr$ (b) 0   **9.** (a) $3 - x^2$
(b) -2 **11.** (a) 1   (b) 6   **13.** (a) -24 (b) 3   **15.** (a) $-a(be - cd)$ or $acd - abe$
(b) 14   **17.** (a) -2 (b) 44   **19.** (a) $ad - bc$ (b) $ad - bc$

10-8   **3.** (a) -11 (b) 11   **5.** (a) -5 (b) -25 **7.** (a) 1   (b) 1   **9.** (a) -2 (b) -20
11. (a) 9   (b) 25   **13.** (a) -15 (b) 0   **15.** (a) 40   (b) 1   **17.** $ad - bc$,

$(ka)d - (kb)d = k(ad - bc)$ **19.** $ad - bc$, $a(d + kb) - b(c + ka) =$ $ad + kab - bc - kab = ad - bc$ **21.** If a column of a matrix is multiplied by a number, its determinant is multiplied by the same number; $ad - bc$, $a(kd) - (kb)c = k(ad - bc)$

10–9 **1.** (a) $x = 2$, $y = 3$ (b) $x = 1$, $y = -3$ **3.** (a) $x = \frac{2}{3}$, $y = \frac{1}{6}$ (b) $x = 2$, $y = -1$ **5.** (a) $x = 1$, $y = 2$, $z = 3$ (b) $x = 2$, $y = 0$, $z = 5$ **7.** (a) $x = \frac{1}{2}$, $y = \frac{1}{3}$, $z = \frac{1}{6}$ (b) $x = 8$, $y = 1$, $z = 1$ **9.** (a) Will give $\frac{0}{0}$, which is undefined (b) $x = (3k)/2 + \frac{5}{2}$, $y = k$ for any real k **11.** (a) Substitution will give undefined quantities $-\frac{21}{0}$ and $-\frac{14}{0}$ (b) No solution **13.** The system will have either no solution or infinitely many solutions, depending on whether the determinants of the "replaced" matrices are all zero or not, respectively. The "replaced" matrix is that obtained by replacing one of the columns of the coefficient matrix by a column containing the constants.

10–10 **1.** (a) cost $= 820 + x + 2y$ (b) at (20, 0), cost $= 840$; at (30, 0), cost $= 850$; at (30, 10), cost $= 870$; at (0, 40), cost $= 900$; at (0, 20), cost $= 860$. (c) Ship 20 units from warehouse I to A (and none to B), and use all of the units in warehouse II, shipping 10 units to A and 40 units to B. **3.** (a) $50x + 40y \geq 1000$ and $x + y \leq 24$. (b) The other two inequalities are $x \geq 0$ and $y \geq 0$. The graph is a triangle with vertices (20, 0), (24, 0), and (4, 20). (c) 4 hours of machine A, 20 hours of machine B (d) 20 hours of machine A for the production, leaving machine B idle (e) There is a minimum value of the cost at both (4, 20) and (20, 0). The line joining them has equation $50x + 40y = 1000$ or $5x + 4y = 100$. Any point on the segment of this line between (4, 20) and (20, 0) will give the same cost. **5.** Let $b =$ the number of acres in vegetable B and $c =$ the number of acres in vegetable C. (a) $b + c \leq 50$ (b) $4b + c \leq 185$ (c) $2b + 5c \leq 205$ (d) $b \geq 0$, $c \geq 0$ (f) Profit $= 15b + 6.5c$ (g) 45 acres in vegetable B, 5 acres in vegetable C

Chapter Review **1.** $\{(\frac{8}{5}, -\frac{1}{5})\}$ **3.** $\{(\frac{1}{2}, -\frac{1}{2}, 1)\}$ **5.** $\{(5, -2, 7)\}$

11–1 **1.** (a) 5 **3.** (a) $x^2 + y^2 \geq 16$ **5.** (a) $(-1, 1)$, $(0, 1)$, $(-3, 0)$, $(-3, 1)$, $(-3, -1)$, etc. **7.** Outside, Inside, On, Outside, Outside **9.** For $k = 10^6$, 10^2, 5^2, 10, 5, 1: circle, center (0, 0) with radius $\sqrt{k}$; $k = 0$: (0, 0); $k = -1$: an imaginary circle; $k > 0$

Preparation Exercises **1.** $\{(6, 2)\}$ **2.** Systems of equations which have the same solution set. **3.** $\{3, -4\}$ **4.** It does not cross the x-axis.

11–2 **1.** (a) (3, 0), (0, 3) **3.** (a) $\{(2, -4)\}$; line tangent to circle. **5.** (a) $\{(-\frac{9}{2} - \frac{3}{2}i, -\frac{9}{2} + \frac{3}{2}i)\}$ **7.** There are two points on the circle for which the abscissa is -4, but only one of those is also on the line. The same is true for 3. **9.** $x^2 + y^2 = 20$; $x + y = 6$; $\{(4, 2), (2, 4)\}$ **15.** $k = 2\sqrt{5}$ or $k = -2\sqrt{5}$

Preparation Exercises **1.** (a) If $x < 0$ $x = -|x|$ (b) If $x = 0$ $x = |x|$ (c) If $x > 0$ $x = |x|$ **2.** (a) If $x < 0$ $x^2 = |x|^2$ (b) If $x \geq 0$ $x^2 = |x|^2$ **3.** 4 **4.** 5 **5.** 5

11–3 **1.** (a) $3\sqrt{10}$ **3.** (a) $p = \sqrt{13} + \sqrt{26}$; isosceles; $\angle A$ and $\angle B$ **5.** (a) AM $= \sqrt{80}$; BM $= \sqrt{80}$. Hence, AM $=$ BM and $(3, -2)$ is the midpoint. **7.** (a) RS $= \sqrt{10}$, ST $= 3\sqrt{10}$, RT $= 4\sqrt{10}$, RS $+$ ST $= \sqrt{10} + 3\sqrt{10} =$

$4\sqrt{10}$ = RT so R, S, and T are collinear.   **9.** Center: $(-5, 2)$; radius: 3
11. (a) $3\sqrt{5}$ **13.** (a) $(x - 1)^2 + (y - 3)^2 = 4$; $(1, 3)$; 2
(b) $(x + 2)^2 + (y + 1)^2 = 1$; $(-2, -1)$; 1   (c) $(x - 3)^2 + y^2 = 8$; $(3, 0)$;
$2\sqrt{2}$ (d) $7x^2 + (y - \frac{1}{2})^2 = \frac{4}{9}$; $(0, \frac{1}{2})$; $\frac{2}{3}$ **15.** $(6, 6)$ **17.** $5x - 11y = 3$

11-4   **1.** (a) (i) 2 and -2; $\sqrt{3}$ and $-\sqrt{3}$ (iii) If (x, y) is on the ellipse, then so are

$(x, -y)$, $(-x, y)$, and $(-x, -y)$.   **3.** (a) $\dfrac{x^2}{9} + \dfrac{y^2}{5} = 1$ **7.** (a) All points

inside the ellipse which is the graph of $\dfrac{x^2}{4} + \dfrac{y^2}{3} = 1$; integral solutions: $(-1, 1)$,

$(-1, 0)$, $(-1, -1)$, $(0, 1)$, $(0, 0)$, $(0, -1)$, $(1, 1)$, $(1, 0)$, $(1, -1)$ **9.** None;
$(-\sqrt{3}, 0)$; $(1, \frac{1}{2}\sqrt{6})$; $(1, -\frac{1}{2}\sqrt{6})$; $(\sqrt{3}, 0)$; none   **11.** (a) Circle with center
$(0, 0)$ and radius $\sqrt{13}$; ellipse with center $(0, 0)$, major axis horizontal

13. (a) $\dfrac{x^2}{4} + \dfrac{y^2}{1} = 1$

Preparation   **1.** $d = \sqrt{(x + 5)^2 + y^2}$ **2.** $d = \sqrt{(x - 5)^2 + y^2}$
Exercises
   3. $\sqrt{(x + 5)^2 + y^2} - \sqrt{(x - 5)^2 + y^2}$
   4. $\sqrt{(x + 5)^2 + y^2} - \sqrt{(x - 5)^2 + y^2} = 8$ **5.** $9x^2 - 16y^2 = 144$
   6. $\sqrt{(x - 5)^2 + y^2} - \sqrt{(x + 5)^2 + y^2}$
   7. $\sqrt{(x - 5)^2 + y^2} - \sqrt{(x + 5)^2 + y^2} = 8$ **8.** $9x^2 - 16y^2 = 144$
   9. They are the same; yes, all are equivalent

11-5   **1.** (a) (i) $(5, 0)$, $(-5, 0)$. If $x = 0$, $y^2 = -16$, hence there are no y-intercepts.
(ii) $(\sqrt{41}, 0)$, $(-\sqrt{41}, 0)$ (iii) $(\sqrt{14}, \frac{16}{5})$, $(\sqrt{41}, -\frac{16}{5})$, $(-\sqrt{41}, \frac{16}{5})$,
$(-\sqrt{14}, -\frac{16}{5})$ (iv) $\pm\frac{4}{5}\sqrt{11}$, $\pm\frac{8}{5}\sqrt{6}$, $\pm4\sqrt{3}$ **3.** (a) $7x^2 - 9y^2 = 63$
5. (a) $12x^2 - 4y^2 = 3$ **7.** (a) $(0, 3)$, $(0, -3)$ **9.** $\{(\frac{5}{3}\sqrt{5}, \frac{8}{3}), (\frac{5}{3}\sqrt{5}, -\frac{8}{3}),$
$(-\frac{5}{3}\sqrt{5}, \frac{8}{3}), (-\frac{5}{3}\sqrt{5}, -\frac{8}{3})\}$ **11.** $\{(4, 0), (-4, 0)\}$ **13.** $\dfrac{x^2}{a^2} - \dfrac{y^2}{c^2 - a^2} = 1$;

$\dfrac{x^2}{a^2} - \dfrac{y^2}{b^2} = 1$

Preparation   **2.** $(\frac{5}{2}, -\frac{49}{4})$ **3.** (a) $\{6, -1\}$ (b) $\{7, -2\}$ (c) $\{1, 5\}$
Exercises   **4.** $d = \sqrt{(x - 3)^2 + y^2}$ **5.** $d = x + 3$ **6.** $y^2 = 12x$

11-6   **1.** (a) $x^2 = -12y$ **3.** (a) Focus: $(0, 4)$; end points: $(8, 4)$, $(-8, 4)$; length: 16
5. (a) Vertex: $(0, 0)$; focus: $(0, 2)$; end points: $(4, 2)$, $(-4, 2)$; directrix:
$y = -2$; axis: $x = 0$ **7.** (a) $(0, 0)$; $(0, 5)$; $(10, 5)$, $(-10, 5)$; $y = -5$; $x = 0$
9. (a) $x^2 = 2y$ **11.** No; no; no   **13.** (a) $\begin{cases} x = -2 + 2\sqrt{2} \text{ or } -2 - 2\sqrt{2} \\ y = 3 - 2\sqrt{2} \text{ or } 3 + 2\sqrt{2} \end{cases}$
15. $(-3, -9)$, $(1, -1)$ **17.** None   **21.** (a) $x^2 = 8(y + 2)$; $(0, -2)$
(b) $x^2 = -4(y - 1)$; $(0, 1)$ (c) $x^2 = 4(y - 2)$; $(0, 2)$ (d) $x^2 = -2(y + \frac{3}{2})$;
$(0, -\frac{3}{2})$

Chapter   **1.** (b) $(\frac{3}{2}, \frac{3}{2}\sqrt{3})$, $(\frac{9}{2}, \frac{3}{2}\sqrt{3})$ (c) $M_1M_2 = 3$ **3.** (a) Ellipse; intercepts: $(5, 0)$,
Review $(-5, 0)$, $(0, 2)$, $(0, -2)$; foci: $(\sqrt{21}, 0)$, $(-\sqrt{21}, 0)$; major axis: x-axis
5. (a) Hyperbola, intercepts: $(0, 2)$, $(0, -2)$; foci: $(0, \sqrt{5})$, $(0, -\sqrt{5})$
(b) Region outside branches of hyperbola of (a)   **7.** $\{(0, 1), (0, -1)\}$
9. (a) $x^2 = 8y$ (b) $y^2 = -4x$ **13.** (c) Parabola: vertex $(-5, 1)$
(d) Ellipse: center $(2, -\frac{3}{5})$

Index

$3x - 1 < 4x + 2$

$-1 < x + 2$

$-2 - 1 < x + 2 - 2$

$-3 < x$

$x > -3$ $\{x \mid x > -3\}$ solution set

graph of inequality is set of all pts on # line whose coord.
satisfy inequality

if you come up with $-x < 3$

$$(-1)(-x) > (3)(-1)$$

whenever you multiply a $^-$ no, across an inequality
you reverse an inequality

p 52-53